A LITTLE HIGH

PAIGE DEARTH

ISBN 9781735079691

Dirt On The Author

Born and raised in Plymouth Meeting, a small town west of Philadelphia, Paige Dearth was a victim of child abuse and spent her early years yearning desperately for a better life. Living through the fear and isolation that marked her youth, she found a way of coping with the trauma: she developed the ability to dream up stories grounded in reality that would provide her with a creative outlet when she finally embarked on a series of novels. Paige's debut novel, Believe Like A Child, is the darkest version of the life she imagines she would have been doomed to lead had fate not intervened just in the nick of time. The beginning of Believe Like A Child is based on Paige's life while the remainder of the book is fiction. Paige writes real-life horror and refers to her work as Fiction with Mean-ing. She hopes that awareness through fiction creates prevention.

Connect With Paige

Find all of Paige's books on Amazon

Sign up for new book releases: paigedearth.com

Follow Paige At:

Facebook: facebook.com/paigedearth

Instagram: paigedearth

Goodreads

Twitter: @paigedearth

More books by Paige

Home Street Home Series (can be read in any order):
Believe Like A Child
When Smiles Fade
One Among Us
Mean Little People
Never Be Alone
My Final Breath

Rainey Paxton Series (must be read in order):
A Little Pinprick
A Little High

For Loi, you are my light.

—Mom

~

For Patti, Frank's wife, because, well, why should your husband get a dedication and not you? Bam! Take that, Frank.

~

For those who have suffered, worried, and lost so much loving a drug addict. Be assured that you did all that you could do, and finally . . .

For those who have beat addiction and found lifelong recovery. May you live well and have understanding, be happy and find your peace.

—Paige

Chapter One

Clinging to the dilapidated chain-link fence, Rainey watched dumbfounded as her father scurried like a rat to the car. Without a backward glance, Peter pulled the door closed on the passenger side and her mother, Miranda, sped away, leaving the confused seventeen-year-old on the streets of North Philadelphia with nowhere to go.

A hooker across the street who had watched the fight lifted her chin and yelled over the traffic, "You okay, doll? You need a sugar daddy to kiss your boo-boos?" she mocked, then broke into laughter.

Ignoring the girl, Rainey looked around frantically. Flustered, she wished she was back in juvie. While she hated being in prison, at least when she was locked up, she had Tootsie to count on. Gathering her courage, she straightened her rumpled shirt and flattened her hair, trying to put her dignity back together. Then she walked toward one end of the block, and right before reaching the corner, a man approached her.

"Hey, you!" he said, scampering toward her. "Come here. I want to talk to you."

She turned around cautiously and watched the tall black man close the distance between them. Her eyes roamed over him as she tried to assess how much of a danger he'd be to her. The man had a medium build and wore baggy jeans and a tight T-shirt. He had a barbed wire tattoo running the length of his right arm. As he slithered a few steps closer, a set of keys dangling from his finger jingled. Stopping a foot away from her, his eyes got dark and serious, looking at her as though they were long-lost lovers.

"Do I know you?" Rainey asked, wondering if he was a squatter from her childhood home.

"I ain't sure," he said with a slow smile. "Do I look familiar, baby?"

The hairs on the back of her neck stiffened.

He continued in a creepy tone, "Everybody in this town knows me. I'm Brewer. What's your name, baby doll?"

Rainey's intuition told her that Brewer was trouble. She stood taller, trying to hide her uneasiness. "Listen, I need to get home before my mom and dad get upset and call the cops," she lied, trying to deter him.

She turned to walk away but the man grabbed her shoulder, twisting her around to face him. "Whoa. Not so fast!" Brewer bellowed. "I wasn't done talking to you. I think you better calm down."

Rainey's apprehension hardened into annoyance. "I am calm. Look, I have to go. I don't have time for this," she said, narrowing her eyes at him.

"All right, hold on now. Let me say this first, I saw that man push you down and spit in your face. I only wanted to make sure you were okay. See, that's what I'm all about, taking care of women. That's right, there are no finer creatures on this earth."

She hiked her hands to her hips. "Great, I'm fine. Thanks for checking."

"But wait," he said firmly, grabbing her arm and holding on. "I saw that asshole get in the car that drove away and leave you standing here looking lost. I ain't sure why someone would treat a girl as beautiful as you like that—he must be outta his damn mind. I would never do that to my woman . . . someone as fine as you," Brewer schmoozed, leaning in closer.

Rainey tried to hide her disgust, wanting to get away from him without setting him off. "I'm not his woman. I'm not anyone's woman," she stated, stone-faced.

Brewer let out a cackle. "I see. You're one of those independent types." He touched the ends of her hair and she jerked her head away.

His comment caused a fresh surge of aggravation, which further fueled her bad mood. "Yeah, that's right." She stared at Brewer for a few seconds, then looked around. A few feet away two hookers hung onto each other, watching her interaction with him. The way they were staring and smiling at her—whispering things she couldn't hear confirmed what she already knew.

Brewer followed her gaze to the hookers, baring his teeth at them and they walked off together. He turned his attention back to Rainey. "Okay baby, I feel you on that one. You like your independence, but that comes with a price. See, I know you ain't got no mommy and daddy waitin' for you to get home."

Rainey crossed her arms over her chest, and her shoulders slumped slightly. Neither action went unnoticed by Brewer.

He moved in closer. "But here's the deal. I can offer you things. See that car over there?" He pointed to a silver Mercedes. "That's the car you'd be driving in if you were my girl."

Losing her patience and having given him too much of her time, Rainey glared at him. "That's your car, huh?" she asked, looking him up and down. "Are you a pimp?"

Brewer forced out a fake laugh. "Baby doll, you sound like you're a hundred years old. Pimp, pimp. Who uses that word anymore?"

"I do, Brewer," she said, spitting out his name like it was poisonous. "I use the word 'pimp.' Here's the thing. I'm having a really shitty day and I think it's better if you leave me alone," she said, turning and walking away.

"Bitch, you don't walk away from Brewer!" he yelled after her.

But Rainey picked up her pace and didn't turn back.

Enraged, Brewer screamed, "That's right, whore. Keep walking. You ain't good enough to be one of my bitches. You can come back and beg me to take you in when your white ass is sleeping in the streets and your belly is hollering at you for food. That's right . . . that's when I'll see you. You'll be sorry. Just wait and see!"

Once Rainey was far enough away and couldn't see Brewer anymore, she leaned against a brick wall to catch her breath. The only thing on her mind was to find a place to stay where she would be safe for the night. She needed time to figure out where she could go next. Shoving her hands into her front pockets, she felt the twenty-dollar bill her mother had thrown in her face before she kicked her out of the car. She wrapped her fingers around the bill and balled it up in the palm of her hand, grateful to have the meager amount of money to fall back on. As Rainey roamed the streets trying to figure out what to do, dark clouds formed over her head. As the day quickly turned stormy, she ducked into a doorway and looked up at the sky. It started to drizzle, but a few minutes later the dark clouds released and the water came down in sheets.

With almost no visibility, Rainey closed her eyes and drew in a breath through her nose. The rain hitting the hot sidewalk gave off a distinct scent that brought her back to her childhood . . . playing at a park on hot summer days with her aunt Sophie. She remembered one time they had gotten soaking wet as they ran for the cover of the car. Inside, they watched the rain coming down as they ate cookies and listened to the sound of raindrops hitting the car roof and windshield. As the storm formed around them,

lightning flashed and thunder banged and all she could recall was being safe inside the car together.

Rainey hated that those days with her aunt were long gone and was left to face the world on her own. She was determined to find her way in the world, and with her courage mounting, Rainey was ready to do what was needed to make a better life for herself and her sister, Ivy.

Chapter Two

Once the storm passed, the sky was blue and the sun beat down on the wet pavement. The people who took shelter scurried back outside, and the circus of life in Kensington resumed. The drunken arguments reemerged, the cat-calling could be heard, and the car horns let out impatient screams. Rainey took it all in, and even while a feeling of being lost settled on her, she was relieved to be distracted by the hustle and bustle of the city streets.

Rainey walked for blocks when she noticed an old church. The white stone front was uninviting and darkened by years of neglect. She considered walking by but noticed a few teenagers entering the front. She climbed the stone steps taking in the trash and dirt clinging to the sides. She imagined how beautiful the structure had been . . . once upon a time. Standing in front of the tall wooden door with elaborate handles, she braced herself and pulled the door open. Stepping inside, she let out a loud breath as the chaos of the abandoned church hit her.

It was as though she'd stepped into another world; it was almost like its own city. The church was brimming with people of various ages. She moved deeper inside, slowly taking in her surroundings. She was amazed that the inside structure, while run down, was intact. Stained glass windows with biblical images stood undamaged as they shone stunning rays of light and colors across the white marble floors and walls. Even though there were people partying and music playing, a peacefulness touched Rainey.

She walked past rows of solid oak pews. Many were filled with people stretching out over them. As she slowly made her way to the front, like she was about to receive Holy Communion, her eyes focused on the groups partying on the enormous marble altar. One man caught her eyes. She

averted her gaze to the floor, and that's when she noticed the used needles and cigarette butts dominating the surface. As she got closer to the front, she spotted piles of feces off to the sides and, that used condoms were scattered everywhere. She paused and scanned the entire space. There were so many people she couldn't help but imagine the community who once used this massive room to pray.

Rainey found a pew in the central part of the church, close to the altar and where only a few others were sitting. She picked a quieter spot and settled in. Two people on the other end of the pew were kissing and lost in their own world, not even taking a breath to notice her. She slouched on the hard bench, trying to find a comfortable position.

She wasn't there for long when a young woman approached her.

"Hey, wasss up?" she slurred. "You're new here, aren't ya?"

Rainey glanced at her, assessing the girl, who looked to be about her age. "Yeah, I got here a few minutes ago. I needed somewhere to hang until . . . I'm on my way to my aunt's house and I ran out of money." She had decided quickly it wouldn't be in her best interests to give the girl too much information. After her encounter with Brewer, she was nervous about letting anyone know she was homeless now.

"Oh, yeah, I totally get what you're sayin'. It sucks when you run outta money, especially when you gotta go out and earn more," she mumbled. "Anyway, this is a pretty cool place to hang, huh? According to the people who've been living in here for a while the church was abandoned after the neighborhood collapsed; not enough people to belong to it. It was only a couple of weeks after the church closed that homeless people took it over." The girl looked around them. "They call this place the Heroin Shooting Gallery. Pretty cool, right?" she said with a giggle.

Rainey gave her a weak smile. "It's hard to believe the people who own this place would leave it. I mean, I can imagine how beautiful it must have been. It's still gorgeous."

The girl nodded. "Yeah, this place seems like home to me. Oh, I'm Claire . . . I've been living here for about a week," she offered.

"I'm Rainey. How did you end up here?" she asked, looking around at the magnificent church with its signs of neglect and decay.

"Ah, you know, I like to party and my parents wanna control me so I split with my boyfriend and wound up here. The first morning I woke up and that fucker had split on me. I should've known he wouldn't be around

long. Him and me weren't too good for each other anyway. We fought all the time so it's better now."

Claire sat and pulled her legs up under her. The two girls talked for a few hours, and by dinnertime Claire had floated off to join a group passing joints.

Rainey reached into her state-issued backpack and pulled out a small bag of pretzels, nibbling on them slowly. Tootsie had given her several things from the commissary before she left juvie.

As the darkness of night fell upon the church, Rainey curled onto her side and used her backpack as a pillow. Exhausted from the trauma of her first day of freedom, she drifted off to sleep.

***

It was five o'clock in the morning when Rainey was jolted from her sleep by blood-curdling screams. She sat up quickly as her heart raced. Her eyes darted around, trying to assess the situation, as the screaming continued. With the moon creating a dim glow inside the church, her eyes followed the sounds until they landed on Claire in a far corner behind the altar.

Claire was on the floor with her back tucked into the corner of the white marble. Her legs were pulled up, and she was covering her head with her arms. Three men, who looked to be in their twenties, were standing over her. One kept kicking Claire while the other two yelled and threw punches.

At first, Rainey couldn't distinguish what they were mad about, but as she listened closer, she understood.

"You're a lying bitch! We know you stole our dope. Do you know what happens to dope thieves in here? This is what happens," he screamed, pulling out a knife and stabbing her. A minute later, Claire lay dead, with more than fifteen stab wounds to her face and body. The three men turned their backs to the altar as their crazed eyes scanned the room. Rainey flattened herself against the pew, as if she could hide from them in plain sight.

As they made their way from the front of the church, all three men headed in Rainey's direction, and she prepared to die in the same way Claire had. Then someone yelled and the men turned in the opposite direction and walked up the middle aisle, to the back of the church. Rainey

was panting and trying to breathe. Grabbing her backpack, she rushed out the side of the church and into the darkness, stopping only for a few seconds to vomit. Then she sprinted several blocks from the church and slipped into a small alley between two row homes.

Rainey shimmied between two trash cans, leaning her back against the wall while her eyes frantically searched for predators. She would stay there, she decided, until the sun came up. Then she'd have to figure out somewhere safe to go.

Chapter Three

The next day, Rainey roamed Kensington, looking for a place where she could sleep. Finding nothing, she turned down a familiar block. Across the street from the house where she grew up, the girl hid behind a large tree, nervous about what she'd see—or worse yet, not see. All she could hear was the boom-boom, boom-boom, boom-boom of her pounding heart. Her arms shook from adrenaline, and in the heat of the thick summer air, a chill ran through her.

Rainey watched the house, hoping that Ivy would come outside. She needed just one glimpse of her sister. She needed to see for herself that Ivy was okay.

Finally, when the sun dipped below the city and the streets were dark, Rainey darted across the street and crept up the splintered front porch steps. Somehow she had expected it to be familiar, but it seemed much different now, worse than she had remembered. The windows were boarded and the front yard was still consumed by trash. Broken beer bottles, crushed cigarette packs, and junk food wrappers littered the tiny patch of dirt and weeds leading to the front porch. On the rusted porch swing sat an empty beer keg. She took in her miserable and strange surroundings, wondering how she'd ever lived there. It was a miracle the house had never been condemned, despite many other homes on the block meeting that fate.

Unable to see anything more than a few vague shadows of movement through the cracks around the boarded windows, Rainey leaped off the porch and sprinted to the back of the house and noticed that one board on a window had rotted and broken away. She dug through the tall weeds of the backyard and finally found an old plastic milk crate. She placed it under the window and stood on the crate to get a better view inside.

Her heart beat wildly as she scanned the kitchen, anticipating the moment when she would see her sister. But Ivy was nowhere in sight. Disappointed, she let out a long breath. As she pulled away from the window a small movement from inside caught her eye. She pressed her face closer to the plywood and focused intently.

Under the kitchen table, Ivy peered out into a crowd of stumbling, half-witted partiers. Her mother rushed into the kitchen and shrieked, "Ivy! Where the hell are you, girl? Don't you hide from me!"

Rainey watched as ever so slowly Ivy crawled out from under the table and looked up at Miranda with large, frightened eyes. Rainey gasped when Miranda bent at the waist, grabbed onto one of Ivy's legs, and whipped her forward with a quick motion.

Ivy instinctively covered her face with her hands as she slid across the dirty floor.

"Don't you touch her," Rainey whispered into the lonely night, her anger moving to a whole new level.

"Get up!" Miranda yelled.

The child obeyed, but Ivy only made it to a seated position before her mother pulled on her leg again. Unable to stay upright, she flew backward and slammed her head against the floor. The child let out a yelp before she burst into tears while holding the back of her head. Everyone in the kitchen turned to watch, but no one helped the child.

When Ivy finally stood, Rainey grabbed her stomach at seeing the condition of her little sister. The eight-year-old was malnourished and looked to be much younger than her age. She wasn't much taller than when Rainey had last seen her. Ivy's hair was long and her bangs were cut at a crude angle. Rainey wondered if her mother had cut them while she was stoned or if Ivy had cut them herself. Ivy wore a skin-tight T-shirt at least a size too small that outlined her protruding ribs, and a pair of cotton shorts. Her kneecaps stood out like two golf balls on her boney legs. There was no distinction in size between her thighs and ankles; she was all skin and bones.

"Go to your room and stay there," Miranda commanded before turning her back on the child.

Rainey watched Ivy weave her way out of the kitchen. When she passed through the doorway, a girl in her early twenties with heavy eyelids swayed a little and handed her a beer, which Ivy snatched before rushing away. Unable to control her rage, Rainey rushed back to the front porch, opened

the door, and walked in. Keeping an eye out for Miranda and Peter, she took the stairs two at a time to the second floor. She opened her old bedroom door slowly, pushing back the dark memories the room held for her.

"Ivy?" she whispered into the darkness. "Where are you?"

A small form sat up and Rainey could only see the whites of her wild eyes.

"It's okay," she said, rushing toward her. "It's me. It's Rainey." She took the child into her arms, but Ivy pushed her away.

"Get offa me," she said.

"What? No, it's me. I missed you so much."

"No, you didn't. You left me. They told me that you hate me so you left me here. And they hate me too, they're mean to me all the time," she said defiantly.

Rainey rubbed her hands together, trying to figure out a way to explain everything to her. She expected their reunion to be happy and wasn't prepared for this. "No. No, Ivy. That's not true. I didn't want to leave you. The police took me away. Mom and Dad wouldn't let me tell the police the truth. They said they'd do bad things if I did," she said, not wanting Ivy to know they'd threaten to hurt her. "I could never hate you. I love you. I thought about you every day."

"Leave me alone," Ivy mumbled, laying her head on a pile of discarded laundry.

Rainey smelled alcohol on Ivy's breath and her head jerked back, remembering the girl in the kitchen who had handed her a beer.

"Ivy, I'm going to get you out of here." Rainey reached into her backpack and pulled out a pack of peanut butter crackers. She held them out to her sister. "Here, I brought you something to eat."

Ivy glanced at Rainey's hand and swiftly snatched the crackers. She sat up and ripped into the package, shoving the crackers into her mouth, chewing a couple of times, and swallowing.

Tears dribbled down Rainey's cheeks watching what had become of her sister. She had been foolish not to imagine that she would find Ivy hungry, alone, and angry.

"Hey, come on," Rainey said. "Slow down. Nobody's going to take them away from you."

Ivy sneered at her and continued to gobble the crackers. When she was finished, she laid back down and fell asleep without another word. Certain

that her sister was sleeping, Rainey crept into a far corner of the closet and moved aside a pile of clothes and broken toys until she found the shoebox she needed. She pulled the lid off, lifting out the picture she'd taken of her aunt Sophie the last time she saw her, the day they had said good-bye. She kissed the photo and slid it inside her bra for safekeeping.

Quietly making her way back to Ivy and longing to snuggle with her sister again, Rainey lowered herself to the floor. Realizing she was a stranger to Ivy the weight of her anguish was bearing down on her with great force. Rainey curled up behind the child, draping her arm protectively over her. The soft breathing of Ivy's deep sleep was like a sad lullaby—with a harsh recognition filled with sorrow, that time had washed away so much of their bond.

***

"What the hell are you doing here?" Peter screamed into the silence of the early morning.

Rainey's eyes flew open; it was still dark outside and her father only appeared as a shadow against the hallway light. Ivy jumped from her spot and backed her small frame into the corner of the room.

"I needed to see Ivy!" Rainey bellowed.

Peter advanced on Rainey too quickly for her to move out of the way and she tried to dodge his booted foot, but it landed in her gut.

"Get out of here, you little whore!" he screamed, glaring at Rainey. "You left your sister three years ago and now you want to come back and see her. Well, she doesn't want to see you! Peter looked at his younger daughter. Do you, Ivy?"

The child shook her head with vigor as Rainey scowled at her father. Rainey was still holding her stomach and trying to catch her breath.

"See?" he said, turning back to Rainey. "She hates you."

"You lied to her!" Rainey yelled, frustrated and ready to fight. "I would never leave Ivy on purpose. I love her."

Peter's fist smashed into Rainey's face before she could react, and everything went black.

Chapter Four

Rainey stirred and gripped her head with both hands to stop the pounding. When the pain had ceased just a little, her eyes fluttered open, and she was facing a brick wall. Where the hell am I? she wondered.

Groaning as she sat up, Rainey noticed she was laying on top of trash. The back of her shirt and jeans were damp and clung uncomfortably to her body. Her eyes scanned the area. To her right was a discarded, rat-eaten lounge chair. To her left was an abandoned rusty water heater. Rainey's blood pumped furiously as she sat in an alley, picking trash off her clothing.

"What the hell?" she whispered.

She painfully got to her feet and looked around, quickly remembering what had happened earlier that morning. Her hand went to the side of her face, and when her fingers grazed the skin, she cringed from the tenderness where she'd been punched. A sense of danger poked at her and Rainey rushed to the end of the alley. According to the street signs, she was at the corner of Indiana and Third.

"Holy shit," she mumbled.

Her parents had dumped her several blocks from their home. They'd thrown her away, like trash, in the Badlands of North Philadelphia. It was the most unsafe and devastated area of the city, worse than the areas nearby. The Badlands were ruled by gangs notorious for committing drug-related crimes and violence.

Tootsie had told her about the vile people who lurked in the Badlands. Most gangs sold drugs, committed unthinkable acts of cruelty, and enjoyed watching people suffer. They often torturously punished victims for what they deemed overstepping their turf. In the Badlands, these gangs were sheriff, judge, and jury.

Rainey looked left, then right, but didn't know which way to go to get out. On more of a whim, she turned right and walked at a quick pace. After several blocks she was becoming nervous that she'd gone the wrong way. Then she saw a small convenience store in the distance and hurried closer. She eyed the black bars on the door and figured this was her best hope for getting directions back to Kensington. She ascended three concrete steps, pulled the door open, and stepped into the store.

Inside, the space was dark and an older man sat behind a bulletproof window.

The man looked up from his newspaper. "What do you want?" he grunted.

Rainey's heart sank. "I, um, I live on West York Street and I'm kinda lost," she said.

"Yeah, and you're probably kinda high too. Get out of my store."

"No, wait!" she said trying to stall, putting her hands in the air and moving closer. "I need your help."

"Oh, yeah. With what?"

"I want to buy something. Something to eat," she said, rummaging through her pockets for the twenty-dollar bill her mother had given her the day before. After checking every pocket twice and finding nothing, she realized that her parents must have taken the money from her before they dumped her in the alley.

Rainey looked up at the man. "I can't find my money. It was in my pocket. Someone must have stolen it from me" she said, choking.

The man's lips pressed together. "Yeah, sure. Listen, girl, if you don't have money to buy something then get the hell outta my store," he stated, pointing at the door.

Defeated, Rainey's head hung as she made her way back outside. She looked up at an overcast sky and at her dreadful surroundings. The broken-down homes on the block and the abandoned warehouses in the foreground seemed a perfect setting for a horror movie. The once thriving industrial part of the city was dilapidated and left to rot. There weren't many people on the streets except for a few small groups of young men. Rainey pulled up her long blond hair, twisted it, and tied it in a knot on the top of her head, trying to make herself less noticeable.

She hugged herself, walking quickly, weaving through the streets, looking for anything that would lead her into the heart of Kensington. With each turn, her surroundings worsened. Finally, seeing an old

two-pump gas station, she jogged toward it. A false sense of security filled her as she sat on the curb at the entrance doors. She thought, at least there's someone inside the building if I need help.

Rainey pulled a sneaker off and removed the piece of paper that Tootsie had given her with an address for her friend Winnie. Tootsie assured her that Winnie would help, and more than anything, Rainey wanted that to be true. She read the address over until she had it memorized, and tried to figure out how she could get there.

She sat at the gas station for an hour, staring into nothingness, thinking of how her parents had twisted everything and made Ivy think she'd abandoned her. Then her stomach churned at the thought of her parents dumping her unconscious in the middle of the Badlands. It was hard to process the things that could have happened to her if she'd been found by the wrong people.

She was lost in self-degrading thoughts when a car with music blaring pulled into the station and parked beside a pump. Rainey looked up and saw a young black woman get out of the passenger side and head inside to pay for their gas.

"Hi," Rainey said as she was approaching.

"Hi. What the hell you doin' in a place like this? You stupid or just high?"

Rainey shook her head. "Neither. I'm lost and I need to get to my friend's house, but I don't know how to get there. I've never been in this part of the city before."

"Little girl, your bright white ass is in the worst section of the city you're ever gonna know. You're outta your mind sitting there like you ain't got nowhere to go. You're a sitting duck waiting for someone to come along and steal your life away from you."

Plagued with a heightened sense of worry, Rainey tilted her head and watched the girl. There was a strong message of concern in her tone, and she wondered if maybe she could trust her.

The girl looked back at her friend sitting in the car and chuckled. "You are too young to be hanging around a place like this all by yourself. Someone will snag you in a minute and you'll be turning tricks on the street before lunch."

Knowing this was her moment; Rainey stood and gave the girl a soft smile. She heard the concern for her safety in the girl's voice, and this gave her courage. "Maybe you and your friend could give me a ride. Here's the address," she said, holding out the paper.

Rainey held her breath, willing to take the risk of getting a ride from strangers. She didn't care; at this point she was more fearful of staying in the Badlands. The girl looked at Rainey, then at the address. She placed her hand firmly on her hip. I gotta go pay for my gas, then I'll ask my friend if she's okay with giving you a lift."

A warm flush of gratitude ran through Rainey's core. "Thanks. I'd really appreciate it."

"Don't thank me yet. See Bone sitting in the car over there?" she said, pointing. "Bone's a tough one to crack. She don't trust nobody. Hell, the bitch barely trusts me, and I've known her skinny ass since we were seven."

The girl chuckled as she disappeared through the door. When she came out a few minutes later she lit a cigarette and said, "All right. You wait here and I'll go talk to Bone."

Rainey waited, bouncing from foot to foot, anxiously worrying that they'd leave her there. After a few minutes, the girl stepped out of the car and waved her over. "Come on. Better hurry before Bone changes her mind!" she yelled.

Rainey dashed toward the car. She leaned down and looked at Bone. "Hey, thanks a lot. I appreciate the ride."

Bone looked at Rainey but didn't acknowledge her.

"Okay," the other girl said, lifting the front seat so Rainey could climb in the back. "I'm Jesse, by the way."

Ducking into the car, Rainey gave her a vibrant smile. "Thanks, Jesse. I'm Rainey. I don't know what would've happened if you two didn't come along."

After they pulled out of the lot, Jesse turned around to face her. "So, where you from?"

Rainey cleared her throat. "I used to live on West York, but I, um, just got out of juvie and my parents won't let me live with them now," she admitted without thinking.

Bone punched Jesse's shoulder. "I fucking told you she was trouble."

Rainey shrank back against the seat, wishing she'd kept her mouth shut. "No, no, I'm not. I spent time in juvie, but it was all a mistake. I swear, I got blamed for stuff that wasn't my fault."

Bone screeched the car to a halt on the side of the road and whipped her head around to face Rainey, who stared back with wide eyes, stunned. "Is anyone looking for you right now?"

"What? No, nobody cares if I'm dead or alive," Rainey shrieked, afraid that Bone would throw her out of the car.

"Why were you in the Badlands? You visiting someone?" she stared at her through narrowed eyes.

Rainey shook her head. "I snuck into my parents' house last night to see my little sister. She's only eight and I haven't seen her in three years. The last thing I remember is my dad punching me in the face early this morning, and when I came to, he had dumped me at Indiana and Third. That's the truth," she said.

"Is that how you got that bruise on your face?" Bone asked.

Rainey touched her face lightly and tried not to wince. "I guess. I haven't seen it."

"Come on," Jesse said to Bone. "Chill out. I believe her. We both know how people blame you for shit that you never did. Stop acting like you're some saint."

A swell of gratitude gushed through Rainey that Jesse was there and willing to help her.

Bone's jaw was tense as she looked squarely at Jesse and said, "This better not turn out to be a mistake. I'm telling you right now, if something goes wrong, I will beat the shit outta you."

Jesse giggled. "You're so dramatic. Give it a rest and just drive."

Bone put the car in gear and headed toward the address in the Harrowgate section of Philadelphia. It was a fraction safer than the Badlands with fewer gangs but just as many drugs. Twenty minutes later, Bone pulled up to an unkempt row home on Joyce Street. She glanced at Jesse, who turned to Rainey. "This is the address."

"Oh," Rainey said, looking around her nervously. "Okay. Well, thanks again."

"Sure thing," Jesse sang.

Rainey leaned up on the front seat. "It was nice to meet you," she said to Bone.

Bone grunted.

Rainey turned and looked up at the house. The porch roof sagged in the middle and she looked down the block. The houses were old and mostly in need of repair. Not knowing what to expect, Rainey was light-headed as she walked toward the solid wooden door with a large pane of glass in the upper top. The glass was cracked and held together, from corner to corner, with a piece of silver duct tape.

Taking a calming breath, Rainey knocked. After a few seconds, when no one answered the door, she rapped again a little harder. She'd just turned around to look back at the street, wondering where she'd go next, when the door flung open. A heavy-set Hispanic man stood in only his boxers. His hair was disheveled and he rubbed the sleep from his eyes.

"Yeah, what do you want?" his gruff voice blasted as he glared at her.

Chapter Five

Rainey's mouth dropped open as her eyes roamed over the large man glaring at her. She'd expected a woman, and now questioned if she had made the right decision to come here. The man was well over six feet tall. His broad shoulders veered outward like the tops of an oak tree in full bloom, and his long, dark brown dreadlocks rested on his shoulders like thick, tangled vines. His eyes were set hard and cold as he waited for her to speak.

"Um, hi. I'm Rainey," she mumbled, swallowing the bile burning the back of her throat. "Um, Tootsie told me to come here and ask for Winnie?"

"Yeah, I don't care. Did that stupid bitch tell you to come here and wake me up at seven o'clock in the morning?" he barked.

Rainey's shoulders rose and her head tilted up to look at him in the eyes. She bit her bottom lip, fighting back tears but too desperate to turn away. "I can't stay at my old house and I don't know where else—"

The man slammed the door in Rainey's face, leaving her dumbfounded. She didn't know whether to stay there or leave.

After several seconds, anger replaced her fear. "You asshole," Rainey whispered, annoyance drying the tears from seconds prior. She was about to turn away when, from somewhere in the house, she heard the guy yell, "Winnie! Answer the door. That dumbass, whore Tootsie gave some loser our address."

"Fuck you," Rainey muttered but smiled, thinking she might not be out of luck after all.

A full minute passed until a young, tired-looking Latina woman in a silky pink robe opened the door and gave her a smile.

"Hey," she said.

"Winnie?" Rainey asked, smiling back, happy to see her.

"Yeah. You wanna come in?"

Rainey nodded, trying not to seem too desperate. "I didn't think you were going to answer."

"Well," Winnie said holding her arms out to her sides, "here I am. You look like shit. Your hair's all tangled and you smell like a garbage can. Where have you been?"

Rainey sighed. "After I left juvie, my parents threw me out on the streets. I spent the first night at that abandoned church, the Heroin Shooting Gallery, someone called it."

Winnie nodded. "Yeah, it wasn't such a good idea for you to go there. I know it's a hub for heroin users."

The girl closed her eyes. "Yeah, I found that out quick—I saw a girl get killed."

Winnie's eyes grew large. "Oh, shit."

"Yeah, so I ran from there and snuck into my parents' house last night. My father sucker punched me. Knocked me out cold and dumped me in an alley in the Badlands. Some girls gave me a ride here. I'm sorry that it's so early but I don't have anywhere else to go."

Winnie scoffed. "Tootsie warned me that you have a lot to say." She eyed Rainey up and down. "Tootsie also told me you ask a lot of questions. Is that true?"

"Yeah, it is," Rainey smirked. She could hear Tootsie saying that to Winnie, and the memory of Tootsie's voice comforted her. The girl was one of a kind, a sister to her, someone she'd always love.

"Yeah, okay." Winnie said, raking her fingers through her hair. "Tootsie called me. She figured you'd show up here a day or two after you got out. Come on in," she said, pulling the door open and standing to the side.

Thankful to be inside the house, Rainey stopped in the entryway and looked into Winnie's face. She took in the girl's smooth brown skin, reflecting her Latina heritage. But what mesmerized her were Winnie's mismatched eyes: one was blue and the other brown. "Your eyes are so cool."

Winnie scoffed. "Yeah, that's what everybody tells me. Come on," she said, leading her to the kitchen at the back of the house.

Rainey followed, looking around her. The house was old and the furniture was worn, but it was clean. Something she'd never had when she

was a child—a clean home to live in. But now she had a good feeling that things were about to change.

Chapter Six

"You have a nice house," Rainey commented as she looked around, hoping she could stay for a few nights.

Winnie looked over her shoulder. "Thanks. It used to belong to my mom. She died, though, and left it to me and my brother."

"Oh, that sucks your mom died," Rainey said awkwardly, not knowing the right words to use with someone who has lost a parent they loved.

"Yeah, it did suck. She died two years ago . . . I was only seventeen. Sometimes it's hard to believe she's been gone that long. She was a good mom. How about you? How old are you?"

"I'm seventeen."

Winnie smiled, showing her broad, straight, white teeth. "I thought the world was over when I was seventeen. Not just because my mom died, but also because I thought I was grown, and no one treated me that way, so that pissed me off. Anyway, that grumpy-ass jerk who answered the door is my older brother, Leo. After our mom died, he was always busting my ass, telling me where I could go and who I could go with. Worst of all, he didn't like me hanging with Tootsie. I couldn't wait until I turned eighteen and he wasn't my guardian anymore. Leo and me own this house together. But my mom always said that because Leo was a guy he'd get married someday and move out and the house would be mine. He's only twenty-three but I don't think he'll ever move outta here. I'm not complaining, he was annoying at first, but he's been good to me and I feel safe with him around . . . especially in this neighborhood. It gets worse every year."

"You're lucky to have an older brother. I'm the oldest in my family. I have an eight-year-old sister. Sometimes I think if I had an older brother or sister things would've been easier."

"Maybe." Winnie moved to a coffeemaker and filled it with water. "You want coffee?"

Rainey shrugged. "I've never had it, but I'm not picky. I eat and drink pretty much anything."

Winnie scrunched her face. "You're lying. You've never had coffee before?"

Rainey shook her head. "My parents preferred cheap whiskey or vodka in the mornings, and they didn't let us have coffee in juvie. The girls in there complained about it all the time, especially Tootsie."

"Ah, Tootsie. Yeah, she wants what she wants, and she needs her caffeine. I love that girl."

Rainey smiled, thinking of her friend. "Yeah, we didn't start off so good. But I eventually won her over."

Winnie gave her a knowing smile. "Yeah, she told me. You must be pretty cool because Tootsie can be a total hard-ass. She doesn't like too many people, but I guess you already know that."

"Yeah, I sure do. I miss her already. I was never afraid when she was around. Now I have to decide what I'm gonna do, where I'm gonna live, how I'm gonna make money. It sucks. I got out of juvie two days ago and woke up in an alley this morning. That about sums up my life."

"Well, you can stay here for a while until you figure out what you're gonna do. You can't live here forever, but you can stay for a month or two if that would help," Winnie offered.

"Really?" Rainey was so happy she almost hugged the girl. Having a place to stay for a couple of months was more than she could have hoped for.

Winnie chuckled. "Yeah, really. I promised Tootsie, I'd help you get on your feet. She told me a lot about you. Like why you were in juvie and all."

Thank God for Tootsie, Rainey thought, letting out a nervous giggle. "See, that's what I mean about Tootsie. She took care of me once she stopped trying to kill me." Then Rainey turned serious. "Don't worry, I'll get a job."

"Of course you'll get a job. You'll have to work so you can help with the expenses while you're living here."

"Right, the expenses," Rainey said, suddenly realizing she hadn't thought about all the things she would need to pay for to live.

"Great. I'm happy that's outta the way. Anyway, what kind of job do you think you can get?"

Rainey shrugged. "I'm not sure. I hadn't thought about it. I've never had a job. I mean, I took care of my little sister, so maybe I can work at a daycare or something."

Winnie's lips pressed together. "That'll be hard given that you just got out of juvie. Places that take care of kids probably don't want someone who just got released from prison on drug charges."

Rainey gasped. "I . . . I . . . I never thought about it like that, I'm so screwed." Her skin prickled. "I gotta think about it. No one is going to want to hire me."

Winnie held up a hand. "Now, hold up. That's not completely true. Do you have a high school diploma?"

"Yeah," Rainey breathed, allowing herself to feel a little hopeful. "I got my GED in juvie. That should help, right?"

Winnie pulled her long, black curly hair back and placed it in a ponytail at the top of her head. "I think so."

"Well, where do you work?" Rainey asked.

"I clean rooms at the Drop Inn Motel. It's a dump not too far from here. They offer rooms by the hour, week, or month. It's a total shithole but I make enough money to pay my bills and still have extra for other stuff."

Rainey tilted her head. "That doesn't sound too bad."

"Please, it's fucking depressing. The rooms are disgusting and the place is filled with people who don't care much about life. And I have to put up with sleezy men coming onto me."

An image of being raped by Freddy and his foul odor that was so hard to wash away flashed across Rainey's mind. "What do you do when they come onto you?" she asked timidly, wiping a bead of sweat from her lip.

Winnie shrugged. "I mean, it depends."

Rainey's eyes widened. "Does that mean you go with them?"

Winnie continued without missing a beat. "You mean, screw 'em? Sure, sometimes. It's no big deal and it doesn't mean nothing. The motel brings in lots of drunks and addicts. Forget I ever said anything."

"Forget it?" Rainey rambled, wanting desperately to understand her perspective. "Aren't you . . . don't you . . . get scared?"

"Of what? Having sex? No, it's just business," Winnie offered. "Besides, I don't have any other skills. I only made it through eleventh grade; I quit after my mom died. I've been wanting to get my GED like you did, but I'm not that good at studying."

Rainey clasped her hands together, happy to move onto another subject. "Hey, I know." She moved closer to the girl. "I could help you study for the test."

Winnie nodded. "Yeah, maybe. Anyway, I might be able to get you a job at the Drop Inn. One of the housekeepers just left."

Rainey tried to swallow the lump suddenly lodged in her throat. Winnie was offering her a way to make money, but she was worried someone would try to force her into prostitution. Still, she needed to make some cash, and right now this seemed like the only way. "Yeah, sure. That'd be great. I can clean. But would I have to prostitute to work there?"

Winnie rolled her eyes. "Of course not. Getting paid for sex is my choice; nobody forces me. It's fine if you wanna just clean rooms, but you ain't gonna make that much money."

Rainey's shoulders relaxed and the tension ran down her arms and out through her fingertips.

Winnie took a sip of her coffee. "I'll talk to my manager when I go in today. He's a piece of shit too."

More out of a desire to do something than anything else, Rainey poured herself a cup of coffee and took a sip, immediately puckering at its bitter taste.

Chuckling, Winnie added cream and sugar for her. "You'll like it better this way. Now let me show you where you'll sleep."

Placing their coffee mugs on the kitchen counter, Rainey followed Winnie up to the second floor.

Chapter Seven

Winnie pointed at the first door on the right, "That's Leo's room," she whispered as they crept past. The door next to that was Winnie's room, and Rainey would be sleeping in the last bedroom at the back of the house. There was a bathroom across the hallway they would all share.

Rainey walked into her room and looked around. There was a single bed covered by an old burnt orange crocheted bedspread. The mismatched dresser and nightstand were worn down to the bare wood in spots, and a faded navy blue pillowcase covered a pillow flat as a pancake. Perched on top of the nightstand was a single-bulb lamp, the only light source in the room. The bare wood floor was worn just inside the door and next to the bed. The brick-colored paint on the walls was washed out and cracked in spots. For all its wear and dreariness, Rainey was still happy to have a place to sleep.

"This used to be Leo's room, before our mom died," Winnie said. "It'll be yours now."

Rainey smiled. "This is great. I've never had a room with a bed in it . . . unless you count my cell at juvie."

Winnie gasped. "You didn't have a bed growing up?"

"No, I didn't," Rainey said, shrugging. "I slept on a pile of old clothes."

Winnie shook her head. "Your parents sound like real assholes."

"Yeah, they are. They're both addicts. They've been taking drugs since before I was born."

"I can't even imagine that. My mom was far from perfect, but she did everything she could to make our lives better," Winnie said.

There was a stretch of silence between the girls.

Finally Winnie said, “Hey, um, I gotta get ready to go to work. I’ll let you settle in. Did you bring your clothes?”

Blood rushed to Rainey’s cheeks. “I only have the stuff I’m wearing. I had a backpack with a few things from juvie like soap and a toothbrush, but my parents kept everything when they dumped me in the alley.”

“Jesus, they’re evil.”

Rainey nodded, and the seriousness of what they had done to her registered.

Seeing the lost look on Rainey’s face, she said, “Well, I have a couple of things that I think will fit you. I can let you borrow them. Then once you make some money there’s a Goodwill between here and work where you can buy your own stuff.”

“That would be great. Thanks a lot.”

Rainey went back down to the kitchen and sat on one of the plastic chairs at the table. She sipped on the cold coffee, excited about getting a job and having her own money.

Later that morning, long after Winnie had left for work, Rainey was still at the kitchen table, deep concern lining her face as she thought about Ivy. Remembering how weak and vulnerable her sister had looked with her gaunt face and bulging eyes, her stomach turned. She was filling her coffee mug when Leo walked in, making her jump. She had forgotten she wasn’t alone in the house.

“You’re still here?” he asked.

“Yeah. Winnie said I could stay for a while as long as I help pay the bills,” Rainey squeaked out.

Leo let out a deep chuckle. “Relax. I know that already. Nothing happens in this house that Winnie doesn’t talk to me about first.” He leaned on the counter and glared at her. “Now, here’s the deal. I work at night so that means I sleep in the morning when I come home. That stunt you pulled this morning, don’t let it happen again. I get home around five a.m. and I’m usually dead asleep by six.”

“Okay,” Rainey said, nodding. “I’ll be sure not to wake you.”

“Good.” Leo walked over to the coffeemaker and lifted the empty pot. “Where the hell is the coffee?”

Rainey looked at him with wide eyes, confused. “Me and Winnie drank it.”

Leo glared at her. “No shit. So make another pot.”

Rainey squirmed on her chair, still staring at him.

"Oh, for Christ's sake, don't tell me you don't know how to make a pot of coffee," he grumbled.

"I've never even had coffee before today. So no, I don't know how."

"Well, get over here and watch me. If you're home when I wake up, I expect there to be a pot of coffee made, jailbird," he smirked.

Leo's aggression agitated her, and Rainey imagined he would be completely obnoxious if he was angry about something that actually mattered. She didn't like him calling her a jailbird and telling her what to do. Knowing she had to hold her tongue with him pissed her off. While she liked Winnie so far, she didn't like him, not one bit. But with nowhere else to go she fought her urge to leave. Living here with Leo instead of alone on the streets was a much better option. This she understood well.

Chapter Eight

Rainey spent most of the day in her bedroom, trying to avoid Leo. She didn't want to turn the TV on downstairs, afraid she'd wake him, and there were no books to read. She spent the majority of the day thinking about Ivy and hoping the child was doing okay. Later, when Winnie returned home from work, Rainey was in the living room sitting on the sofa and staring into nothingness.

"Why are you sitting in the dark?" Winnie asked, turning on a lamp next to the sofa. In the light, she could see the stress around Rainey's eyes.

Rainey looked up, surprised. "I don't know. I was just sitting here, thinking."

Winnie's eyebrows lifted. "You look upset. What's wrong?"

Rainey ran her palm across her forehead and nodded. "Well, actually, I'm worried about what I'm going to do now."

"Well, you can stop worrying." Winnie plopped down next to her and grinned. "Tomorrow you're starting a new job."

Rainey scooted to the edge of the sofa with her hands clasped together, unable to keep the smile off her face. "Are you serious?"

"Yep. I talked to my manager today and he said you can start tomorrow, cleaning rooms."

Rainey placed her hand on Winnie's forearm. "Thank you for helping me. So did your manager tell you how much money I'll make?"

"Our manager's name is Titus; he pays under the table."

"What does that mean?"

Winnie threw her head back playfully. "He pays us in cash."

"Oh, great," Rainey said, trying to sound nonchalant. She hadn't considered getting paid any other way. "How much?"

"He said he'll give you twenty-four bucks a day."

"Is that good?" Rainey asked, trying to do the math.

Winnie shrugged. "Well, it's four bucks an hour, but we have to work seven days a week from nine in the morning to three. So that's forty-two hours a week at four bucks an hour, which makes"—Winnie looked up at the ceiling—"a hundred and sixty-eight bucks a week. After you pay your portion of the electric and water bills, plus you gotta pay for food you won't have much left over. So I guess it kinda sucks, but it'll do for now. You'll just have to wait and see how it goes."

"Oh." Rainey thought for a moment. "Is that how much money Titus pays you?"

Winnie rubbed her tired eyes from the long day. "Titus pays me six bucks an hour, but I've been there for two years and I have a lot of guys who go there because they like me, so I bring in a lot more business." Winnie stood and her belly growled. "Anyway, did you eat?"

Rainey shook her head. "I wasn't sure if I should take any of the food from the refrigerator."

"Good call. Until you start putting in money, we should eat together. That way, Leo won't throw a fit. He's not good at sharing his food. He can be a dick about it."

I bet Leo can be a dick about a lot of things, Rainey thought.

***

As Rainey laid in bed that night, one issue kept pulling her back into the damp darkness of her life. She couldn't process what her parents had done to her over the past couple of days. She should have learned from her time in juvie that her mother and father would sacrifice anything for drugs. Instead she made excuses for them, because not to meant accepting that she was all alone in the world. Not having a family frightened her more than the thugs on the streets of Kensington. Rainey had never expected much from her parents and knew that they rarely, if ever, did the right thing for their daughters. But she never anticipated that they wouldn't let her see Ivy, and this made her feel stupid and gullible.

Her parents' actions planted a pebble of hate inside her belly, and the roots were growing stronger as she went over the events in her mind. She wanted to get even with them. She wanted her parents to have the same pain they'd inflicted on her.

After a sleepless night, Rainey got out of bed and tiptoed to the bathroom. She washed her face and dabbed at the dark circles under her eyes with cold water. Back in her bedroom she dressed quickly and went down to the kitchen to make a pot of coffee, just the way Leo had shown her.

Winnie came down about an hour later. "Girrrrrrl, look at you, making coffee and shit."

Rainey smiled and tilted her head to the side. "Leo made me learn how to make coffee in case I'm home when he's still sleeping."

Winnie winked at her. "Leo is a douchebag that can make his own coffee. You ain't his servant, don't let him push you around. He can be like that—he likes to be the boss."

Rainey pursed her lips and shook her head. "So you want me to tell him to make his own coffee? And then he'll throw me out and I won't have anywhere to go."

Winnie flicked her hand in Rainey's direction, gesturing to shoo her thoughts away. "He ain't gonna throw you out. Now that I'm of age we gotta agree on everything that goes on in this house. He was counting on you never telling me about having to make him coffee. Don't worry about Leo, I'll handle him."

Now, we gotta get moving. Titus is a real bastard if you're late."

***

Rainey and Winnie stood in front of the Drop Inn Motel, looking up at the four-story building. Air conditioners hung from small windows and the stucco façade was a urine yellow. At first, Rainey's attention was drawn to a man and a woman sharing a bottle of whiskey on a small patch of grass in front of the building. Then her eyes moved to a rusted metal sign hanging from the roof above the entrance, "Drop Inn Motel." She wrinkled her nose.

"This place is a dump," Rainey said.

Winnie smirked. "No kidding. Come on. Let's go inside. Wait until you get a load of Titus."

Winnie took a few steps forward, but Rainey didn't follow. Somehow Rainey didn't think it would be this bad. There was a criminal element to

the place. Looking around her, she worried she'd signed up for something that could land her back in prison.

"Are you coming?" Winnie asked, her voice rising.

Rainey looked at Winnie carefully, wondering if there was more to the Drop Inn Motel than her new friend had told her. "Yeah, of course, I'm coming," she said, jogging to catch up.

Inside the motel, Rainey took in her surroundings. To the left was a room with a television and an old sofa. The seat cushions were ripped and there were cigarette burns on the floor in front of it.

"Try to ignore how horrible this shithole is," Winnie whispered. "I know it can be shocking."

Rainey shook her head. "What's shocking is how much it reminds me of my house when I was a kid. Practically no furniture and the nauseating smell of smoke and booze."

Winnie leaned in. "And roaches?"

Rainey nodded. "Yeah, plenty of those too. I just realized that the only good thing about juvie, except Tootsie, was that the place was pretty clean."

"So the thing is," Winnie said, leading her deeper into the motel, "never bring a bag or purse here and never, ever put your clothes anywhere other than on a hook. We don't want to carry home bedbugs or roaches on our stuff."

Rainey smiled, her reluctance to work at the motel fading. "Yeah. You don't have to worry about that. I don't even have a purse and I would have no reason to ever take my clothes off in here."

Winnie scoffed, "Got it. Now let's go meet Titus."

Chapter Nine

Rainey trailed behind Winnie as she led them toward the back of the building until they stood in front of a closed door.

"Try not to let Titus get under your skin. Remember, he can be an asshole," Winnie advised.

"I'm sure I'll be fine. I've known some real assholes in my life," she said, snickering.

Winnie smirked and knocked on the door. When it flung open, Titus glowered at them. Rainey had to stifle a gasp. Titus was covered in hair, an extraordinary amount of black hair, on every exposed part of his body. He even had a bushy mound of hair poking out from the neckline of his shirt, and sprouts of hair shooting from his ears. He eyed Rainey suspiciously, then stepped aside to let them enter his dreary office.

"This is Rainey," Winnie said.

"Yeah, no shit," he grunted and moved closer to Rainey, violating her personal space. "You just got out of the can, huh?"

Rainey cringed at his sour breath, "Yeah, I did. I need to work. So here I am."

Titus sneered at her. "You a smartass?"

With another whiff of rancid breath wafting up her nose, Rainey stepped away from the repugnant man. "No, but I'm not gonna let you talk to me like I'm a piece of shit," her annoyance coming out loud and clear.

Titus stepped forward, closing the gap between them. "Yeah, I think you're a smartass. Just by the cocky way you answered me. So listen real good, girlie," he said, pointing his finger at her face. "I don't put up with bitches who think they can give me lip."

Rainey cocked her head to the side and assessed him. She hated his large round head with his deep hairline almost touching his eyebrows and the big gap between his two front teeth. Her upper lip curled and her nose wrinkled, already deciding to stay as far away from Titus as possible.

"Come on, Titus," Winnie interjected to break the tension between them, "cut her a break. You know she's just here to do her job."

"Oh, yeah?" Titus said, ignoring Winnie and circling Rainey, who had curled her hands into fists just in case. "How do I know she ain't here to cause trouble? What makes you so sure?" he asked, looking directly at Winnie.

"I already told you, Tootsie vouched for her."

"Uh-huh. And?"

Rainey watched out of the corner of her eye as he lurked closer.

Finally Winnie put her hands on her hips and raised her voice. "And you know that Tootsie would never send anyone to live in my fucking house that she didn't trust."

"How do I know she ain't gonna steal nothing? Since the bitch is straight outta prison."

"What's she gonna steal?" Winnie countered. "A set of filthy sheets. Oh, maybe she wants your ripped, cum-crusted towels. Stop being mean. Between cum and the period stains, ain't nobody want your damn shit."

Titus stood behind Rainey and cupped her ass with his hands. Outraged, she jumped away, then spun around to face him with her eyes blazing. "Don't you ever touch me!" she said, seething. She clenched her teeth and stared at him with untamed hate. "You hear me?"

"Oh, calm down, you prude," he said, letting out a nervous chuckle and realizing he'd pushed her too far. "You ain't got nothing I want anyway."

Winnie grabbed Rainey's hand. "She doesn't want you manhandling her, asshole. So leave her alone. You have a really shitty way of welcoming new employees. It's no wonder nobody wants to work for you."

Titus let out a low-pitched, grotesque laugh that chugged out of his mouth like the muffler of a car backfiring, then turned to Winnie. "Get her scrawny ass outta here before I change my mind. There's plenty of bitches out there that would like the job."

"Oh, please. I just told you, there isn't anyone that wants to work for you in this dump," Winnie remarked, pulling Rainey out of the office.

In the hall, Rainey was boiling with anger. "What the fuck was that?"

"That's Titus being the dick he was born to be. I warned you about him. The only good thing I can say about him is he'll protect us if anyone gets outta line."

"I can protect myself," Rainey said, with her belly burning from all the anger smoldering inside her.

"Yeah, I'm sure you can," Winnie said, side-eyeing her in a way that gave Rainey the perception she didn't believe her. "But we get some real losers in here. And besides, if the day ever comes that you can't handle someone, the douchebag inside that office will. Anyway, I'll show you where the clean," she air quoted the word, "towels and sheets are. We have a closet on each floor."

Rainey nodded and followed Winnie as she unlocked the closet door on the first floor. Inside, the shelves were filled with mix-matched sheets and grungy white towels. Winnie removed a key attached to a plastic red key ring from a hook on the side wall.

"This is your master key to get into all the rooms and the linen closets on every floor. Whatever you do . . . don't lose it or Titus will make you pay to rekey all the doors after he rips you a new ass."

Rainey turned the key over in her hand. "Got it. What else?"

"Let's see . . . Titus gives us these papers every morning so we know which rooms need to be cleaned," Winnie said, handing two of the four sheets to Rainey.

"What are we supposed to use to clean the rooms?" she asked, looking around.

Winnie pulled a bucket from the bottom of the closet.

Rainey peered inside at the generic cleaners, frayed sponges, and stiff, scruffy rags. "Okay, I guess I'll start on the fourth floor, then I'll go to the third?"

"Yep, that'll work. There's a bucket with the same shit in each closet so you can leave that one here."

Rainey nodded, making a mental note of everything. "Anything else?"

"Yeah, you need to check in with Titus every hour."

Rainey cringed and her brow furrowed. "O God. What for?"

"We have a lot of people who rent for an hour or two, so those rooms need to be cleaned after they check out, which means you go in, remake the bed, and replace any towels they used. No need to change the sheets."

"Okay, that's disgusting."

Winnie shrugged. "Hey, just following orders. That's what Titus wants us to do."

Still grossed out by the thought of multiple people laying naked on the same set of sheets, Rainey cringed and headed toward the stairwell. Up on the fourth floor she looked around at the dark burgundy wallpaper patterned with bright red velvet roses that lined the dimly lit corridor. The floor was covered in worn carpeting with a green and gold floral design. Rainey thought she might pass out from the clash of the rug and wallpaper, and left lying there on the grubby carpet for someone to find.

Even though Rainey was no stranger to grime and crud, the filth of her home had been familiar. On top of the filth was the sleaziness of the motel and its clientele, which was heightening her uneasiness. Still, it was a job, and a job she'd gotten quickly. Rainey shook off the jitters, straightened her back, and walked down the hall with purpose to the linen closet.

Inside the first room marked on her sheet of paper, the tattered bedspread was heaped onto the floor. The windows were covered with heavy navy-blue drapes, and even in the morning sun, the room was dark and dank. The smell was a mixture of sweat, sex, and poverty.

"This place is disgusting," Rainey said aloud.

She moved about quickly, pulling the sheets from the bed and remaking it, trying not to think about what she might be touching. When she lifted the wet towels from the bathroom floor a brown spider with thick, hairy legs scurried out from under it and into a corner.

"What? Are you related to Titus with those hairy legs?" she chuckled, squashing the bug with the toe of her sneaker. If there was one thing Rainey wasn't squeamish about, it was bugs.

As she cleaned each room, she piled the dirty towels in the hallway. After an hour, she went to check in with Titus as instructed.

"You have any rooms you need to add to my list?" she asked, glaring at him from the doorway, remembering how he took the liberty to touch her earlier.

Titus looked up at her. "Yeah," he said, pushing a paper across the desk, "I have a few on three."

Nodding curtly, Rainey took the list and turned to leave.

"Hold up, girlie," he barked, and reluctantly Rainey turned to face him. "Did Winnie tell you how the laundry works?"

Rainey shook her head. "How?" she asked impatiently.

Titus leaned back in his chair. "The door next to my office is where we keep the washer and dryer. Bring all the towels and sheets down and keep them separated by floor. Throw everything in the dryer, fold 'em up, and put them back in the closet. We only wash shit on Fridays. You got that?"

"Yeah, I got it. Keep everything dirty for your customers," Rainey quipped.

Titus grunted. "Go on and get back to work. You got a big mouth, you know that?"

Rainey stared him dead in the eyes, determined not to let him get the upper hand. "Yeah, I know."

As she was walking toward the stairwell, Winnie turned the corner.

"How's it going?" Winnie asked.

"Fine," Rainey said. "I can't believe we only wash sheets and towels once a week. Really, if the customers knew, they'd be pissed."

Winnie just shook her head and snickered. "It is gross, but honestly, the customers don't give a shit. They're all either high or drunk, and a lot of the guys bring hookers here. I've talked to some of the girls over the years and they'd rather be giving blow jobs in this dirty motel than in a dark alley with no one else around."

"Shit, I didn't think of it that way," Rainey said, understanding it better.

"Yeah, well, that's how things play out in this town. You gotta do whatever it takes to get by. You know what I'm saying?"

Rainey nodded. "I'm starting to understand what it means," she stated, and headed upstairs to complete her cleaning. She knew that Winnie wanted her to accept the reason she slept with men for money. But Rainey thought it was better not to address it. Knowing that whatever Winnie did with men was none of her business and she'd never try to tell her what to do. In return, what she did was none of Winnie's business either, and she had learned that some things were better left unsaid.

Chapter Ten

Over the next six months, Rainey got accustomed to living with Winnie and Leo. After getting a taste of paying less for expenses, both brother and sister had no desire to ask Rainey to leave. Besides, she and Winnie had become closer, and Leo and Rainey had learned to be cordial to each other. Even though paying her share of the bills left her with only forty dollars a week, with food still left to buy, she managed to tuck a few dollars away.

Rainey made it a habit to go to her childhood home every Wednesday after work. She would hide near a tree across the street, waiting and hoping to see Ivy. To her disappointment, she hadn't spotted her sister yet.

On a cloudy Wednesday in late spring, she watched her mother and father get into their jalopy and drive off. In the six months she'd been watching the house, she'd never seen them leave, and so, with her heart in her mouth, and knowing this was her chance, Rainey darted across the street and let herself inside. The usual crowd of drifters, squatters, and daytime druggies were scattered throughout, and she slipped past with no one noticing her. She rushed up the steps to the second floor, opened her old bedroom door slowly, and peered inside.

"Ivy?" she whispered.

A small form sat up and Rainey rushed to her. She sat on the floor next to her little sister.

"How are you?" Rainey asked.

Ivy's eyes narrowed. "What do you want?"

It was like Rainey took a punch to the face. More than anything, she wanted Ivy to be happy to see her, like when she was just a little girl.

Composing herself, she said, "I came to visit you. Are you okay?"

"You don't care anyhow," Ivy said, sulking.

"Of course I care about you. I think about you all the time." She put her arm over Ivy's shoulder, but the child quickly yanked her body away. Rainey was using every ounce of energy to hide her disappointment and heartbreak. "You know what?"

Ivy kept her head down, but Rainey noticed her peeking.

"I brought you something."

From inside a paper bag, Rainey pulled out a box of graham crackers and a jar of peanut butter. Ivy's eyes widened, and seeing her reaction, Rainey pulled a cracker from the wax paper and smeared peanut butter on top with the plastic knife she'd brought.

Ivy took the cracker from her and ate it quickly.

"Do you want another one?" Rainey asked, already preparing a second cracker.

Ivy licked the peanut butter from her dirty fingertips, nodding furiously.

Rainey handed her the second cracker, then said, "I'm gonna leave the rest of the crackers and peanut butter with you. Come on. I'll show you where I used to hide our food."

They made their way to the closet, and once the food was stashed, she turned to Ivy.

"Are Mom and Dad treating you okay?"

Ivy shook her head. "Sometimes they lock me in the basement when they have lots of people here so I won't bother them."

Rainey's heart seized, remembering how scary it was for her to be locked in the attic. "Do you stay down there long?"

"Yeah, for a long, long time, and the basement is dark." Ivy lowered her voice, "There are cats in there."

"Cats? We never had cats in the basement before," Rainey commented.

"Yeah," Ivy said, shrugging. "The kind that make squeaky noises and have big teeth."

Putting the pieces together quickly, Rainey gasped. "You mean rats?"

Ivy shrugged again. "I guess. Some are gray and some are black and they got real long tails. It's kinda dark down there so I can't see them so good," Ivy said, leaning into her sister. "Their tails look like snakes coming out of their butts. I hate those things. They scare me a lot."

Rainey gripped Ivy's shoulders firmly. "Listen, don't ever go near them. They're not cats, they're rats. They're dirty and they will bite you."

Ivy's eyes widened and she hugged herself. "I'll kick 'em if they come near me."

"That's right. You kick as hard as you can."

Ivy rested her head against her older sister. "Do you want to live here with me? I can share my room with you."

Rainey thought for a moment, choosing her words carefully, not wanting to diminish Ivy's hopefulness. "Mom and Dad think I'm old enough to live by myself. So they won't let me live here. But you know what?"

Ivy put her thumb in her mouth and sucked on it. She shrugged.

"If there was anyone in the whole world that I could live with it would be with you."

Ivy said nothing, just continued to suck.

"How come you're still sucking your thumb?" Rainey asked, trying to lighten the mood.

"I don't know; 'cause I like it," Ivy answered, thumb still in her mouth.

"I love you," Rainey said, hopeful that Ivy would believe her.

Rainey pulled Ivy closer and let out a breath of relief when Ivy allowed herself to be cradled. A few minutes later, she was asleep. Rainey held onto her for a while, then gently laid her down, covered her with clothes, and sneaked out of the house before her parents returned.

As she walked back home, thoughts of Ivy consumed her. She wanted to figure out a plan to get Ivy away from her parents. The thoughts of her sister trapped in the basement gave her a queasy stomach and a thickness in her throat. By the time Rainey got home, she was disappointed with her inability to come up with a good idea. She'd waited for three years to get out of juvie so she could do something for her and now she was just getting by, barely taking care of herself.

One thought was stuck on repeat in her head. I need to make more money so I can buy Ivy some things she needs, to ease some of her pain.

Chapter Eleven

Back at Winnie's house, Rainey found her friend in the kitchen.

"Winnie, I need to make more money so I can buy Ivy things like food and clothes and stuff. Maybe even be able to move her out of my parents' house soon," Rainey said, desperation ripping through her.

"Okay," Winnie said, looking up from the donut she was eating, "What do you wanna do?"

Rainey shook her head. "I don't know. Maybe I'll get another job. I can work nights."

"Yeah, I guess you could be a cashier at one of the stores on Kensington Avenue."

"I thought about that, but who's gonna trust me with money after being in juvie?" Rainey was pacing the kitchen floor. "I thought that all juvie did was keep me locked up for no good reason, but now it's ruining my chances of getting a better job. What the hell?"

"It's not all bad," Winnie said, placing her donut on a napkin. "You're still living here after all this time. That's a good thing, right?"

Rainey looked into her friend's eyes. "Yeah, it's a very good thing. I'd be on the streets if it weren't for you. But I'm not making enough money to get an apartment on my own to bring Ivy with me, plus I'm not old enough." She stopped pacing. "Unless . . . you and Leo would let Ivy live here?"

Winnie shook her head. "You know that ain't gonna fly. Leo doesn't want any trouble from your parents, and honestly, neither do I. Besides, there isn't anyone here to watch her."

Rainey's shoulders hunched forward. "I know, I know."

"Even if you moved into an apartment, you'd need to pay someone to babysit her while you're working."

"Ugh," Rainey sighed, then flopped in a chair and covered her face with her hands. "I'm afraid something bad is gonna happen to her. They put her in the basement that's filled with rats."

Winnie gasped. "Okay, so, there is one option. Stoker's been asking about you. Remember him? He's got a serious crush on you."

"Stoker?" Rainey said, sitting up straighter, trying to picture him. "The guy from the Drop Inn? The one who wears all the leather?"

"Yeah, that guy is hot. And he wears all that leather because he's a biker."

Rainey knew who Stoker was now. And he wasn't just a biker, he also was a biker in the Devils Angels. As far as she knew, they were considered trouble. Stoker was different, though; he wasn't just hot, he was a nice guy and had been around since she'd started working at the motel, and from the first day, he always acknowledged her. The problem was Rainey didn't understand how he could help her earn more money unless Winnie was suggesting prostitution.

Rainey shook her head. "I know he's a biker in the Devils Angels and they're into some bad shit. Sometimes I overhear them talking about people they need to take care of, and I don't know what it means but it doesn't sound good."

Winnie shrugged. "It depends on how you see it. Yeah, they do some illegal shit, and yeah, they protect themselves and their members. But they also don't beat up on old women or poor people like some gangs do."

"What about drugs? Don't most gangs make their money selling them?"

Winnie wagged her finger at Rainey. "Not the Devils Angels. They take drugs, but they don't sell them. Besides, Stoker only drinks, he never does drugs."

The girls moved into the living room, and Rainey let out a loud sigh. "I must be missing something. How's Stoker gonna get me a better-paying job?"

Winnie sat on the sofa. "He knows a ton of people and has a lot of connections. You should talk to him."

"You're not suggesting I have sex with him, right?"

"No, I know you aren't into doing that. All I'm saying is you should talk to him."

"Does Tootsie know him?" Rainey asked.

Winnie rested her head on the arm of the sofa. “Probably. Tootsie knows everybody.”

Intrigued by the idea that Stoker could help, Rainey sat down next to her. “I’m not sure. I wouldn’t even know what to say.”

“Look,” Winnie said. “Just talk to him. Tell him what’s going on with Ivy and see if he can do anything to help. That’s all you have to do.”

Rainey closed her eyes trying to imagine what she’d even say to the man. “Okay. Maybe. I’ll think about it. I just don’t want to get myself involved in any bullshit. You know?”

“Yeah, I hear you. But you gotta remember, there are weak people and strong people. It’s all up to you. You have to decide if you wanna be a kitten or a lion. If you want to help your sister, then at some point you have to make some hard decisions. People like us, like you and me, good things don’t just fall from the sky. Good things come from pain and sacrifice. Do you think I’m fucking a bunch of guys because I like it? I don’t like it at all. I do it so I can save money so that someday I can have a better life. Maybe even talk Leo into selling this place so I can go live somewhere warm, like Florida. You know, be in a nice house where I can walk down the street without worrying about getting mugged.”

“Yeah, that would be nice,” Rainey said thoughtfully. “I’ll talk to Stoker the next time he’s at the motel.”

Winnie raised her eyebrows, giving her a skeptical look.

Rainey giggled and raised her right hand. “I promise. I’ll at least talk to him and see if he has any ideas.”

“Good girl,” Winnie said.

“I didn’t say I was going to do whatever he thinks, I only said I’ll talk to him.”

She stood and pulled Rainey to her feet. “Well, at least that’s a start. How about we cook spaghetti for dinner?”

Rainey chuckled. “If by ‘cook’ you mean heat a jar of sauce and boil pasta, then I’m in.”

As the two girls walked back into the kitchen, Rainey had a sliver of hope that Stoker, regardless of his membership in a biker gang, might actually help her, so she could help Ivy.

Chapter Twelve

The next weekend Stoker showed up at the Drop Inn. Rainey saw him on the fourth floor and he was carrying a bottle of whiskey in one hand with a woman in her mid-twenties closely behind him. The two were chatting softly and the woman let out a sensual giggle. Opening the motel room door, he turned to her and lifted her long brown hair from her shoulder, kissing her neck. The woman was slender, and wore a hot pink tight-fitting dress that accentuated her curves, and black patent leather heels. As they stood in the hallway kissing, outside their motel room door, Rainey couldn't help but wonder what it would feel like to be kissed by Stoker.

Rainey gawked at Stoker. He looked amazing in jeans, a leather vest with no shirt underneath, and his shoulder-length blond hair. He had blue eyes and a firm, square jaw. His body bulged with muscles—not the body-building kind of muscles, but the kind you see on a surfer, firm, lean, and sexy. She had to agree with Winnie: Stoker was hot, now that she had taken a good, long look at him.

Rainey pretended not to pay attention to the twosome, but she kept glancing in their direction. One time when she looked over, Stoker caught her eye. Suddenly embarrassed, she quickly looked down and hurried down the hallway and into the next room on her list. An hour later, as she was returning from her check-in with Titus, she saw the woman in the tight-fitting dress leaving Stoker's room.

Stoker was leaning against the doorway. "See ya later, sweetheart," he said with a grin.

Rainey glanced at the woman who turned and gave Stoker a magnificent smile before continuing down the hallway. Rainey thought the woman was the prettiest prostitute she'd ever seen—it was no wonder Stoker liked her.

Stoker turned his attention to Rainey. "Hey, missy. How are you?"

A jolt of excitement ran through her at the sound of his voice and the way his eyes fixed on hers. He was like a magnet pulling her closer. Rainey cautiously moved near him. "I'm good. Was that your sister?" she asked, cracking a smile, trying to hide her jitters.

Stoker grunted out a laugh. "That's funny. Nah, my sister was the successful one of the family. She lives in Lancaster with her three kids. Her old man split on her about a year ago."

"Oh," Rainey breathed. "Yeah, sorry."

"What the hell are you sorry for?" Stoker chided.

She shrugged, "Making a bad joke?"

Stoker's eyes dragged over her, making Rainey self-conscious. He nibbled on his bottom lip as he took her in. "So you wanna come in for a while?" He lifted his eyebrows gesturing to the room behind him.

Rainey wrung her hands together taking in his features. Holy shit, he's so sexy. "I'm . . . well, I'm working right now."

"And what? You don't get a break?"

Her heart fluttered. She really wanted to go into the room with him. "Yeah, sure, but I have a lot of work to do."

Stoker raked his fingers through his hair. "Oh, come on. It ain't no big deal. Come in and sit down for a few minutes."

Rainey ran her sweaty palms down her pant legs, then slowly entered the room. Stoker closed the door behind them.

"I think you're cute," he said, moving to the bed and grabbing the bottle of whiskey from the nightstand.

Rainey let out a nervous, schoolgirl giggle, and crossed her arms over her chest. "Thanks, I guess."

"You look nervous," he said. "You ain't got no reason to be nervous. Why don't you come over here and have a drink? It'll help you calm down."

Rainey shook her head. "I don't drink, but thanks."

"Okay, then I'll have a drink by myself. Anyway, how did you end up working here?"

She adjusted her stance, her nerves getting the better of her. "Winnie got me the job."

"How do you know Winnie? You go to school with her or something?"

"No," Rainey said. "I met her through a friend."

"A friend, huh?" Stoker paused and gave her a suggestive smile, and she thought her legs would give out on her.

He leaned back on his elbows and gave her a full view of his ripped stomach. "Okay, well, since you ain't too talkative, I'll fill you in on me. I grew up in West Philly. My dad split on us when I was five, and my mom had lots of boyfriends at our house." Stoker lifted his glass and took a gulp of whiskey. "Anyway, there was this one asshole who used to bust my balls. You know, smack me around and call me a pussy. I was only a kid, but I never backed down from the prick. I vowed one day I'd get back at that lousy fuck."

"Why are you telling me all of this stuff?" Rainey asked, hoping he wasn't expecting her to tell him all about her childhood.

Stoker shrugged. "Just trying to make conversation. You're way too uptight."

"You don't even know me. How would you know if I'm uptight?"

Stoker grinned. "Ah, that's where you're wrong. I know some shit about you. I know you were in juvie. I know you ain't got a boyfriend and I know you can't stand Titus."

Annoyed with his cockiness, Rainey's face flushed and she glowered at him with steely eyes. "So what? You know a few things about me. That doesn't mean anything."

"Whoa," Stoker said, standing and taking a few steps in her direction. "Look, I thought you were hot, so I asked around about you. I'm not trying to piss you off."

Rainey wanted to stay angry but was flattered by the compliment. A small smile sneaked onto her lips, but she wiped it off quickly.

"Fine. I went to juvie. And that fucked up my life and now I have to work here. And, yes, I think Titus is a scumbag." Stalling, she chewed on her bottom lip. "Anyway, I heard you know a lot of people and I was wondering if you could help me get a better job. One that pays more money."

A satisfying smile crept to his lips. "Well, I might be able to help you," he hedged. "I'll tell you what . . . let me think about it and ask around a little. Is there anything you can't do?"

Rainey moved toward the door. "Not really, but"—she looked at him with a fixed gaze— "I don't prostitute."

Stoker's laughter roared, filling up the entire room and making her smile. Then he patted the bed beside him, "Why don't you come over here and sit down next to me?"

Reluctant, but driven by curiosity about what made him tick, she sat on the bed. Her heart pitter-pattered sitting so close to him. His broad chest

and toned upper body made her want to touch him. The instinct was new to her, but she didn't mind it.

Stoker nodded. "I'll make a note that you don't prostitute. In the meantime, though, maybe I can take you out to dinner or something."

Rainey stood, suddenly needing a way out. She was inexperienced with men, and he was making her hormones soar. "Um, maybe. I don't know."

Stoker stood and put his hands on her shoulders. "Have you ever had a boyfriend?"

Rainey, under pressure and embarrassed, shook her head; the desire to kiss him was overwhelming. "I was fourteen when I got sent to juvie so I never dated." She unknowingly rubbed her neck; she'd never been attracted to anyone in a sexual way, and she wasn't sure how to handle herself.

"That's okay," he cooed.

Rainey, wanting to get back to her work, stepped away from him. She needed to get out of that room, catch her breath, and pull herself together.

"You look scared. I ain't gonna hurt you."

"I'm not scared, and I never thought you were gonna hurt me," she said. "Look, I have to get back to work. Thanks for trying to help me."

"And that dinner?" Stoker said, smiling broadly.

"Fine. Just dinner, though." All of her senses were on fire, and she hoped her face wasn't showing it.

"Great. I'll be back in a few days and we can figure something out."

Rainey left the room. With the door closed behind her, she stood in the hallway trying to settle her shaking hands. Her insides were tingling. He was so good-looking. She hadn't noticed how handsome he was before now. Rainey wasn't sure if she was more excited he could get her a better-paying job or that she would have dinner with him.

***

That night, Rainey told Winnie about her conversation with Stoker.

"That's great!" Winnie said. "Are you gonna go out with him?"

"Yeah, but it makes me really nervous. I've never dated anyone."

Winnie smiled and tilted her head. "Do you have a crush on Stoker? You do, don't you?"

Rainey waved her off but could not keep herself from smiling. Something about the way Stoker looked at her filled her with desire.

"You do! You like him. That's great," Winnie said. "Just take it slow. I mean, he is hot and all, but he's really into hookers too."

Rainey's crush on him came tumbling down. How could she have been so stupid as to forget that? Obviously Stoker had been playing her. Why would he want to get involved with her when he can just go out and pay for sex? "Yeah, he was with a hooker today. Jeez, I'm an idiot."

Winnie's faced pinched. "No you're not, just take it slow. Don't get all caught up in what could happen and just go with it. You worry way too much."

"All I want is for him to hook me up with a better job."

"Uh-huh," Winnie smiled.

Rainey smiled back, but she was worried about her future. She recognized there was an energy between her and Stoker, and was apprehensive about letting herself get involved with him. She needed to keep her thoughts and actions focused on making a better life for herself and hoping that one day she could take care of Ivy.

Chapter Thirteen

Three days later Stoker returned to the Drop Inn. He went alone and hadn't rented a room. Instead, he walked the floors looking for Rainey until he found her. He knocked on the open door softly and when she didn't answer, he let himself into the room and closed the door behind him. In the bathroom, Rainey hummed as she wiped out the sink.

"Hey, gorgeous," Stoker crooned.

"Shit!" she yelped, whirling around and throwing her hands in the air. "Don't sneak up on me like that."

Stoker chuckled, a deep, throaty sound so sexy it gave Rainey goosebumps and a yearning to throw her arms around his neck.

"Sorry about that, doll. I didn't mean to scare you. I came to see if you wanna have dinner with me tonight."

Rainey ran one hand over her hair and pulled on the ends, trying to seem casual while her insides were jumping. "Yeah, tonight would be good."

Stoker grabbed her hands. "So I'll pick you up at the house . . . at Winnie's?"

Rainey looked at their hands nestled together and blushed. A shudder ran through her body as though being energized with a high-voltage wire.

"Ye . . . yea . . . yeah," she stuttered.

Stoker smiled, leaned forward, and kissed her cheek gently, lingering for a moment.

His smell was alluring and she inched her face closer. When he pulled back, Rainey clasped her hands together and let out a nervous giggle.

"I'll pick you up at seven," he said and walked out.

Rainey stood looking through the door into the bedroom for several seconds after he was gone. Then she turned and grabbed onto the sink

for support and looked at herself in the mirror. Stop being so weird, she thought. It's only dinner.

***

That evening, she sat on the sofa impatiently waiting for Stoker to pick her up. It was almost seven thirty when she turned to Winnie. "Stoker said he'd be here at seven. He ain't coming."

Winnie looked up from her magazine. "Oh, stop it. He's probably running late. He'll be here."

Rainey went to the window and pulled back the curtain, scanning the street. "If he isn't here in fifteen minutes I'm changing and going to bed."

"Chill, girl. Don't get yourself all twisted. Just give him some time."

Rainey sauntered into the kitchen several times to glance at the clock on the stove, her disappointment deepening each time. At nine o'clock she accepted that Stoker wasn't coming. She looked at Winnie. "I'm going to bed."

Glancing back, Winnie gave her a soft nod. "Yeah, sorry it didn't work out."

"Whatever. It's no big deal."

"You know, it's okay to be upset. You don't have to hide it from me," Winnie assured her.

In the distance, the girls heard the hum of a motorcycle. Their eyes locked as the sound of the bike got closer.

"He's here!" Winnie said victoriously.

"Shit, I wish he hadn't shown up. I'd already made up my mind that I didn't want to see him ever again," Rainey stated, her nerves now getting the better of her.

A minute later there was a knock at the door.

Winnie jumped up. "You stay here." She pushed her magazine into Rainey's hands. "Sit on the sofa and pretend like you're reading."

When Stoker walked into the living room, Rainey kept her eyes on the pages of the magazine.

"Hey, doll. Sorry I'm late," he offered.

"What time is it?" Rainey asked in a disinterested voice.

Stoker looked at his wristwatch. "Ah, around nine."

"Oh. It's kinda late to go out. I have work tomorrow," she said in a cool tone, looking up at him.

Stoker sat down next to her. "It ain't that late. Look, I had some shit I needed to deal with and I got tied up. Come on, let's just go out for a while."

Unable to contain herself, Rainey frowned. "Stoker, we were supposed to go out two hours ago."

Stoker put his arm around her and she smelled liquor on his breath. This made her wonder if he'd been at a bar drinking and had forgotten about their date.

"Come on, don't be a tight ass. We got the whole night."

Rainey laid the magazine down, energy thrumming through her. Half of her wanted to slap him and the other half wanted to throw her arms around his neck. "No, we don't," she said tightly. "I already told you that I have work tomorrow."

Stoker pulled Rainey into him. "Ah, come on. Let's just take a ride on my bike," he said, glancing at Winnie, who was in the doorway staring at them.

Rainey pulled away from him. "I don't know about that . . . it smells like you've been drinking. Are you drunk?"

Stoker laughed. "No, doll. I ain't drunk. I promise."

Relenting to her longing to be with him, Rainey pushed her hair over her shoulders. "Fine, but not for long. Okay?"

Stoker's eyes took her in. Her long blond hair laid easily down her back. Her tank top fitted her slender body and her tight jeans emphasized her curves.

"Whatever you say," Stoker said, kissing her shoulder. Rainey thought she'd lose herself, her frustration from a moment ago, gone. He was seductive and she loved that he was laser focused on her now . . . as though she was the only person who mattered to him.

***

Outside, Rainey soaked in Stoker's rugged elegance as she watched him climb onto his motorcycle. His thin waist and thick thighs. The jeans that hugged his backside. So many things that she'd never noticed about a man before, but now, everything about Stoker captivated her.

"Climb on," he said, flashing her a smile.

Rainey approached, then gingerly put her leg over the seat.

"You gotta hold onto me real tight, doll."

As Rainey wrapped her arms around his waist, her body lightened and her senses stirred, an awareness about herself she'd never experienced before. It was delicious, and she liked it.

"Where are we going?" she yelled over the rev of the engine.

"Somewhere special."

Rainey tightened her hold on Stoker and rested the side of her face on his leather jacket, wondering if this was what love felt like.

Chapter Fourteen

After riding for fifteen minutes, Stoker pulled up in front of a row home. They were in the Strawberry Mansion section of Philadelphia. She'd never been there before now, but it seemed an extension of Kensington by the looks of the neighborhood. She looked up at the adjoined homes and noticed that the first-floor windows were boarded and covered in beautiful graffiti art, the lawn was mostly weeds and dirt with trash strewn in random places, and the porch was overcrowded with lawn chairs. Music blared from inside the building. Rainey's stomach spun; she'd been expecting a diner, maybe even a nicer restaurant, but not this.

Stoker parked his motorcycle, got off, and held out his hand for her. "Here we are . . . I told you I was taking you somewhere special. My club owns most of the houses on this block and we're having a little party tonight. I don't normally bring girls home."

Rainey gave him a worried look then she raised her eyebrows and a mischievous smile formed on her lips. "Probably because you see a lot of hookers."

Stoker broke into laughter. "That's true. No fuss, no muss. I ain't too good at relationships."

Rainey tucked that tidbit of information away with the understanding that their relationship would remain casual. Disappointed, she wished she'd stayed home.

Stoker walked toward the front porch, "Let's go, doll."

Rainey grabbed his arm. "Look, I'd rather you'd call me by my name, I don't like being called 'doll.'" She looked up at him and smiled. "Okay?"

Stoker's face grew serious, and for an instant she thought she'd insulted him. Then he put his hand on the small of her back, and his other hand

lifted her long blond hair from her neck. Leaning in, his lips grazed her neck as he whispered, "Rainey, do you wanna go inside with me?" he purred in a deep throaty voice.

Rainey's knees wobbled, and at that moment she would have followed Stoker anywhere. With butterflies in her stomach, she said, "Yeah, sure. I wanna go."

Stoker took a solid hold of her hand and led them into the house. There were men in their early to late twenties dressed in denim and leather. She noted that they all had chains hanging from their wallets, just like Stoker. Rainey's eyes fell on the women, who looked like they were ready to rumble. Mostly all of them had dark eyeshadow and big hair, teased and sprayed into place. They wore tight jeans, had exposed cleavage, and each had piercings and tattoos covering their arms and chests. Watching them, Rainey already knew that she didn't have enough denim, leather, or makeup that could make her look like she fit in. These women possessed a hard, raunchy sex appeal that was alluring and scary.

Rainey unconsciously slid her hand into Stoker's and he squeezed it gently.

"You ain't worried, are you? Nobody's gonna hurt you here," Stoker said, glancing at her.

Rainey chuckled. "No, I'm not worried. I grew up in a house filled with squatters and addicts shooting up everywhere, some rough people too."

Stoker raised his eyebrows. "Oh, yeah? Any of those people ever hurt you?"

Rainey pivoted, not wanting to talk about Freddy or Jiggy with him. She didn't want to share too much. "There was a lot of partying at my house and a lot of drug dealing." She eyed him and asked, "Do you use drugs?"

"Nope." Stoker shook his head. "Used to take every drug I could get my hands on, but not anymore." He lifted an index finger in the air, as if remembering something. "I never shot up, though. I liked to snort my drugs or pop a pill. I did some stupid shit until my biker brothers beat the addiction outta me. I drink, but that's it. How about you?"

Rainey blew out her breath and shook her head. "No, I've never even tried drugs. I've seen what it does to people. My mom and dad showed me what I'd never want to be."

"Well, I like that you don't do none of that shit. I mean, if you did like dope, then this," he said, waving his hand between them, "could be

a problem. That's part of the reason I'm not real good at relationships. All the chicks around here like to party."

Rainey searched his eyes, wanting to believe he was telling her the truth. She wouldn't be with anyone using drugs.

"Hey," Stoker said, "enough of this serious talk. Let's go grab a beer."

Rainey cleared her thoughts and decided quickly to be honest with him. "I don't drink beer. I've never tried that either."

"Really? All right. That's cool."

"Maybe there's soda somewhere," she suggested.

Stoker smiled, almost laughing. "Yeah, I ain't so sure we got any of that, but let's go check."

Stoker stayed by Rainey's side throughout the party. He introduced her to a few people who seemed nice, but after saying hello, they didn't talk to her. While Stoker was waiting for Rainey to come out of the bathroom his friend Andrew approached him.

"What are you doing? Guarding the blond chick? Afraid someone is gonna snatch her fine ass out from under your nose?" Andrew joked.

Stoker grinned. "Fuck you, man. She doesn't know anybody here and you're all a bunch of fucking derelicts."

Andrew nodded and took a swig of his beer. "This your new ol' lady?"

"You're an asshole, Drew," Stoker whispered, followed by a quiet snicker. "I don't want you to scare her off. Who knows what'll happen? Right now the two of us are just checking each other out."

"You bang that ass yet?" Andrew asked.

"Shut up, man."

"Oh, now you're waiting to tap an ass. That ain't the Stoker I know."

Stoker lit a cigarette. "Yeah, well, this chick is different. She ain't a hooker."

The door opened and Rainey smiled at the two men.

"This is my friend Andrew. We bunk together," Stoker said.

She moved closer to him. "Hey, Andrew. I'm Rainey."

"Yeah, good to meet you. You can come around here whenever you want." Andrew eyed her up and down, and Rainey watched Stoker's face change into a scowl. He's jealous, she thought. Good.

Stoker pushed his friend in the shoulder. "Don't be a jerkoff," he wisecracked.

"Okay, okay," Andrew said. "I'll split and leave you two alone. I was only playing with you, Rainey. It's good to meet you. Maybe I'll see you around."

After Andrew walked away, Stoker turned to her. "Drew's cool. He just ain't used to me bringing babes home."

"Babes?" she repeated, smiling.

"Aaaaah, sorry. Women. Is that better? I don't wanna insult you again."

Rainey shrugged, flattered he considered her a babe and feeling smitten toward him now.

"Anyway," Stoker said, putting his arm over her shoulder, "my room is in the house next door. You wanna go check it out?"

Rainey's breath hitched. She'd been comfortable being in the large crowd of people and had forgotten that Stoker might want more. "Um, I'm not sure."

"Listen, we ain't gonna do nothing you don't wanna do."

Rainey looked into his smoldering eyes. "Okay, but I need to go home soon, so just for a while."

The two left the party and went next door. It was dark inside except for the moonlight shining across the hallway from a second-floor window. Rainey could still hear the faint sound of the music from the party as Stoker led her up to the room he shared with Andrew. Her heart pulsated rapidly as they stepped inside the bedroom and he closed the door.

"I've been wanting to kiss you all night," he said, gently pressing her against the door. "That okay?"

His mouth was so close to hers she could almost feel his lips before they touched. She nodded, and in the next moment they shared their first kiss. Having never been kissed before, Rainey was self-conscious. When he pulled away, she looked into his eyes, trying to see if she'd done it right.

"I've never kissed a guy before," Rainey muttered.

Stoker cracked a smile. "Well, I guess you're a natural. Plus, you taste like fucking sunshine."

Rainey pushed on his chest. "Yeah, right."

Stoker ran his hand down her back and over her ass and she didn't mind. "How old are you, anyway?"

"Seventeen," she said, waiting for him to kiss her again.

"When you gonna be eighteen?" he asked, leaning in closer.

"In a month," she said nervously. "How old are you?"

"Hmm, well, I'm twenty-eight." He lifted her chin with his hand. "Too old for you?"

Rainey shook her head. "I don't think so. Do you think you're too old for me?"

Stoker stepped back from her. "Nope, especially since you're almost eighteen that makes you old enough to make your own decisions."

"I've been making most of the decisions for me and my little sister since I was nine."

"Kinda young to be doing that," he commented, yearning to kiss her again.

"I was young for a lot of things. My parents were never there for us. Now my little sister, Ivy, is living with them by herself, and I worry about her," she rambled.

"Hey, listen," Stoker said, "let's talk about your sister later. Why don't we relax on my bed and listen to some music?"

Rainey's face drained of color. "I'm not ready for that."

"Ready for what? I already told you. We ain't gonna do nothing you don't want to do." Stoker nibbled on her earlobe, and her breath pulled in and she held it. He was so seductive that she could barely breathe. "We could just hang, and you know, kiss a little."

Her eyes eased closed and she reveled in the sensations that Stoker sent through her body. "Okay, but just kissing."

Stoker led Rainey over to his bed and she sat on the edge. He bent down and pressed her back onto the mattress. Then his mouth met hers and suddenly she was lost in unfamiliar territory . . . the feeling of being wanted and craving another person so badly, it hurt.

Chapter Fifteen

Rainey wanted to stay in Stoker's arms all night. She loved how his mouth fit so perfectly with her own. And the way his strong hands gently touched her breasts over the top of her shirt. After a long time together, she asked him to bring her home. When he dropped her off in front of the house, he gave her a broad smile.

"See you soon, Rainey," he cooed.

"Okay," she whispered, watching him closely, loving the way her name flowed from his lips and not wanting him to leave. Then she leaned toward him and he met her mouth with his.

Once they parted, Rainey turned on her heel and trotted to the house. Inside, she rushed up the stairs and knocked softly on Winnie's bedroom door.

"Yeah?" Winnie said, groggy from sleep.

Rainey opened the door and bolted to the side of her bed.

Winnie rubbed her eyes. "What time is it?"

"It's one o'clock," she said in a hushed voice, unable to keep the smile off her face.

Winnie sat up. "So I guess things went good with Stoker tonight?"

Rainey nodded. "He's such a good kisser. You can't even imagine."

"Oh, yeah? Do you have someone to compare him to?" Winnie teased.

"No, but who cares?" she said, giggling.

Winnie chuckled. "I'm sure he is a good kisser. Did you have sex with him?"

"No. I hardly even know him. Besides, I'm not on birth control or anything. I like Stoker a lot, but the last thing I need is to get pregnant."

Winnie flopped back on her pillow. "Well, you need to go to the clinic and get your ass on birth control. You know, so you don't get preggo."

"How much does that cost?" Rainey asked.

"The clinic?"

"Yeah, and to get on birth control," Rainey answered, a little embarrassed.

"The clinic is free and the birth control pills will cost you about twenty-five bucks a month. They practically give that shit away so that us Kensington girls don't get knocked up. It's cheaper than addicts and homeless teens having babies that they can't take care of."

"Will you go with me?" Rainey asked.

"Yeah, I don't have any guys coming to see me tomorrow, so we can stop there on our way back from work."

Rainey cringed. "I worry about you . . . that one of those guys you have sex with will hurt you someday. I wish you didn't have to do it."

"Yeah, and I wish I was six feet tall, blond-haired and blue-eyed with billionaire parents, but I ain't, so I gotta do what I gotta do," Winnie said, fluffing it off as a joke.

Rainey moved onto the bed next to her. "So, then you're on birth control?"

"Hell, yeah. How do you think I know about the clinic? But still when I have sex I never do it without a condom. No telling what those guys got."

Rainey nodded, thinking about some of the men who paid to have sex with Winnie. "I hate some of the guys at the Drop Inn."

"Well, that's because you don't make money from them. I agree with you that some are really annoying. I never set out to sell sex, it happened because I needed the money. One day I was doing it to pay my bills, and before I knew it, I was doing it with more guys so I could buy stuff I wanted," Winnie admitted.

Rainey leaned up on her elbow, understanding how life can change in an instant. "I hope I never have to do that with anyone. After what happened with Freddy, I told myself I would always have control of who I had sex with. I was lucky nothing happened with Jiggy. Who knows where I'd be today?"

Winnie gave her a grave look. "I get it, but your experience with sex is from a fucked-up place. I think if I had been raped like you were, I probably wouldn't be able to have sex with any of those guys either. But back to Stoker, you better be careful with him, make sure he wears a condom when you finally do have sex. He's been with a lot of prostitutes."

Rainey grimaced. "Yeah, I didn't think about that. Honestly, it doesn't bother me that he's been with a lot of women. I don't have anything against prostitutes; a close friend of mine in juvie was one. I always pictured myself with a strong guy that would never let anything bad happen to me." She smiled at her friend. "I think he would be that kind of guy. I really like him . . . a lot!

***

A few days later, Rainey and Winnie, soaked from the pouring rain, walked into the women's clinic. Rainey stepped up to the window and told the woman behind the glass why she was there.

The middle-aged woman looked at her with a blank expression, and Rainey fidgeted under her penetrating gaze. Finally, the woman passed her a clipboard. "Fill out these forms. You can have a seat and someone will be out to get you when the doctor can see you."

"Why do I need to see a doctor?" she asked, caught off-guard.

"You want birth control, right?"

She nodded, wondering if all of this was really worth it just to have sex with some guy she barely knew and who had already told her he wasn't the relationship type.

"Well, the only way you're going to get it is if you see a doctor first," the woman said, sounding annoyed.

"How much will this cost?" Rainey lowered her voice. "My friend said this clinic is free. Is that true?"

"Your friend is right. Your appointment is free because we are funded by the city and other organizations."

"Thank you," Rainey said letting out a nervous breath.

Rainey took a seat next to Winnie to fill out the forms. Winnie leaned into her and whispered, "You better say you're eighteen or else they'll want a parent's permission."

Rainey glanced at her. "Damn, you think of everything."

Inside the examination room Rainey was tense, not knowing what to expect. A nurse finally sat with her and asked general health questions, handed her a gown, and instructed her to undress.

"Why do I have to get undressed? I just want to get birth control," Rainey said, wanting to get out of there quickly.

The nurse gave her a warm smile. "Honey, at this clinic you can't get birth control pills without a pelvic exam."

Rainey looked down at her hands as panic traveled from her core into her throat. Her voice struggled against her larynx, as though the tube leading from her mouth to her lungs was filled with sludge. She hadn't been touched between her legs since Freddy had violated her. "Is that going to hurt?" she managed.

"Well, it's not comfortable, but women do it every day." The nurse patted her shoulder. "Dr. Astor is a good physician and she's gentle. You'll do just fine, I promise."

Rainey didn't anticipate that lying on the table with her legs in the air and spread apart would be more uncomfortable than the actual exam, but it was for her.

"You can sit up now," Dr. Astor told her once she had finished.

Rainey quickly lifted her legs out of the stirrups, sat upright covering herself with the paper sheet, and looked at the doctor with anticipation.

"So have you used birth control in the past?" Dr. Astor asked.

Rainey winced and squirmed on the table as the doctor watched her, suddenly unsure of herself. She shook her head.

Dr. Astor placed her hand over Rainey's. "Have you been sexually active yet?"

"No," Rainey said, but then realized that wasn't true, not really. "Yes. I don't know. I mean it wasn't like I wanted to," she squeaked out.

The doctor was observing her closely, sensing the girl had a grim story. "I don't understand. Can you tell me more about it?" she asked, moving closer.

"It's a long story, and um, I have to get going soon," Rainey said timidly.

Dr. Astor's eyes widened and Rainey looked away, nervous she'd have to tell her all the details about what Freddy had done to her. So she offered what she was willing to share. "It's not like he was my boyfriend or anything," she explained. "He was a lot older than me."

Dr. Astor kept a steady gaze on Rainey, then said gingerly, "I see. Do you mind me asking how old you were when you first had sex?"

Rainey's cheeks flushed and she bit her bottom lip. "Thirteen," she whispered, images of Freddy's body bearing down on her flashing through her mind, despite her efforts to suppress them.

"I see," Dr. Astor said, not taking her eyes off of the teen. Unable to bear it, Rainey turned and stared at the wall. Her eyes welled and the tears

spilled over, crying harder when the doctor draped a thin blanket over her shoulders. "Did someone force you to have sex with them?" she asked gently.

Rainey nodded, turning to face the doctor again. "It's fine, it was a long time ago."

"Did you tell your parents?"

"Yeah, they knew."

"Well, did they press charges against this man?"

"No. I taught myself how to get over it," Rainey said.

It was true. Rainey had spent years suppressing the emotions attached to the memories, and when they did surface, she watched those moments from a distance, never allowing herself to fully accept the psychological scars that were left behind.

The doctor gave her a curious look. "Is there anything I can do to help you? Perhaps you'd like to talk about this with one of our therapists?"

Rainey shrugged off the blanket and stood from the table. "No thanks," she said bluntly, realizing this visit had become much more personal than she had expected. "Can I get the birth control pills?"

"Yes, of course," Dr. Astor said, then gave her a sympathetic look. The doctor glanced around the room, trying to stall, wanting to do more to help the girl. "If you change your mind and want to talk with someone, we are here to help."

Rainey gave her a tight smile, wanting to get out of there. "Thanks for the offer, but I'm good."

"I'm sorry, Rainey, but I have to ask how you made yourself get over being raped, as you described it. I have to say, that's a little concerning."

Rainey looked directly at the doctor and back down at her hands. "Well, I taught myself how to pretend like it never happened. It took me a while, but I practiced not thinking about it, and after a while, it felt like a dream. You know, like when you wake up and you know you had a bad dream, but you can't remember most of what happened."

"I see," Dr. Astor said, and Rainey could sense she was waiting for more, but there wasn't more to tell her. "I'd like to do something for you. Something so that you can work through what was done to you."

Rainey shook her head. "Thanks, but I'll be fine."

Thankfully, the doctor left the room without asking any more questions.

Alone in the examination room, Rainey exhaled loudly. Talking about Freddy was hard on her. She'd never admitted to an adult what had happened to her or what would have happened to her again if Jiggy hadn't been disrupted by the police that night. Getting busted and being sent to juvie was both a blessing and a curse.

Back in the waiting room, Rainey took the first month of pills from the woman at the counter, gave her twenty-five dollars, found Winnie, and left as quickly as she could.

As the girls walked back to the house, Rainey couldn't get the images of Freddy's long, stringy hair and yellow-stained teeth out of her head. She shuddered at the memory of his breath, which was a mixture of drugs and mouth rot. Then she wished Dr. Astor had never asked her those questions and that she hadn't told the woman so much. Rainey had been doing fine, and now she couldn't get Freddy out of her head.

Chapter Sixteen

It seemed as though until Rainey got out of juvie, the only consistent thing she had in her life was being let down. She understood disappointment well; it meant living with looming heartbreak that created heightened anxiety as she waited for the next bad thing to come her way. Being let down by other people was both something she'd come to expect and what she hated most.

Rainey had learned to tuck her trauma away in a safe place so she could survive each moment that followed. Shortly after she had been raped, she'd buried the filthy, smelly reality of the assault deep inside, and keeping it locked away her life went on.

Now Rainey's visit with Dr. Astor stirred a memory she'd worked so hard to keep hidden from herself. Once she allowed the memory of Freddy to emerge, the violent moment that changed her self-worth took away her focus. She obsessed on the rape. She was stuck on knowing that her parents used her to pay their debts. With no skills to combat the old horror that took up residence in her mind, she spiraled downward into a place the likes of a swampland. An ugly world where the trees were strangled by thick gray vines and she didn't know what waited for her below the depths of the black water. She was floating vulnerably, waiting for something to go horribly wrong, for someone to grab her and drag her to the lowest depths, to the muddy bottom, where she would be stuck and where no one could save her.

"Hey, Rainey," Stoker's voice rumbled, coming up behind her.

Torn from her depressing thoughts, Rainey jumped. "Crap! Don't creep up on me like that when I'm working."

Stoker put his arms around her waist. "That wasn't the hello I was hoping for," he said, leaning in and kissing her.

She stared at him, trying to shake the remaining thoughts from a moment ago.

Stoker pulled his head back, looking more closely at her. "What's wrong? Did something happen?"

Rainey shook her head, but tears spilled down her cheeks. Her thoughts of Freddy since she left the clinic two days prior had worn her down. Now, seeing the concern Stoker had for her made her break down.

"Hey, hey. Come on. Let's sit down," he fussed, leading her over to the unmade bed in the motel room.

"I can't," she bawled. "If Titus finds me sitting on the bed and not cleaning this filthy room, he'll fire me."

Stoker strode to the door and shut it. "Titus doesn't have a fucking clue what you're doing. Don't worry about him. Come on," he said, taking her hand and pulling her to the bed.

Rainey allowed herself to follow his commands, and as if in a trance, plopped down next to him, hunching her shoulders forward.

"Tell me what's bugging you," he said, rubbing her back.

Rainey shrugged him off and shook her head. "I can't."

"Why?"

"I'm afraid you'll hate me," she admitted.

"Look, unless you trashed my bike there ain't nothing you could've done to make me hate you," he said, attempting a joke.

Rainey looked into his face with bloodshot eyes. "I went to the clinic in Kensington."

"Okay, and what happened?"

Rainey looked across the room, let out a heavy sigh, and bent her head forward.

An alarming thought ran through Stoker's head. She has a terminal illness. "Are you . . . sick?" Stoker asked, sounding worried.

His tone snapped Rainey out of it. "What? No, no. I'm not sick."

Stoker's gaze met hers. "Okay, so what were you doing at the clinic? Let's start there."

Rainey raked her fingers through her hair, not wanting to share the details but knowing she had to be honest. Then she blew out a breath, emptying her lungs. "I went there to get birth control pills."

"All right. So that doesn't sound so bad."

"It wasn't that . . . it's just that the doctor asked me some questions and, there's this thing that happened to me when I was younger."

"What thing?" he asked in a terse tone.

Rainey stood and crossed to the other side of the room. "I was raped by this older guy and I haven't thought about it in a while. Anyway, the doctor made me remember it, and it's messing with my head."

Stoker leapt up. "Who the fuck is this guy? What's his name?"

Rainey's eyes widened. She hadn't expected his reaction. She wasn't planning on telling him, and now he was livid. While she liked that he went into a defensive mode, she wasn't sure what to do. "You're making me nervous. Yelling and getting mad isn't going to help me."

"I'm sorry," Stoker said. "I'm pissed off. Just tell me what I can do."

Rainey shook her head. "There's nothing you can do. It was a long time ago. I haven't even thought about it that much over the years. And, then this doctor I never met asks me a few dumb questions and I"— she paused and looked away from him—"I blurted it all out like diarrhea. Bits and pieces of what happened poured outta me and I had no control . . . I'm struggling with it a little."

Stoker wrapped his arms around her. "A couple of things," he said, his voice even, which helped calm Rainey. "First, you have no reason to be scared. You're my girl and I'll keep you safe. Second, I want you to tell me this guy's name."

"I'm your girl?"

He looked into her eyes, "Yes, you're my girl."

Rainey's heart took flight at his answer, but she kept quiet . . . she'd already said too much. Just like with the doctor, she regretted having said anything. When am I going to learn to stop telling people more than they need to know?

"What is this scumbag's name?" he asked again. His voice was gentle, but his eyes held an intensity Rainey had never seen before.

"What does that matter?" she asked, squirming a little. "It was a long time ago."

"Great. Then tell me his name."

She considered for a moment, torn between not wanting to involve Stoker and hoping that he might make Freddy sorry he ever touched her. "His first name was Freddy, but that's all I know about him."

"He's bald on top with long hair down the sides?"

Rainey's eyes bulged; Stoker knew him. "He's not a friend of yours, is he? O my God, please tell me he isn't part of your club."

"He sure ain't. That motherfucker ain't no friend of mine. I know his skank ass. He deals a lot of meth. The guy is an asshole. And now I know he's a perverted, pedophile bitch too," Stoker growled.

"You're not gonna do anything, are you? He'll come after me," Rainey cried, panicking over what she'd done.

Stoker moved closer and pressed his chest against hers. He lifted her chin, looked into her eyes, and spoke to her with the gentleness she craved. "You listen to me and hear me real clear. He's known as Fast Freddy on the streets because he's quick to fuck people over. But the most important thing for you to understand is that Freddy won't ever come after you. He'll never say your name or look in your direction. That's a promise."

Rainey trembled as her body melted into Stoker's. She wanted to believe him. She needed to believe that Stoker would keep her safe.

She thought, maybe he won't let me down, like so many people have done before him.

Chapter Seventeen

For the next three weeks, Stoker stood outside the Drop Inn waiting for Rainey to finish work. A smile would spread across his face when he'd see her bounding down the cement steps.

"Thanks for being around so much," she told him one afternoon while they were lounging on the sofa at his house.

"I told you that you ain't got nothing to worry about—and I meant it," he reassured her.

He took her hand and pulled her across his lap. His lips brushed just below her collarbone, making Rainey shiver. She leaned in and kissed him, marveling for the millionth time she was finally with someone who wanted to love and protect her.

"So you have a birthday this week, right?" he asked.

Rainey beamed. "Aw, you remembered. How romantic," she joked.

"Sure, I remember. I thought we'd do something special to celebrate."

Rainey laid her head on his shoulder and wrapped her arms around him tighter. "Like what?" she asked, letting out a short giggle.

"There's a motel in the Poconos where our club stays when we travel. I was thinking we could go there for a weekend," he offered.

Rainey smiled, but her elbows were plastered against her sides, knowing that a whole weekend in a motel together would mean they would have sex. This unnerved her. She liked the innocent kissing and touching. She had hoped it would last much longer.

"What?" he asked, looking down at her. "You afraid of something?"

Rainey shrugged, trying to find the words. "I'm not afraid . . . just . . . you know, nervous. We've never been away together. Um, I've never stayed in a motel before . . . with a guy. Besides, I'd have to see if I can get off work," she added as a backup excuse.

Stoker ran his hand over her thigh, which sent a thrill through her. "And you're nervous about sex?"

Rainey took a playful swat at him. "Well, yeah, I am. It's a big step for me and, let's face it, the only sex I ever had was torturous. I'm afraid I'll freak out or something."

Stoker looked into her eyes the way he always did when he was serious. "Sex ain't what you experienced. What Freddy did to you was just getting his rocks off. When you make love it's the best thing in the world, for both people."

"It sounds nice, but what if I don't like sex? What if I'm too scared to go through with it?" she asked, worrying about losing him.

"Let's just take it one step at a time. Okay? Don't get too worked up over it. Besides," he said with a smile, lightening the mood, "I'm a great lover," he bragged.

"Oh, yeah? Were you a great lover to the hookers you slept with?" she asked in a kidding tone, but deep down wanting to know the answer.

But Stoker's eyes grew dark and he was serious again. "Nah. See, you have it all wrong. I've always been nice to women, whether I pay them for sex or not. Doing it with hookers, that's just sex between two people—a business arrangement."

"Well," Rainey said, "are you still . . . having business arrangements?"

"No. I gave that up for you."

Her heart fluttered in her chest; it was what she was hoping he'd say. She let out a small chuckle; she'd been wondering for weeks if he was "seeing" anyone else.

"So we're only dating each other then?" she asked.

"Well . . . yeah. I didn't think about it like that, but sure, I don't want to be with nobody but you," he said, looking into her eyes so she'd know he was serious. "And you won't see nobody but me, right?" he asked as a confirmation rather than a question.

She smiled softly. "Right," she said, pulling his head to hers and kissing him. "I'm really happy."

"Me too. Now, about that weekend away . . ."

Rainey nuzzled his neck. "Okay, I'll ask Titus for a couple of days off," she committed.

***

The following Saturday, Rainey left her house with a small backpack she'd borrowed from Winnie. Stoker handed her a helmet and they set out for her birthday weekend. When they pulled up to the motel, Rainey got off the motorcycle and stared at the lighted sign that stood high on a thick metal pole. It was supposed to say SPIN MOTEL, but the P was burned out and she read, SIN MOTEL. Well, that's just great, she thought, wondering if this was a bad omen. Realizing that was silly, she followed Stoker inside, where the man behind the counter looked them over. She stood off to the side, listening to the two men negotiate a room rate—to her they sounded like cavemen grunting at each other.

"Three nights," Stoker said.

"Buck fifty a night," the man answered.

"Cash discount?" Stoker huffed.

"Can't."

"C'mon. We give you lots of business, man," Stoker pressed.

The man behind the counter responded with an incomprehensible mumble, mumble, mumble, grumble.

Stoker pushed three one-hundred-dollar bills to him, and a key was placed on the counter.

A few minutes later Rainey and Stoker walked outside.

"What the hell was that?" Rainey asked, chuckling. "I barely understood a word either of you said in there."

Stoker glanced at her. "Really? Well, that was man talk."

"Man talk?" Rainey said, scrunching her brow. "C'mon."

"Yeah, now climb on," Stoker said, pointing to the bike.

Still amused, Rainey hopped on and they drove through the parking lot to a one-story brick building with bright red doors.

Stoker parked the bike, got off, and grabbed her hand. "We're in room eight."

She pinched her bottom lip between her thumb and forefinger and gave the red door a pensive look. She had thought about sex almost the entire ride, and now, looking at the door to their motel room, it all became very real. "Okay, let's go," she said cautiously.

Inside the room, Stoker threw his leather bag and her backpack onto the dresser. "I need to hit the head," he said walking into the bathroom.

Alone, Rainey looked around the room. The paneling on the walls had been painted a steel gray. Just below the ceiling line, there was a small air conditioner jammed through the wall. A short navy blue sofa with worn

pillow cushions sat next to the queen-size bed covered by a quilt with a blue and burgundy Native American Tribal Navajo design.

Rainey sat on the edge of the bed and waited. A moment later, Stoker opened the bathroom door and she looked up at him. "You're beautiful," he said.

She blushed. "I am not."

Stoker strode over to the bed and pulled down the thin bedspread. She watched, wordlessly, as he pulled his T-shirt over his head. She took in his body as he unzipped his jeans and stepped out of them. She gawked at him in his boxer briefs with her arms crossed tightly over her chest as he climbed between the sheets. I was hoping we'd ease into sex, she thought.

"I'm gonna take a short nap. You wanna join me?" he asked, lifting the covers.

She was feeling foolish, but Rainey's hands dropped to her sides and she let out the breath she'd been holding. Knowing he only wanted to take a nap, she softened, "Sure, that sounds good."

Still dressed, she kicked off her shoes, lifted the sheet, and slid under. She scooted closer to Stoker and rested her head on his bare chest. At first her body was stiff, but after a few minutes without him groping her, she relaxed into him. Stoker ran his hand over her long hair, then rolled onto his side and looked into her face. He kissed her slowly, then his passion took hold of him. As they were kissing, Stoker's hand slipped under her T-shirt and she lifted her arms signaling he could pull it over her head. Then he unlatched her bra and gently slid his warm hands over her breasts. Rainey moaned and pushed his head to her chest. Placing his mouth over one of her breasts, her back arched, and her hands slid down his back, resting on his butt. As he moved in closer, she could feel his erection against her thigh. In the moment, between them, all of her concerns faded.

Rainey ran her hands over Stoker's biceps, to his elbows, and along his forearms until their fingers were entwined and they kissed until they could barely breathe.

He got up on his knees and unzipped her jeans. Instinctively, she lifted her pelvis from the bed as he slid the denim past her ankles and tossed them onto the floor. His body hovered over hers. His tongue followed a line from her belly button to the top of her panties. He paused for a moment and looked up at her; her eyes were gently closed and her mouth slightly open as she let out a sensual breath. His fingers slid under the waistband of her panties and he effortlessly glided them off of her body. Rainey pushed his

boxers down to his knees with her feet, and Stoker quickly clawed his legs out of them.

Stoker reached for his pants, plucking a condom from a pocket. Moments later, he was back on top of her and she let out a soft moan as he tenderly entered her. He made love to her for several minutes, then pulled himself away, shimmying down the bed, and placing his mouth between her legs. Rainey let out a long groan as his tongue and fingers made her feel magical. Letting go of all doubts, just before climaxing, Rainey Paxton allowed herself to be vulnerable.

Stoker moved his mouth back up to her lips and kissed her. She opened up to him fully, and as he shifted himself inside of her again, he whispered, "I love you."

Rainey's eyes flew open. "I love you too."

Chapter Eighteen

The next morning, just before dawn, Rainey woke to the silence of the motel room. Not completely awake, she stretched her arms and legs. As she did, her hand bumped into something. Alarmed, she turned her head quickly and she saw Stoker's head lying on the pillow next to her. Her quickened pulse slowed as her eyes scanned his biceps covered in tattoos, his broad chest, and his long blond hair. Joy washed over her. She wasn't in juvie or her parents' home; she lay beside the man who vowed to protect her. The man who told her he loved her. Filled with a sense of security, Rainey slipped her arm over his waist.

Stoker opened his eyes and dragged her closer to him. "Morning," he said, in a deep scorching voice.

"Good morning," she said softly with sleepy eyes.

With the day's first light illuminated behind the semi sheer yellow curtain, Rainey stared into his eyes, searching for the love he had vowed to her the night before. Stoker playfully rubbed the short whiskers of his face against her cheek.

"What are you looking at?" he joked.

"You," she squealed. "I'm looking at you. Trying to see if the person who said he loved me last night is the same guy."

Stoker rolled on top of her and playfully pinned her arms down; kissing the underside of her forearms. "I'm still the same guy. And you know," he said, planting tender kisses on her neck and chest, "that guy from last night is thinking about a little morning lovin' before we go grab breakfast."

A hot rush of desire burst through her. "I guess that would be fine," she teased.

Stoker, pleased to hear the longing in her voice, grinned and rolled up on his side.

Rainey gazed in anticipation, wanting that blast of ecstasy she had experienced the night prior. She knew then that if she would ever be addicted to something it would be the way Stoker made love to her and how he brought her to the height of pleasure. Stoker reached between her legs and lightly touched her. His faint stroke, so barely there, made her moan with delight. Then he stopped.

Rainey's eyes snapped open and his mouth came down on hers. As she responded to his kiss, Stoker pressed his fingers inside her. Then he caressed her again and her hand found his penis and she moved with the same gentleness of his touch.

Stoker lightly nibbled on her nipple while he brought her to the edge of glory with his practiced hands. Rainey put her hand on the back of his head while her body quaked as she climaxed, feeding her with the natural drug she now craved.

Breathlessly, she pushed Stoker over and moved on top of him. She placed him inside of her and moved her hips up and down until Stoker could no longer resist the surge of sheer bliss as he exploded. Rainey stopped and laid her head on his chest with him still inside her. She listened to his quickened heartbeat and smiled to herself.

"You were right," she said. "Sex is great when you actually want to do it with the other person." Rainey rolled off of Stoker and stood, his eyes roaming over her young, taut body as she rummaged through her backpack, pulling out clean clothes. "I'm going to grab a shower so we can go eat."

She looked at Stoker lying naked on the bed. He pushed his blond hair back with his hand and gave her a wink that made her insides tremble.

"Stop it," she said, smiling. "Do you have any idea how sexy you are?"

Stoker grinned. "No. Why don't you come over here and show me?"

Like a fly to a picnic table covered with cake crumbs, Rainey dropped her clothes on the small blue sofa and went back to him. Time stood still as they made love. By the time she crawled out of bed to take a shower it was almost noon.

Thirty minutes later, they sat across the table from each other at a diner less than a mile from their motel. Rainey took a bite of her grilled cheese sandwich and smiled at Stoker.

"I worked up an appetite," she kidded.

Stoker pursed his lips. "I have no idea what you're talking about," he said, forcing a straight face.

Rainey held out one of her French fries and Stoker leaned across the table and took it into his mouth along with her fingers. When she went to bring her hand back, he grabbed it quickly and kissed the top. She peered at him through smoldering green eyes. He turned her hand over and used the tip of his tongue to lick her palm.

"I'm trying to eat over here," she said in a strangled voice.

Stoker snickered. "Okay, you go ahead and eat. You need to keep up your strength." He took a bite of his fried chicken. "When I was a kid I couldn't get enough of this shit," he said, waving a chicken leg.

Rainey's smile dimmed.

"What's wrong?" he asked.

Tilting her head, she said, "I don't know. I guess you talking about being a kid made me think of Ivy. I've never told you about her . . . not much, anyway."

"Okay. Well then, you need to tell me everything," he said, but didn't make eye contact.

Rainey leaned forward on her elbows. Averting her gaze was a sign he didn't want to discuss it. "I'm serious, Stoker. She's going through some really bad shit. You know, I worry that Freddy is doing the same thing to her that he did to me."

Stoker took another bite of chicken and locked eyes with her. "Nah, you don't have to worry about Freddy bothering you or your sister ever again."

Rainey put her grilled cheese down on the plate. "What do you mean?"

"What I mean is," he said, shoveling a forkful of mashed potatoes into his mouth, "he ain't around to bother anyone."

Her heart hammering, she was torn between celebrating that Freddy would never be a problem again and fear of what Stoker had done to make that happen. Still, she needed to know whether Freddy could come back again. Rainey leaned back and lowered her voice to a whisper. "What did you do to him?"

Stoker wiped his hands on his napkin. "Rainey, if you keep asking questions it's going to piss me off. I already told you what you need to know. Let it drop," he said sternly.

Rainey was shaken by his change in demeanor and decided to let it drop. She knew that Stoker had taken care of things. It wasn't about that . . . it was that she needed to know what exactly happened to the man who had brutally raped her.

Chapter Nineteen

A few months later, Stoker took Rainey to a party at the Devils Angels house. More often than not, he kept her away from his biker brothers; in fact, he rarely left her to mingle alone.

"You want something to drink?" he asked her when they arrived.

"I'll try a beer."

Stoker looked her up and down. "Really? That's a change."

Amused by his reaction, she gave him a soft smile, "Well, I just thought I'd try one. It's not like I asked for a hit of heroin."

Stoker chuckled, leaving Rainey standing alone while he went to the kitchen to grab two beers. She kept glancing at the doorway, waiting to see him come back.

"Hey, blondie," a biker named Rubble said, stumbling up to her.

Rainey's eyes moved over the short, stocky man with black hair and brown eyes. His T-shirt didn't cover his stomach, which was hanging over the waistband of his jeans, and his fingernails were caked in grease from fixing motorcycles and cars.

"Hi," she said, wishing she'd gone with her boyfriend into the kitchen.

"Where did Stoker go?" Rubble asked.

She gestured toward the kitchen. "To grab a beer."

Instead of going to the kitchen, Rubble slithered closer to her—entering her personal space. She leaned away from him, but froze when he reached out and took her hair between his fingers, then ran it through his open mouth, over his tongue. Rainey wasn't sure if she should punch him in the face or walk away.

"Stoker used to share," Rubble said with a disgusting grin. "Maybe he will again."

Coming to her senses, Rainey yanked her head back. "What are you doing?"

Rubble snickered. "Relax, blondie. Until Stoker's ready to share, you're considered hands-off. That doesn't mean I can't have a taste, though."

Rainey's gaze pivoted to the doorway as Stoker strode through, his eyes watching Rubble. He stood close to the biker, glaring at him. Not smiling, not blinking . . . just angry. Rainey backed away, not wanting to be in the middle of whatever this was.

"Rubble giving you a hard time?" he asked, not taking his eyes off of his biker friend.

Glancing at Rubble, she didn't answer, unwilling to get in the middle of a potential argument.

"Well?" Stoker said to Rubble. "Are you giving my girlfriend a hard time?"

"Don't get your panties in a wad, brother. Me and your squeeze were just chatting, getting to know one another."

Stoker cocked his head to the side, still glaring, knowing that Rubble was stoned. "Okay, man. You take it easy on the meth tonight. And . . ." he leaned in closer, "don't ever go near her again."

"What are you, my mother now?" Rubble growled.

"Fuck you, Rubble," Stoker said, stepping closer to him. "You know better than to start any shit with me. You better check yourself, brother."

Rubble stood tall, breathing through his open mouth with his eyes fixed on the wall. "You don't gotta be a dick."

Stoker advanced on him and gingerly guided him up against the wall across the room. He whispered into Rubble's ear. "Don't be dumb, man. Know your motherfucking place. I like this girl. She's with me, so back the fuck off."

Rubble put his hands up. "Cool, cool, man. I was just testing the waters. You usually share all the ass you find. I just thought maybe she was another catch that you'd release to the rest of us. But I get it, you got a thing for this one. Now listen," he moaned, with a crooked-lipped smile, "when you get over her, I want you to let me know first."

Stoker gave him a tight smile. "Yeah, buddy, you'll be the first to know, but don't count on that happening."

As Rubble stumbled away, Stoker looked back at Rainey. "Sorry about him. He gets stupid when he's stoned."

Crossing her arms over her chest, Rainey said, "Yeah, they all get stupid when they're stoned. I know all about stoned people, remember?" she said, still put off by Rubble's behavior toward her.

Stoker swaggered up to her. "Aw, come on. Don't let him ruin our night. What did he say to you?"

"He said you pass your girlfriends around," she spat.

"Ahhh," Stoker purred, putting up his index finger. "See, that's where you're confused. I pass around hookers. You're my girlfriend."

Stoker nibbled on her earlobe, and though she tried hard to keep a straight face, Rainey broke and giggled. "Whatever," she said, brushing off the incident. "Are all of your friends like that?"

"Not all of them, but some. Any of these men would give their life to save mine. That's what the Devils Angels do for each other. We're family, so try not to be too offended. He didn't mean no harm," Stoker stated.

"Okay, sure, but I don't know why you're sticking up for him. He was a total asshole."

Rainey's belly swirled as she waited for him to respond. She wondered if she'd lose if Stoker had to choose between her and one of his biker brothers. She didn't know why his choices felt like such a betrayal. He'd been with the Devils Angels for more than ten years and with her for not yet six months.

"Why the sad face?" he asked.

Rainey shrugged, aware that she had no desire to talk to Stoker about his loyalties. "I don't know. I just want to go home. I'm really tired and I have a headache."

Stoker placed his beer down. "You got it. Let's get moving."

***

Standing at her front door, Rainey watched Stoker ride away and wondered if she was overthinking his reaction. She'd wanted him to agree that Rubble was a total asshole, but he hadn't. She was in love with Stoker and was afraid she'd lose him if she put up too much of a fuss. One thing she knew was that he didn't tolerate drama.

As she laid in bed that night, she decided to call Stoker after work the next day and make sure things were still okay between them.

Chapter Twenty

The next day, when Rainey finished her shift at the Drop Inn, she went into Titus's office. Finding his office empty, she used his telephone to call Stoker.

"Yeah?" he said when he answered, sounding hurried.

"Hey," Rainey breathed, relieved to hear his voice.

"Hey, baby. You want me to come get you?"

"Actually, I was hoping to talk to you for a minute. I have some things on my mind . . ." Rainey said.

With hearing the strain in her voice, Stoker said, "I'm coming to get you. Stay right where you are and don't move," he commanded. Then, without waiting, he hung up.

"No, wait! I don't need you to be upset . . . Hello? Stoker?" She looked at the receiver in disbelief. "He hung up on me. Is he fucking kidding me?" Rainey pushed the sleeves up on her shirt, spun on her heels, and left the office, slamming the door behind her.

Infuriated that he'd hung up without letting her finish talking, and needing to burn off her pent-up energy, she defied his orders and walked home in a blind rage. As she rounded the corner of her street, she saw Stoker's bike parked in front of the house. She stomped inside and glared at him and Winnie sitting in the living room having a beer.

"What are you doing here?" she hissed at Stoker.

"Whoa? What the fuck? I went to your work and you weren't there so I came here to make sure you got home," he said, defending himself.

"Oh, really? You're so worried that you're sitting here drinking a beer," she spat. She took the steps two at a time, rushed into her bedroom, and shut the door.

Leo flung his door open and barked into the hall, "What the hell is all this noise about? What's your problem, Rainey?"

"Dude, back off," Stoker said, having run upstairs after her.

Leo spun toward the voice, and seeing it was Stoker, his shoulders lowered and he raised his hand in the air. "Hey, yeah, sorry about that. I was sleeping."

Leo knew who Stoker was and what he could do. He stepped back toward his bedroom as Stoker walked toward him.

Stoker's face was calm and he drew in a deep, satisfying breath. "I know you're Winnie's bro so I'm gonna make this easy for you. Don't ever talk to my girl like that again." Stoker flashed Leo a menacing smile. "We have an understanding?"

"Yeah, man. We're good," Leo said, sticking out his hand for Stoker to shake.

When Leo went back into his room, Stoker tapped lightly on Rainey's door before turning the nob and stepping inside. "Rainey? It's me."

She was facedown on her bed and didn't acknowledge him at first.

"Rainey," he said again with a bit more force.

"Leave me alone," she said, her voice muffled by the pillow and trying to rein in her annoyance with him.

"Aw, come on. I was just giving you some time to get home and Winnie offered me a beer. If you weren't home in ten minutes I was going to get on my bike and find you."

She rolled onto her side and glared at him. "Look, here's the thing. I need to be able to talk to you. I told you I wanted a few minutes, that I had some things on my mind, and you got upset before even knowing anything. You told me to stay where I was and not to move, then you hung up and I'm standing there confused and not understanding what set you off. Nothing bad was happening to me. All I wanted to do was talk. It's disturbing and it scares me that you can't control your anger. Hear me out first, okay?"

Stoker made his way over to her bed and sat on the edge. He placed his warm hand on her hip, making her look up at him. "I'm sorry; you're right. But I heard stress in your voice and I went into overdrive. From now on I'll listen first, but only if you promise to be very clear about whether you're in danger."

Rainey considered what he said. "Okay, so from now on I'll say nothing bad is happening before I tell you anything."

He nodded. "Good, I like that. Now, I'm sorry I hung up on you. When I get worried about people I love, I'm gonna do something about it," he said firmly.

She peered at him, feeling the ice in her veins melting ever so slightly. "I'm not saying I don't like when you look out for me, because I do."

Stoker raised his eyebrows. "I know. Anyway, I have some news for you."

Rainey begrudgingly sat up. "What?" she muttered.

"I've been working on getting you a gig so you can make some extra money. You know, so you can help your little sister."

"And?" she asked with anticipation.

"And I think I might have something lined up for you."

She tilted her head. "Is it legal?"

"Yeah," Stoker said, though she noticed that he averted her gaze and rubbed at the stubble on his chin. "You'd just be passing on information to different people that go to the Drop Inn."

"What kind of information?" Rainey didn't think it sounded like a legitimate job.

"That doesn't matter. Just think of it like you're a letter carrier, because that's all it is."

Rainey shifted, still skeptical about the offer. "I don't want to be in the middle of drug deals or anything like that. I'd rather find another way to earn money."

He sighed heavily. "Rainey, you won't have to touch any drugs or weapons or anything else. It's only letters and it took me weeks to convince my people that you could be trusted. You'll make ten bucks for every letter you deliver. That's all there is to it."

Rainey sucked in a breath. "Wow. How many letters would I handle?"

"Not sure. Four or five a week."

"Holy shit!" Rainey squealed, quickly doing the math in her head. "That's like two-hundred dollars a month. Now I can save money to get Ivy out of that house of horrors."

"Okay, so the deal is, you give the letters to who we tell you to. You don't ask me any questions. You don't ask the people you meet at the motel any questions. You consider yourself a mailman and keep your mouth shut. Got it?"

Rainey thought about all the money she'd be making and her hesitation vanished. "And there's no way I can get in trouble?" she asked, checking one last time.

Stoker shook his head. "They're just letters with information that will mean nothing to anyone except the recipients."

He would never tell Rainey that the letters she was delivering would contain nicknames for other criminals or addresses to be used in various illegal activities, from assassinations to major weapons sales. Stoker had convinced The Devils Angels they needed another letter runner and she was the perfect person to handle it for them.

Chapter Twenty-One

Rainey bit down on her bottom lip. "Okay, I'll do it," she said before changing her mind. "Hey, I have a favor to ask you."

Stoker stood and pulled Rainey to her feet. "What's that?"

"Well, I haven't seen Ivy lately and I'm worried about her. She said my parents lock her in the basement and I'm afraid they'll put her down there and forget she's alive."

Sensing how much this meant to her, Stoker placed his hand on the small of her back and kissed the tip of her nose. "I'll find out what's going on."

Rainey's eyes widened. "You will?"

Stoker nodded. "Yeah, don't worry about a thing."

"How will you find out?"

"Doesn't matter."

"Just like it doesn't matter what happened to Freddy?"

"That's right."

"Hmm. Okay, whatever you can do would be great, thanks. I don't have anyone else I can ask to help."

Stoker patted her butt. "I got this, but I gotta run. The club has a meeting tonight so I need to get back."

Disappointed he couldn't stay she gave him a curt smile. "Right."

Stoker looked her in the eyes. "Hey, you know the club is a big part of my life. That's what you're signing up for if you want to be together. We've talked about this."

"I know, I'm sorry. It's just that I like being with you," she said.

Stoker held her hand as she walked him outside, then gave her a quick kiss on the mouth before straddling his motorcycle, promising to see her the next day.

When Rainey went back inside, Winnie was on the sofa, watching television.

"Well, look whose back," Winnie said. "You were really upset when you came home. What happened?"

Rainey was embarrassed, but sat down next to her. "I called him and he pissed me off, so we had a fight."

"Yeah, no shit. Did the little couple make up?"

"Stop it. You're not funny," she said, smiling.

Winnie gave her a scrutinizing look and Rainey knew she had more to say.

"I have a question," Winnie said. "How come you never sleep at Stoker's?"

Rainey jerked her head back. She'd never actually considered it before, but it was true. She had never slept overnight. Not that she really wanted to; the biker house wasn't homey, as it was at Winnie's.

"I don't know. I guess because there's a bunch of other guys living there with him. Besides, he's never asked me."

"Oh, doesn't it bother you that you never get to spend the night with him?"

Rainey laid across Winnie's lap. "Well, it didn't bother me until you brought it up."

"Sorry."

Rainey looked up at her friend. "You know, it doesn't matter. The thing is, I like having my own space as much as I like being with him. I mean, like tonight after we made up, I thought he'd take me back to his place for a while, but he has some dumb meeting, and that was disappointing, but now I get to hang out with you," she admitted.

Winnie huffed. "Not tonight. I have a date, so you're on your own."

"Oh, man. You're leaving me here with Leo?"

"Nope, he's going out with his friends."

Rainey closed her eyes. "Well, this is good. It'll give me time to call Tootsie. When I talked to her last week she was down. I know there's something she isn't telling me."

"Yeah, let me know what you find out. I talked to her two weeks ago and she sounded weird."

Alone on the sofa, Rainey thought more about Tootsie. She wished the girl was living with her and Winnie; she knew they'd all have fun together. She hadn't told Tootsie about Stoker yet but intended to that night. She

had waited because it always seemed self-serving to share good news with Tootsie while she was locked up inside juvie. But it was time to tell her, she loved Stoker and wouldn't want things to go too far without Tootsie knowing.

Chapter Twenty-Two

After finishing dinner, Rainey waited with anticipation as the phone rang. A girl with a young, squeaky voice picked it up on the fourth ring.

"Hello, young girls being tortured, who you looking for?"

Rainey laughed. It was a running joke in juvie to answer the phones this way.

"Hi, I want to talk to Tootsie," Rainey said.

"Yeah? Everyone wants to talk to her. She gets like a million calls every night." She laughed. Then she dropped the phone, and the sound clanged in Rainey's ear as it hit against the wall.

"Hey, Tootsie!" the girl yelled. "Another phone call for ya!"

Rainey waited, listening to the familiar sounds of life in juvenile detention. The banging of metal doors, girls screaming, and the foot traffic moving past the prison wall phones.

"Yeah?" Tootsie breathlessly huffed into the phone.

A warm sensation filled her at the sound of Tootsie's voice. "Hey, girl. It's me!" she sang.

"Hey, what are you up to? You're calling me on a Saturday night? Everything okay there?" she asked, a concerned tone in her voice.

"Yeah, yeah, everything is fine. Winnie's good, I'm good," she assured her.

"Yeah, that's what I like to hear," she said. "I'm happy you're outta here, but"—she lowered her voice to a whisper—"I really miss you."

"I miss you too," she said. Hearing the despair in Tootsie's voice made Rainey's throat thick. As she spoke her voice cracked. "I have a lot going on out here. You know, working and taking care of myself. Some of this

shit was easier in juvie where everything was there and all we had to do was some chores."

"Hmm, I'll tell you what. I'll trade you any day of the week," she said playfully.

"You're right. Sorry for even bringing it up," Rainey said.

"Fucking true, I'm always right. Come on now, girl, I'm messing with ya. I know it ain't easy to be young and taking care of yourself. I joined a gang because of it, remember?" She chuckled. "So how was your week? Whatcha' got going on?"

Rainey's eyes lit up; this was her chance to tell her friend. "Well, there is this guy I met and been dating for a while," she giggled in spite of herself.

"A while, huh? I see. How come you didn't tell me?"

A jab of dread nailed Rainey in the pit of her stomach. "I didn't tell you because I felt bad. I know what it's like to be locked up and I didn't want to gloat or brag or make things worse for you."

"I understand and appreciate that, but you're my girl and I wanna see you happy. Sure, it would've made me a jealous, but it ain't gonna ruin my world. I want to know what's going on in your life. Did you forget how boring this place is?"

Rainey let out a light chuckle. "Okay, so let me tell you about him then. I met him at the Drop Inn and he's gorgeous and . . . I . . . I'm in love with him."

"You don't want to be involved with gangs and then you let your skinny ass fall in love with a biker?" she teased.

"Wait! How do you know he's a biker? Do you know Stoker?"

Tootsie groaned. "I told you a million times I know just about everybody. Stoker's an okay dude, I like him, ain't never did nothing to hurt me or my people. He don't run in my circles but my people and his people do business together sometimes. Point is, I ain't worried about you seeing him. He treatin' you good?"

"Yeah, he is. He's nice," Rainey said, relieved that Tootsie approved of him.

"How's your sister doing? You see her?"

Rainey was touched at the mention of Ivy. She told Tootsie more about her sister than anyone else. "I've seen her a couple of times. She told me those assholes lock her in the basement. I haven't spotted her in a while though. I think of the crap that my parents put me through and it makes

me sick to my stomach to think that she might be going through the same shit."

"Well that sucks, but it must feel good that Stoker had Freddy taken care of. That fucking pervert. Shit, shit, shit," she muffled into the phone. "Fuck, I didn't mean to say that, Rainey. That can bring some heavy stuff down on me."

"Relax. You know I'd never tell anyone anything you told me. Besides, Stoker told me he made sure Freddy would never bother me or Ivy again." Now her curiosity was running wild. "Do you know what he did to Freddy?"

"Seriously? How is it I know more about your man than you do?"

There was a tightness in Rainey's chest. "C'mon, tell me already before I burst."

Tootsie sighed. "Okay, so I understand Stoker's club said that Freddy OD'd. That he shot up like triple the amount of coke that no one can handle, now that's just bullshit 'cause a dealer like Freddy knows his limit. Anyway, then his house mysteriously caught on fire and his body was burned to a crisp."

Rainey covered her mouth with her hand. "I can't believe it," she breathed, both mortified by how it happened and grateful he was gone.

"You can't believe that Freddy's dead or that your man took care of business?"

Rainey closed her eyes. "Both."

"You know, girl," Tootsie said, "you still have a problem with people being dealt with the right way. Your problem is you're too nice, you never want nobody to die."

"No, I don't want people to die because of me. There's a difference." Rainey's thoughts were racing between relief that Freddy could never get to Ivy, and fear that Stoker had murdered a person on her behalf. Deep down, she'd suspected that Freddy was dead, and now she knew for certain. She was trying to focus on what Tootsie was telling her, but her mind was too busy processing the news she'd just been given. Rainey had become consumed with guilt. She now understood the power her words had with Stoker.

"Rainey?"

"What?"

"Did you hear what I just said?"

"No, sorry."

"I'm being transferred to an adult prison in Wyoming to serve out the rest of my sentence. Like what the fuck? They may as well send me to another planet. Anyway, I need you to send me letters," Tootsie said. "You know, phone calls are good, but when I get a letter, I can hold it, almost like I have a piece of you with me."

"I'll mail you a note every week, I swear, but only if you write back to me," she added.

"I ain't that good of a writer," Tootsie mumbled. "But I'll try, just don't let me catch you making fun of me."

"Oh, please, I'd never do that behind your back," she laughed. "I'd do it right to your face. Seriously, though, it sucks that they're sending you so far away. Can I bring you anything before you get transferred?"

Rainey could hear Tootsie's heavy, raspy breaths in the phone and the sounds made her heart ache.

"Yeah," Tootsie said, her voice tinged with sadness. "How about you bring me some of those white cotton socks and a new bra, size thirty-four C. You know, one of those nice ones from a fancy store."

"If by 'fancy store' you mean the Vintage Fashion Discount Store downtown, then you got it."

Tootsie giggled and, at the sound of her laughter, Rainey was grateful she could make her laugh and saddened that her friend was facing time in something other than a youth facility.

"When can you come?"

"I'll be there next weekend."

"Great. I'll put you on the list for Sunday afternoon then?"

"That works."

"Hey, I gotta go, it's almost lights out. In case you forgot visiting hours start at two."

"I remember. I'll see you then."

After the girls hung up, Rainey pressed her body against the sofa. So many thoughts ran through her head. She remembered how nervous Phoenix was about being transferred to an adult prison once she turned eighteen, but noticed Tootsie didn't have that same panic. She knew it was because Tootsie probably had fellow gang members in the prison where she was being transferred. And, as crazy as it seemed, knowing this gave Rainey comfort.

Chapter Twenty-Three

At the Devils Angels meeting that night Stoker lit a cigarette and sat back on the sofa next to Boulder, the club's president.

"Any other business?" Boulder asked.

"Yeah," Stoker started. "I want Andrew and Rubble to do some work for me.

"What's that?" Boulder asked.

"I need some recon. I need some information on a kid."

Andrew took a swig of beer. "How old is this kid?"

"I don't know. Nine or ten, I think."

"Damn, Stoker. Now I'm on kid duty?" Andrew moaned.

Stoker glanced at him. "No, you're on Rubble duty. He's gonna get you into the nasty crack house where she lives and you're gonna make sure he doesn't do or say anything he shouldn't. And keep him the hell away from the dope. He needs his head clear."

Rubble threw a look at Stoker. "Really? Come on, man."

Impatient, Boulder sat forward on his chair and broke in. "No more of this bullshit. You two," he said, wagging his finger at Andrew and Rubble, "get together with Stoker and figure out what's needed."

Andrew nodded. "You got it."

"Anything else?" Boulder asked the roomful of men, but no one spoke. "Okay, meeting over." He turned to Stoker. "Let's have a chat."

The two men left the house and stood on the porch together.

"This your girl's kid?" Boulder asked.

Stoker nodded, looking out into the street. "It's her little sister."

"Well, things are getting serious between you two then?"

"Yeah."

"You trust this girl?"

Stoker faced Boulder. "Yeah, man. I trust Rainey completely. She's a good girl."

"So are you saying the club is ready to meet her?"

"Yep, that's what I'm saying," Stoker stated.

"All right. You keep Andrew and Rubble until they get you what you're looking for. If you need more men just say so."

The two men clasped their right hands together and did a chest bump before going back inside to join the others.

***

Stoker pulled Andrew and Rubble into the kitchen. "So you guys are going to stake out a house in Kensington. I need you to look for a kid named Ivy."

Andrew nodded while Rubble opened a beer and flung the bottle top at the trashcan.

"How do you know the kid?"

"It's Rainey's sister," Stoker said.

Rubble let out a cackle. "Come on, man. Now we're doing recon for some chick you're banging?"

Stoker advanced on Rubble with speed and force. He jacked him up against the kitchen wall. "Who the fuck do you think you're talking to? You think this is a fucking democracy. Is that what you think this club is about? Your job is to do whatever the club needs you to do. Don't forget that."

Rubble stared at Stoker with wide eyes and mouth agape. "Yeah, yeah, Stoker. It won't happen again. Sorry, man."

Stoker let Rubble go with a little push and stepped back, then pointed his finger in Rubble's face. "If you ever talk about Rainey like that again you'll have hell to pay. I told you at that party she's different and I meant it."

Andrew started for the kitchen door. "Let's go, Rubble. We need to talk about how we're gonna tackle this. Hey, Stoker, is it okay if we pull Snoopy into this. He's got three kids so if we do find this girl at least he'll have some idea of what to do."

Stoker patted Andrew on the back. "Yeah, good idea."

Stoker stood alone in the kitchen thinking about Rainey. He'd just gone out on a razor-thin limb for her and hoped she was as dedicated to him as

he was to her. There were rules she would need to follow, but that would be the true test of how much she wanted to be with him.

Chapter Twenty-Four

The following evening, Rainey and Stoker were eating at a local restaurant.

"So, I talked to Tootsie," Rainey said, still mulling over their conversation and what Tootsie had shared.

Stoker smiled. "That's great. How is she?"

"Well, I promised her I'd visit her on Sunday. They're moving her to an adult prison in Wyoming soon."

"Oh, yeah? That's too bad. How are you getting there?"

Rainey shrugged. She hadn't actually thought that far ahead. "I don't know. The bus, I guess."

"Nah, I don't want you on the bus."

Rainey laid down her fork. "Why not?"

"Because people know you're my girl and I don't want you taking the bus anymore."

Rainey's breath caught in her chest. Why would Stoker think he could tell her what to do? Yet part of her also found his overprotectiveness flattering. Her emotions with Stoker were sometimes conflicted and, she wondered how someone she loved so much could make her feel good and bad at the same time.

She fumbled for the right words. "Okay, so what am I supposed to do? Fly there?"

Stoker scoffed. "No, I'm gonna take you. You'll do your little visit and I'll wait outside."

"My little visit? Why are you being so weird tonight?"

Stoker grabbed his beer and gave her a look. "I ain't being weird," he said, taking a sip. "There are rules and they need to be followed. You have to understand that anything I want you to do is for your own good."

She jerked her head back. “Anything you want me to do? You sound like a Neanderthal. What’s gotten into you?”

He lifted his chin and looked at the ceiling, then back at her. “I can see how it sounded,” Stoker said, his voice softening, “but I don’t mean it the way it came out. All I’m saying is being my ol’ lady changes things. You need to be more careful.”

She liked that he was overprotective and Rainey’s eyes lit up with a twinkle of mischief. “Ol’ lady? Are you calling me old now?" she laughed.

“Oh, that? It’s nothing. It’s a club thing; that’s what we cavemen call our women,” he joked.

She let out a giggle. “Okay, fine. You can drive me, but you don’t have to be so pushy about it though.”

Stoker stood and leaned over the table. He planted a kiss on her lips. “When it comes to you, I’m gonna be pushy. You mean everything to me. I ain’t been in love in a long, long time.”

When he sat down again Rainey looked at him in a new light, cupping her elbow with one hand and tapping her lip with the forefinger of her other. “You never told me you’d been in love before.”

“Yeah, I don’t like to talk about it.”

She smirked. “Did she break your heart?”

“No, she died.”

Rainey gasped. “O my God. What happened?”

Stoker sighed. “It’s a long story. Let’s just say it’s why I’m so pushy when it comes to you.”

Looking at Stoker, the way his eyes hardened as he spoke, Rainey wondered if someone had killed his old girlfriend, possibly as revenge against him. This idea shook her to the core. With a dazed look, she lowered her voice to a near-hysterical whisper. “Did . . . did someone kill her?”

Stoker didn’t answer. He stood and threw twenty-dollars on the table. Then, grabbing Rainey’s hand, he led her out of the restaurant. He started the bike quickly and sped away toward his house. They were both silent until they were inside Stoker’s bedroom. He was sitting on a chair, while she lingered in the doorway, feeling unsettled not knowing why the woman he loved before her was dead.

“Look, there are things you need to understand,” Stoker said after a long silence. “First off, we can’t be talking about all this shit in public. And yeah, I was in love, and yeah, she died. Nothing else matters. The only thing

that's important is that I love you and I will do whatever is needed to take care of you and keep you safe."

"Okay, but I am safe. Nobody is going to hurt me. There aren't that many people who even know I exist." Rainey paused, but Stoker didn't respond. "I didn't mean to upset you, but knowing your old girlfriend died freaked me out. Am . . . am I in danger because I'm with you?"

"Come on, Rainey," he said throwing his hands in the air. "Stop asking so many fucking questions about everything. Okay? Sometimes I need you to do things. End of story. Period."

Rainey's head dropped and she hugged herself. But when she looked up again her teeth were clenched and nostrils flaring. "So now what? Why didn't you tell me about this before? Am I just going to walk around scared someone is gonna kill me?" she asked, flouncing across the room and flopping on the bed.

"No, there isn't any reason for you to be scared as long as we are careful. You and me love each other and we have fun together. That's all you need to think about."

Rainey nodded, knowing their conversation was over. She hated when he shut her down and wouldn't give her the information she wanted. She got off the bed and walked to him. "I hate it when we fight," she said. He rested his forehead on her abdomen and she dug her fingers into his hair. Lowering her head, she kissed the back of his neck. Stoker wrapped his arms around her waist and pulled her body forward against his own. He kissed her and soon he was pulling her shirt off.

"Stop it!" she giggled. "What if Andrew walks in?"

Stoker looked up at her. "He doesn't share this room with me anymore. Now that I have you, this room is all mine. I kicked him to the curb. Seniority."

"That's not nice. You probably hurt his feelings," she stated.

He let out a short, hearty laugh. "Rainey, bikers don't hurt each other's feelings by telling them to get another roommate. We're all thick-skinned. This ain't no place for pussies," he said.

She stood and led him to the bed. After they'd made love, they laid under the sheet, their legs entwined. She breathed in his smell, loving how he always smelled as good as he tasted. She closed her eyes and moved her body farther into his.

"I know I'm not supposed to have any questions for Your Majesty," she said playfully, "but I do. So if I can't ask you anything, then what?"

Stoker let out a loud sigh. "Well, I'm gonna introduce you to Kiki. I'm sure you've seen her. She's been with the Devils Angels a long time and she'll show you the ropes. You can ask her questions, but not too many. Okay?"

Rainey smiled, giddy inside. "Does this mean I'm part of your club now?"

"No, baby. Girls aren't in the club. Girls love fellows that are part of the club. Kiki is just like you, she loves one of my brothers," he explained.

Rainey rested her head on Stoker's shoulder. She was excited to officially meet one of the other girls. The few Devils Angels parties she'd been to, Rainey had remained close to Stoker's side. Mostly, all the bikers and their girlfriends had ignored her. But now she hoped she might finally have a girlfriend she could talk to who lived in Stoker's world.

Chapter Twenty-Five

It was the night Rainey would be meeting Kiki and some of the other Devils Angels women. She was nervously pacing the sidewalk outside of her house when Stoker slowed his motorcycle to a stop and put his feet down to balance his bike.

"What's going on?" he asked.

"Nothing. Why?"

"Because I saw you walking back and forth from down the block," he said, grinning. "Relax, babe. Everything is going to be fine."

Rainey thudded to a stop. "Oh, really? So, what if Kiki hates me? Does that mean we can't be together?"

"Why the hell would you think I need Kiki's permission to do anything?"

Rainey cocked her head to the side, confused. "Isn't this like a test for me tonight?"

"Okay, let's get something straight. You meeting Kiki is a big deal but only because she has a lot of power with the other women. But to be clear, Kiki ain't my boss and I don't give a shit if she likes you or not. You're mine. Period." Stoker got off of his bike and walked toward her, his eyes roaming over her. "Damn, you're hot," he said.

Rainey shoved her hands in her pockets and looked down at her clothing, "I wasn't sure what to wear. I didn't want to be too girly or too tough."

Stoker dipped his chin down and looked into Rainey's eyes. He ran his hand down her blond hair that had been pulled to one side and hung in a smooth, thick braid. She'd chosen jeans with holes at the knees and a black button-down, midriff shirt. Now she was questioning her choices.

"Well, I think you look great, kinda tough until you get to the tennis shoes; that's your softer side," he joked.

Rainey moved one foot out to show him. "I know my shoes look stupid, but I don't have any other going-out shoes." She looked back up at him and smiled. "But you look handsome," she purred.

"Baby, I don't care how I look," he said.

"That's not true. You put gel in your hair to keep it back. And you wear big rings and a big necklace and a chain on your wallet that hooks on your jeans," she pointed out.

Stoker puffed out his chest. "Yeah, I don't consider that caring about how I look. It's more like tribal wear."

"Oh, really?" Rainey said, blinking her eyes at him.

"My biker brothers are my tribe and we all roll together. Come on, let's get going," he said, grabbing her hand.

As Rainey straddled the bike behind him, she said, "You know, Tootsie hated me at first," she admitted, still worrying about meeting the other girls.

"They ain't going to hate you. Besides, the only person you need to care about is me."

Stoker lifted his feet and pulled away from the curb. As they rode back to his house Rainey thought about Kiki, wondering why she was so special to the club.

When they arrived, Rainey discovered the party was just like the others she'd attended. Loud music, lots of people smoking, drinking, and laughing. Stoker took her by the hand and led her into the basement, which she'd never been in. The basement was finished with a living area, pool table, bar, sofas, and coffee tables. She learned later that the basement was reserved for the higher-ranking members. Half a dozen bikers were playing pool as several girls watched them.

Stoker led her to a woman standing with one high-heeled foot propped up on the wall behind her and smoking a cigarette. She had short brown hair and wore a black leather jacket with nothing under it except a black bra. Rainey tried to take her in without gawking; her first impression was that the woman looked angry.

"Kiki," Stoker said, "this is Rainey."

Kiki leaned forward and kissed Stoker on the cheek before turning to Rainey. Kiki's eyes took in every inch of the girl. Her scrutinizing gaze sent a chill up Rainey's spine. When she continued to stare at her without speaking, a flash of heat ignited in Rainey's chest and rose to her face.

Finally, unable to take the silence, Rainey said, "It's nice to meet you."

Kiki smirked. "She's cute," she said to Stoker with an edge of sarcasm.

"Yeah, and she's smart," he said, putting his arm over Rainey's shoulder. "And she's my girl," Stoker stated sharply, looking directly at Kiki.

Kiki took her foot off of the wall and stepped toward Rainey. "Yeah, I know. I'm just messing with her." She butted her cigarette out in an ashtray. "Good to meet you too. Let's go grab a drink."

Rainey gave Stoker a pitiful look as she followed Kiki to the bar at the other side of the basement.

"What can I get you?" Kiki asked.

Rainey rubbed her forehead, not really wanting anything. "Um . . . um . . . what do you have?"

Kiki leaned over the bar, making sure Rainey got a full view of her large breasts. "Honey, this isn't a restaurant. Do you want a beer or a shot of whiskey?"

"Oh, I'll just have a beer," she said, planning to hold it most of the night.

Rainey put the bottle to her lips and took a small sip as Kiki watched her.

"So," Kiki said, "you're the girl that wrangled Stoker?"

Rainey pulled her head back slightly, surprised by the comment. "I don't know what you mean."

Kiki pointed to a group of girls across the room. "See those babes? Just about every one of them tried everything they had to make that man theirs."

Rainey followed Kiki's pointed finger to six twentysomething girls, who were glaring back.

"Oh, I didn't do anything to Stoker," she said, feeling suddenly like she was being accused of trapping him.

"I know that, and you know that, but they don't know that. All they see is an outsider who's been consuming one of our men. Now, I know that ain't your fault, but it's still something you're gonna have to deal with. I mean, after all, they'll give you respect because Stoker is second in command in this club. That in itself limits how bad they can treat you."

A bead of sweat dripped down the small of Rainey's back. She hadn't known Stoker was second in command, and now, learning that, made her want to know what else she didn't know about him.

Rainey shrugged. "I'm not sure what I'm supposed to do. They don't even know me and just because I'm with Stoker doesn't mean they should treat me like shit."

Kiki's face reddened; she didn't like the new girl coming in and thinking she was going to set the rules. "Yeah, that's how it goes. You'll need to deal with it."

Rainey bristled at her remark, took a mouthful of beer, and swallowed, wondering what the hell she'd just gotten herself into.

"So, which one is your boyfriend?" Rainey asked, ready to change the subject.

Kiki lifted her eyebrows. "The guy with the tire mark tattoo running down his arm," she said, now pointing in his direction.

Rainey glanced at a stocky man with long brown hair, talking to Stoker. His eyes were set wide and he had full lips. "What's his name?"

"Boulder. He's the president of this club."

She looked at Kiki and nodded. Then Rainey bit on her bottom lip. So that's the guy in charge of everything.

The woman added pointedly, "He's also Stoker's boss."

Rainey returned her remark with a tense grin. To her, Kiki's words sounded like a warning.

Chapter Twenty-Six

"Come on," Kiki said, walking away from her. "I'll introduce you to the girls."

Ready to face the others and get it over with, Rainey strode across the room. All the girls sneered as she approached, except one, who lifted her chin in a small nod. She was a tall, slender redhead dressed all in leather. Rainey thought she seemed at ease with herself and not annoyed with her like the others. As the two made eye contact, she gave her a small smile, which the girl returned.

Kiki held her hand up as she stepped into the group. "You all keep in mind this is Stoker's ol' lady. I ain't in the mood for any shit tonight." Then she let her hand drop and sat in the only open chair. "So this is Rainey, the girl we all heard about," she said with an edge in her voice.

A few girls made eye contact with Rainey, but no one extended themselves until the one who had smiled at her stepped forward and put her hand out. "I'm Taz, good to meet you."

Rainey took her hand, hoping the awkward scrutiny of the others would end. "Hi. Taz is a cool name."

Taz let out a little giggle and rolled her eyes. "Well, my real name is Theodora, Taz is the shorter version."

Rainey thought about it a second but could not make the connection between the formal name and the nickname. "Oh, cool," she said, not sure of how else to respond.

"Come on, follow me, I gotta take a pee."

Grateful for an escape, Rainey turned and walked with the girl.

"These girls can be real bitches," Taz said. "I'm sure Kiki told you that Stoker is a hot commodity around here; he has been for years. He stuck

with prostitutes that aren't part of this club. He's avoided getting involved with any of the chicks that hang here. And then you came along."

Taz gave her a tentative look at the mention of prostitutes, but Rainey was unfazed.

"Yeah, I know that about him. It doesn't bother me. It wasn't like I went after him or anything. He saw me at work and told my friend that he wanted to meet me. I thought he just wanted to get laid, which wasn't going to happen. Anyway, we started talking and spending a lot of time together."

"You like him a lot, huh?" Taz asked.

Rainey blushed as she nodded. "Yeah. I just don't understand why all the girls are pissed at me. It's not my fault that Stoker didn't want to be with any of them."

Taz laughed. "Girl, that don't matter. They don't think normal. See, in the Devils Angels, it's all about status and power. Since you're Stoker's ol' lady, that pisses the girls off. Most of them have been here for years and they're still just mamas."

Rainey nodded but was confused, not understanding what Taz meant. "Okay, wait. What's a mama?"

"A mama is someone who is allowed to hang out with the club, but we don't belong to any of the members. Sometimes the guys call us sweet butts too. They mean the same thing."

"Okay," Rainey said, working it out in her head, "that means an ol' lady is someone who is a girlfriend?"

"Exactly! And here's the thing, all the girls want Stoker because, for one, he's hot as hell, and two, his position in the club. Now that you're his ol' lady you'll get special privileges the rest of us don't get. You and Kiki are the only two that share those."

Rainey grinned. She liked the sound of that. "Oh, yeah? What kind of privileges?"

Taz averted her gaze. "Maybe Kiki should be filling you in," she said, suddenly guarded.

"Aw, come on. I'm not sure I have that 'thing' with Kiki. You know? Just tell me. I won't let anyone know that you said anything. I swear," she said raising her right hand.

Taz hesitated, biting her lip. "Okay, but remember you promised to keep your mouth shut."

"I'll remember," Rainey pledged, anxious to learn more about Stoker's world.

"Well, for one, you won't get passed around to the other members."

"What does that mean?"

"All the rest of us girls pretty much sleep with whichever member takes us to their room."

Rainey's hand moved to her heart. "What if you don't like them?"

Taz laughed. "Well, then it really sucks. Look, it isn't as bad as it sounds. We all came here knowing that we would get passed around and hoping to become an ol' lady."

Rainey rubbed her cheeks with her palms; she couldn't believe what she'd just heard. She had a need to be in control of who she had sex with, and this petrified her. "That sounds scary. I would never be able to have sex with whoever wanted it. Like Rubble, he's so disgusting, I would never be able to sleep with him."

Taz put her index finger to her lips. "Shhhh. You can't talk about club members like that, not even you. Okay?"

Rainey's pulse quickened as she looked around them, afraid someone overheard her. "Yeah, yeah," she mumbled.

Taz put her hand on Rainey's shoulder and whispered. "Don't worry, I'll never tell anyone. You and me are gonna be friends so we need to trust each other, right?"

Rainey liked Taz so far. She'd already given her a lot of information. "Yeah, of course we can trust each other." Her gaze nervously ping-ponged from the bathroom door to a poster of a naked woman in the hallway. She focused on Taz again "So what else should I know?"

"Well, you get to sleep in Stoker's room while the rest of us crash on the sofa or floor in the basement. I mean it's nice down here, and once in a while a member will let me stay the whole night in their bed after I have sex with them, but that's usually only because they're too drunk to tell me to leave." Taz paused, then giggled. "Okay, I like you. So, I'll tell you a secret . . . I have a massive crush on Andrew. He's Stoker's old roommate."

"Have you told him?" Rainey asked, happy Taz was trusting her already.

Taz shook her head. "I'm too scared he'll be like, bitch, you've slept with too many of my brothers for you to be my ol' lady."

Rainey paused and chose her words carefully. "I doubt that he'll care. From what you told me, that's normal for the club." She gave her a genuine

smile, "I think you're really nice and you're obviously beautiful. You should talk to him. You know, feel him out and see where his head is at."

"Really? You think so?" Taz looked across the room at Andrew and back at Rainey, who gave her an encouraging nod. "Okay, I'll do it."

"He'd be an idiot not to listen," Rainey added. She looked to her left and saw Kiki watching them, and turned back to Taz. "We're gonna have to get back to the others soon. Anything else I should know?"

"Well, there is one thing," Taz said, pausing. "It's kind of a big deal. You and Kiki are the only two who get to keep the money you work for."

"I don't understand. What does that mean?" Her muscles tensed, waiting to hear the explanation.

"We all have jobs. Lots of us are prostitutes. We have to give our money to Boulder and Stoker. It's a requirement. In return, they buy food and pay for the house and stuff like that."

"Stoker takes your money?" Rainey asked, a little louder than she'd meant. She looked around for Stoker, unable to believe that he'd do something like that.

Taz's eyes grew wide. "Keep it down, if anyone hears you I'll get in trouble. Don't make me regret telling you this stuff."

Rainey nodded and whispered to Taz. "You're right. I'm sorry. It won't happen again. And you don't need to worry, you can totally trust me."

Taz glanced at her, hoping she was sincere. "We better get back to the others."

When the two girls returned to the group, Rainey looked across the room and caught Stoker's eye. He strode over to her and laid his arm over her shoulder.

"Everything going okay?" he asked, leaning in to kiss her while the other girls looked on.

Rainey got close to his ear and whispered, "I don't think the other girls like me too much. Apparently you're the most wanted man in this room."

Stoker looked over his shoulder at the girls, turned back to Rainey, and met her lips again. He pulled her closer as his eyes remained steady on the women at the bar. He was sending a signal that no one better overstep their boundaries with his new girl.

Rainey kissed him back with a sense of security washing over her.

Stoker nuzzled her neck. "How was Kiki?"

Rainey shook her head. "I don't know. She was nice, kind of."

Stoker scoffed. 'Nice' isn't a word that's ever been used to describe Kiki. She's cool and all, but she's a raving bitch. She wants to control all of the girls."

Rainey lifted her eyebrows, happy Stoker acknowledged exactly what she already thought about Kiki. "No kidding. Do you think she'll try to control me too?"

Stoker shrugged. "Probably; she's got the highest rank. My advice to you is to do what she asks for the most part and carefully pick the shit you ain't gonna do. Otherwise the two of you will be fighting over everything."

"That sounds awful."

He looked into her eyes, growing serious. "It's not that bad. Look, you're with me now. Like I told you before, I'm a big part of the club and you're gonna have to bend a little. The good news is all the other girls have to listen to you. But don't contradict anything Kiki tells them to do. She knows these girls better than you and they'll eventually try to play you two against each other."

Rainey sighed. She'd never thought that being with Stoker would become this complicated. She loved him, that was for certain, but she didn't love the club. "I don't know," she said, looking into his eyes, "I didn't expect there to be so many rules and this much drama."

Stoker placed his hands under her chin to keep their gaze steady; there was a slight simmer of authority in his eyes. "You'll be fine. All you gotta do is follow the rules. That's the way it is here," he said, kissing her lips gently.

Rainey pulled her face away from his hands, feeling as though he wasn't giving her an option. "All right. Will you take me home?"

Stoker shook his head. "That wouldn't look good. This is the first time you met the girls; if you don't stay the night with me there'll be rumors. You want to fit in, don't you?"

Rainey paused, taking her time to respond. "I want to fit in with you, not all of these other people. Is that so bad?"

"Of course not. But there's a whole package that comes with me," he said, cupping her butt and lifting her off her feet.

Rainey looked into his face for a few seconds, then smiled. "Yeah, that's fine. I'll try to fit in"—she pointed her finger at him—"but I'm only doing it for you."

Stoker put her back on her feet and kissed her. After he walked away, she turned and looked at Kiki, who was leering at her. Walking back to the

others, Rainey wondered how she'd tolerate someone telling her what to do, after fighting so long for her freedom.

Chapter Twenty-Seven

Early the next morning, Rainey had Stoker take her home as soon as they woke. Inside her house, she went directly into the kitchen for coffee.

"Well, good morning," Winnie sang.

"Hey, good morning. Thank God you made coffee," Rainey said, reaching for a mug.

Winnie sauntered over and leaned on the counter beside her. "Sooooo, you slept at Stoker's last night?"

Rainey shrugged. "Yeah. It's not as big of a deal as you think, though. I met some of his friends and he thought it would be better if I slept there."

"His friends, huh?" Winnie gave her a look that Rainey knew well; her friend wanted details.

She took a sip of coffee, wondering how much to tell Winnie about what really happened. "Yeah, some of his friends' girlfriends too."

"How were they?" Winnie asked, already knowing the answer, having met them.

Rainey lowered her head, a little embarrassed to admit the truth. "I don't know, it was weird. Most of them didn't even talk to me. According to Kiki, they're all mad that Stoker picked me. There was one that was nice, though."

"Which one?"

"Taz. Do you know her?"

Winnie gave her a small smile. "Yeah, I met her a couple of times. Nice girl. Pretty harmless."

Rainey tapped the side of her coffee mug with her fingernail. "How about Kiki?"

"Yeah, I know her pretty good," she said without offering more.

"And?" Rainey asked, pitching her voice higher.

"Well, she ain't my favorite person in the world." Winnie glanced over at Rainey. "She's pretty aggressive; not the nicest person you'll ever meet. I mean, all I can say is you should never trust her."

"What does that mean? Trust her with what?" Rainey asked.

"I mean, never trust the bitch with your secrets."

Rainey looked at her thoughtfully. "How do you know so much about her?"

"Through one of the bikers."

"Did you date one of them?" she asked.

"Um, yeah, kinda. I was friendly with Stoker from when we were young, before he was anything in the club. I started dating one of the bikers and we got serious. I spent a lot of time at the clubhouse," she explained.

"How come you stopped dating him?" Rainey asked.

"I didn't like the rules. He was great, and then all of a sudden he wanted me to do shit that I wasn't about to do," she said.

"Who was it?"

"Jacob. He's a nice guy but he was totally into this 'the club is my whole world' thing. He didn't see anything wrong with what the club makes women do."

"Like give them your money?"

Winnie took a sip of coffee. "Exactly. I wasn't doing that shit. I'm out working and they wanted to take everything I earned. I didn't need them; I was living in my own house. Anyway, because I was friends with Stoker for so long, I talked to him and he talked to Boulder for me. So if I wanted to be out, I had to break up with Jacob."

"What do you mean 'to be out'?"

Winnie cocked her head to the side. "Out as in no longer part of the girls that belong to the motorcycle club. They're like a pack of groupies. I hated it. Anyway, you won't have the same problems because you're with Stoker. You'll have other problems, but you won't be passed around to some of those other dirtballs."

"What other problems?"

Winnie took in a deep breath and blew it out slowly. "There'll be expectations because you're supposed to set an example for the other girls."

Rainey scoffed. "I don't think the girls will be looking to me to give them pointers. Besides, they were all older than me . . . like in their twenties," she added, remembering how none of them even bothered to talk to her.

Winnie chuckled. "That's where you're wrong. They're all gonna watch everything you do. You captured the man that no one could tie down. I bet they're all curious about you . . . how you are . . . how you act . . . how you dress. They'll be taking everything in."

"That sounds creepy," she chuckled. "Like I'm the head of a cult or something."

"Nah, it ain't creepy, that's just biker life." Winnie paused and looked at her so closely that the flesh on Rainey's arms prickled. "Are you having second thoughts about Stoker?"

Rainey shook her head. "Not about him, I'm totally into Stoker. I just don't like all this other stuff that comes with him. And I don't like how Kiki is the boss of the girls."

Winnie nodded.

"It's just that, well, it took me a long time to get away from people who controlled me and I'm not about to give my power over to some chick I don't even know."

Winnie put her hand on Rainey's shoulder. "Don't look at it that way. Just pick your battles. It's not like she's gonna tell you to sleep with someone or shoot up heroin. It's more like she'll want you to meet her at the club to gossip about the other girls. She'll probably give you the dirty work of telling someone when they've done something wrong."

Rainey's hand went to the base of her own throat. "I don't want to tell any of the other girls what to do. I don't care what they do. I just want to be with Stoker without all of this other crap."

"Rainey, you're not just with Stoker now, you're with the club. That's what it means when you get introduced to the other girls. Didn't he explain that to you?"

Rainey froze. "Not like that, but he mentioned there were rules and I asked a million questions. Then he said that I was going to meet Kiki and she'd fill me in on some of the details."

"Yeah, well, he was probably scared you'd run the other way if he told you what was gonna happen. But it's real now. Your part of something bigger and even though it comes with stuff you don't like, those people will have your back and won't let anyone hurt you, ever."

Rainey massaged her temples with her fingertips, trying to process how her life had changed without her even realizing it. "I mean, I guess that's good. I know it's great to have people who have your back. But it seems like there's a lot of stuff that I still don't know about and, that rattles me."

Winnie walked toward the doorway and as she left the kitchen, she said, "That's probably something you should talk to him about, you know?"

Alone, Rainey lifted her coffee mug and looked into the caramel-colored liquid. "Yeah, I know. Me and Stoker definitely need to talk," she murmured.

Chapter Twenty-Eight

Later that afternoon, Rainey paced in front of the park bench where Stoker sat. Finally, he said, "Ah, something bothering you?"

"Yeah." Rainey stopped abruptly. "I don't want you to get mad at me, but I wish I knew that meeting with Kiki and those other girls meant that I was pledging into the motorcycle club."

Stoker smiled and shook his head. He stood and put his hands on her shoulders. "You weren't pledging to the club; you were pledging to me and I just happen to be part of the club."

Rainey sighed. "You know what I mean. Why didn't you tell me?"

Stoker shook his head. "What did you think, Rainey? You said you wanted to be with me. You told me you loved me. I told you there were rules that needed to be followed if we were gonna be together. You never said no to any of that and then, you wanted to know more and so I made it happen. I thought that's what you wanted."

"How could you think it was what I wanted if we never talked about what it all meant?"

"Well," Stoker said, lighting a cigarette, "you and I being in love told me that you wanted to be together."

"Yeah, but I didn't know all the details. You never said I had to be your ol' lady . . . it's such a stupid name to be called. I hate it," Rainey said, frustrated.

Stoker leaned in and kissed her cheek. "Ol' lady," he whispered.

"Knock it off," Rainey said, swatting at him and stepping back. She was too pissed off to be swayed by his charms. "I'm serious. You should've warned me about this crap. I should've known."

Stoker took her hand and led her to the bench. He sat and pulled her down next to him. "Okay, so let's talk about it now. What's got you so worried?"

"Well, let's start with you and Boulder having hookers working for you and taking all of their money," Rainey said, getting fired up just thinking about it. "What the hell is that?"

"That's how things work. Some of the girls who hang out with us go out to earn money to support the club. Everyone has to contribute in their own way. You won't be required to give us money, you'll be required to do different things, like keeping the other girls in line."

"Oh, great," Rainey hissed. "That's the last thing I need is to be in charge of a bunch of girls who already hate me." She stood and paced again, unable to contain her energy. "And another thing, don't you think it's shitty that those girls are screwing all those men just so you can buy beer or whatever it is you spend their money on?"

Stoker sat back. His lips were pinched into a straight line, leering at her. "It's not about the money. No one is forcing them to hang around with us. That was their choice."

"Then what's it about?"

"It's about control. The whole club is based on control. The members, the mamas, the ol' ladies, even the kids. Boulder has control over me and I have control over everyone else. It's just the way it works. It's been that way since the club was formed. All clubs have rules."

"Well, I don't want to be controlled," she stated with certainty. "So what now?"

Stoker dropped his cigarette on the grass. "So now nothing. I already told you there isn't anything you need to do or worry about. You're with me."

Rainey faltered, confused now. "So I don't have to do what Kiki tells me to do?"

Stoker looked down at his hands to avoid being too abrupt and then looked back up at her. "Kiki? That ain't nothing. She'll tell you what she needs and you'll tell the other girls to do it. It's like management."

"Oh," Rainey said in a huff while sitting back down. "Is there anything else I should know about? I know the other girls have to sleep with whoever in your club wants them."

Stoker shook his head. "Nope, you belong to me."

That set Rainey off again. "No, I don't belong to anyone," she said, turning away from him.

Stoker gently grabbed the back of her head and pulled her face to his. Rainey resisted for a few seconds before giving in. He kissed her, and after a moment she pulled away.

"I thought you loved me," he said.

"I do."

"Then just relax and stop being so uptight."

Rainey flushed and looked away. She was annoyed by everything he was saying.

"Hey," he breathed as she made eye contact with him, "do you trust me?"

Rainey put her hand over his heart. She had told him exactly what was on her mind and now was worried that she'd said too much and that she'd lose him. "Yes, I trust you. But this is so much to take in."

"Then stop worrying about everything and just go with it. I'm right here with you. Everything is going to be fine. Okay?"

Rainey nodded and rested her head against his chest, wanting their fight to be over.

After a few minutes Stoker said, "I want you to move in with me."

Jerked from the calm she'd lulled herself into, Rainey looked up at him. "What?"

"I know it's a big change," Stoker said, stroking her hair. "But it won't be what you're thinking. The club owns most of the row homes on our street and you and me will take one of them over. It'll take a few weeks to move the guys out to other rooms, but we'll do it."

"Our own place?" Rainey mumbled, trying to absorb this new information. She wanted to be excited about this move, but the club loomed over her.

"Yeah, just the two of us. You can fix it up the way you want and make it your own," he added, trying to sell her on the idea. "You'll move in with me to the house I'm at now and then we'll move to our own place when it's ready."

"I . . . I'm . . . I'm not sure what to say." Rainey could hardly believe he'd just made her the offer, let alone wrapping her mind around actually moving in with him. It was a big step and she was unnerved by the decision she'd have to make.

Stoker grinned. "I think you're supposed to say that you can't wait. You're my ol' lady and we need to represent as one. You understand?" he asked firmly.

Rainey gave him a blank stare. She wanted more time to decide. "Can you not call me your ol' lady? I really hate it," she said, trying to deflect from giving an answer right away.

Stoker smiled. "Yeah, when it's just the two of us, sure, but I can't promise that when we're around my brothers. And another thing, don't talk back to me around any of the guys or mamas either. That wouldn't be good."

Rainey said nothing, hoping he wouldn't ask her to verbalize her agreement. She didn't like this side of Stoker. She stood stone still, even though her stomach spun wildly. She tried to convince herself that it wasn't all that bad. She would have a place of her own and that was big. Then she thought about moving out of Winnie's house, and her emotions were mixed. She was comfortable with Winnie and Leo. Despite everything she was learning about Stoker, Rainey believed she needed to give their relationship a chance before she could decide to toss Stoker out of her life.

"Well?" he asked with a slight tension to his voice, hoping she wouldn't disappoint him.

"Yeah, sure. I'll move in with you," she said, placing her arms around his neck.

Stoker kissed the top of her head. "I have some news for you. We had our eyes on your sister."

Rainey's head popped up. All of the emotions and fears of moving in with Stoker flew from her thoughts. "You saw Ivy? When?"

Chapter Twenty-Nine

Stoker gave Rainey a broad smile. "I sent some of my guys into your house acting like squatters. Your little sister was in the basement. They fed her and gave her a few bottles of water. They said she was doing okay. You know, dirty, hungry, scared; all the things you'd expect of a kid getting locked in the dark."

Rainey's hand flew to her chest. "You have to help me get her outta there."

Stoker sighed. "It isn't going to be that easy."

"Why?" Rainey cried, desperate now that she knew Stoker's guys had seen Ivy. "Can't Ivy live with you and me when we move in together?"

Stoker shook his head. "I haven't told you the whole story yet." He paused and took a breath, and in that moment Rainey thought she'd explode with anticipation. "The thing is, Jiggy was there and he recognized our guys. Snoopy had to lie and say they checked out of the club for a night so they could party. He didn't think Jiggy bought it, though."

"So? Fuck Jiggy! Why do you care about him?"

"I don't care about him," Stoker said, a mean glint in his eyes, telling Rainey he meant it, "but I do care about my club. Now that Jiggy knows we have gone into that house, if Ivy disappears, they'll come to the club looking for her. The club can't take a risk on one kid."

Desperation clawed at her; she wanted her sister back, period. "Stoker, please. It's not just any kid, she's my sister, and I raised her since she was born."

"I get it," he said. "But to the club, it is just a kid. A kid that ain't even biker blood. Me and Boulder talked about it, and we both agreed that it'll start a war we don't need."

Angry that Stoker hadn't fought harder for her sister, she spewed, "Am I supposed to live with you and forget about Ivy? Is that what you're saying?"

"No. We'll send in one of our girls regularly to check on her."

"What makes you think Jiggy won't know you sent a girl in?"

"The club has a lot of connections. We don't need to get into all of that. But I promise we'll get updates on her."

Rainey brushed her hair from her face and looked at him with anger. "So I'm never going to be with my sister. Is that what you're telling me? Because I won't agree to it."

Stoker stood and put his arms around her. "No, that's not what I'm saying. What I'm telling you is until the kid gets older, we're gonna have to wait to make any moves."

"Older? How much older?"

He looked away. "I don't have all the answers for you. I'm trying my best here to balance the club and wanting to help you."

His words resonated with Rainey. It was true that if it weren't for Stoker she wouldn't even know if Ivy was dead or alive. She took in a few breaths and rested her forehead on his chest. "Can I at least talk to whoever you sent in to see her? I have questions," Rainey said, near tears with images of Ivy alone in the basement haunting her.

"Yeah, you can talk to Snoopy. He took point because he has kids and I wanted to make sure whoever I sent would know how to talk to your little sister."

***

Winnie's eyes popped out and her hands sat firmly on her hips. "You're moving in with Stoker?"

"Yeah, I told him I would," Rainey answered, now questioning her decision again.

"Don't you think that's too fast?"

"I thought you liked Stoker," she said defensively, but knowing Winnie made a good point.

"I do, but that doesn't mean I think you should live with him. And, that'll mean getting deeper and deeper into the club, which makes me

nervous. It should make you nervous too. I don't think you understand what you're doing . . . what you're committing to."

Rainey, sensing that Winnie had her best interests at heart, put her fingers over her lips. "I know this is crazy. It's all happening so fast and I love living here with you. It's just that I love him and I want to be with him."

Winnie's face shifted to one of concern. "Are you getting married? Is that what you think is going to happen?"

Rainey shrugged. "I don't know. We've never talked about that. I'm only eighteen."

"Exactly," Winnie said. "You're young and he's your first freakin' boyfriend. I thought you wanted to do something better with your life."

"Wow, that was mean." Rainey didn't mind Winnie giving her advice but now it seemed insulting, and she dug her heels in farther. "Living with Stoker doesn't mean my life is over. Come on. You're being kinda harsh."

Winnie shook her head. No I'm not. Living with Stoker means dedicating your life to him and his dumb biker friends. Do you understand that?"

"If I'm going to live with him, then yeah, I'm dedicating my life to him. As for his biker friends, he said we'd get our own house and that I would help with the other girls."

"Oh, yeah? Did he tell you that as his 'ol' lady' you're required to cook for him and those goons he hangs with? Did he tell you that you can never question him or disrespect him or talk back to him?"

Rainey thought back on his warning of not talking back to him around his brothers or the other women, and a good dose of doubt trickled through her. "I guess he did, sorta. He did say something about that to me," she said, feeling embarrassed at the hole she'd dug for herself. To save face, she added, "But that's about his authority. I can argue all I want when we're alone."

Winnie clucked her tongue. "Do you hear yourself? Do you actually think Stoker is going to let you question him or tell him what to do? If that's what you think, then you're delusional."

Rainey sighed, and plopped down on a chair, confused about what she wanted now, but also annoyed with the things Winnie had said to her. "I thought you were my friend. I thought you cared about me."

Winnie knelt in front of her. "I am your friend and I do care about you. I want you to be happy, and I'm scared that tying yourself up this tight with Stoker is going to be a problem for you. The thing is, once you're in with someone of his rank, you can't just step out."

Rainey's gut told her Winnie was right, but her heart insisted on defying her instincts. "How about if I try living with him for a while and if I don't like it, I'll come back here?"

Winnie stood and stepped away from her. When she spoke, her voice was hard. "You're not hearing me. This decision is a permanent one. All I'm saying is think about it long and hard before you take that plunge."

Chapter Thirty

The following week Rainey had packed her clothes and was sitting in the living room with Winnie when Stoker showed up in a van. Despite her worries about the club, Rainey was excited about starting a life with him.

In her bedroom, surveying the few green trash bags, Stoker asked, "Where's your other stuff?"

"This is it," she said with a grin. "To me it seems like a lot. I came here with nothing and now I have clothes."

Stoker was quiet as he hoisted the bags over his shoulders and went downstairs. When they reached the living room, he greeted Winnie, but she only lifted her chin in response.

"What's up with you?" Stoker asked.

"Nothing."

"Okay, then why are you giving me the cold shoulder?"

Rainey stood behind him in the doorway, watching Winnie intently. She knew what Winnie was upset about and was worried what she might say to Stoker.

Winnie got up and stood in front of him. "I'm worried for Rainey. I think her moving in with you is a mistake."

Stoker chuckled. "Isn't that fantastic? You think I can't take care of her or something?"

"That's it, right there," she said, her voice rising. "I think Rainey can take care of herself," she said, meeting her friend's eyes for half a second. "But it's too soon for her to move in with you. She hasn't been out of juvie that long. You're her first boyfriend. And let's not forget, you're second in the Devils Angels. That's a big deal and your girl doesn't understand what that means."

"Okay," Stoker said, smiling slyly and leaning against the doorway. "Why don't you tell me what that means for her then?"

"It means she belongs to you. All of her."

"Yeah, so what? That's what happens when you find someone to love. You belong to each other. Rainey and me talked about this," he said, glancing at his girlfriend.

Rainey used all of her willpower to keep quiet because Winnie was on fire and needed to say what was on her mind. Plus she wanted to hear Stoker's explanations to the hard truths being thrown at him.

Winnie banged her foot on the floor. "You know what I'm talking about."

"No, actually, I don't. Listen, you and I go way back. We've been good to each other and I'm not going to keep Rainey from seeing you if that's what you're worried about."

Winnie glared at her girlfriend. "See? He's not going to keep you from seeing me. That means he can if he wants to. Don't you get it?"

Rainey sat on the sofa and looked from Stoker to Winnie. Overwhelmed with everything that was happening, tears slid down her cheeks. Her voice came out small but crisp, "This is supposed to be a happy day for me. Stoker isn't my boss." She turned to the man she loved. "Do you think that? Do you think you can tell me what to do or who I can see?"

He laid down the bags, strode into the living room, and sat on the sofa, looking at Rainey with compassion in his eyes. He sighed. "Look. Winnie's right. Things are going to be different. Being in the club changes a lot of stuff."

Rainey shifted uncomfortably as he spoke; she hadn't expected this.

"But," he continued, and Rainey hung onto that "but" like a lifeline, "I can promise you that I have no desire to boss you around. I waited a long time to meet someone like you and now that I have you, I don't want to lose you. That's it. It's that simple."

Rainey's face lightened and a sad but telling smile put him at ease. She loved Winnie but this was her decision and Stoker just laid his heart on the line and she believed him. She turned to Winnie; her friend's arms were crossed over her chest, and she gave Rainey a shrug.

"Okay," Winnie said, "but remember what you promised, Stoker."

Stoker stood and saluted Winnie. He picked up the green trash bags and walked toward the front door. "Now can we get outta here? We got some celebrating to do."

Rainey rushed over to Winnie and hugged her. "I'll see you at work."

Winnie nodded, her eyes welling as she tried to fight back tears. "I'll miss you living here."

"Me too," Rainy said, swiping the tears from her cheeks.

***

Inside her temporary home with Stoker, she put her clothes away as he lay on the bed, watching.

"How long before we move into our own place?" she asked.

"Should be no more than a week."

She smiled as she approached the bed, and when she laid next to him, he pulled her close.

"You ain't gotta worry about all that shit Winnie was talking about. Yeah, we got rules that you'll have to follow, but it's nothing big."

"Winnie said I have to cook for you and the club members. Is that true?"

Stoker gave her a sexy grin. "Yeah, now and then you will. Do you know how to cook?"

Rainey shook her head. "So there better be someone who can help me."

"Don't worry. We can work that out."

"Do you ever worry about anything?" she asked.

"Sure, there are plenty of things that weigh on my mind. Just not silly shit. What do you worry about?"

Rainey pushed herself up on her elbow. "I worry that me and Kiki won't get along. She's okay, but I get the feeling I'm not her favorite person."

"Why would you think that?"

Rainey laid on her back and looked at the ceiling. "I can tell. She wasn't friendly. It was more like she was doing something she was told to do."

Stoker sneered. "Well, she was doing something she was told to do. Now, aside from that, Kiki can be harsh. She doesn't trust anyone until they've earned it. She's got her way of doing things and doesn't like anyone changing shit around. You'll get used to her."

"What if I don't?"

Stoker leaned up and kissed the tip of her nose. "That's not an option. I know you'll make it work."

Chapter Thirty-One

The next morning, Rainey was in the kitchen drinking coffee when Stoker strolled in and grumbled a garbled, "Morning."

"Morning," Rainey said in a cheery voice. She'd decided that since she was here anyway, it didn't make sense to freak out about everything. She told herself to just roll with things for now. "Hey, can you give me a ride to work?" she asked.

Stoker pulled a mug from the cabinet and glanced at her. "Yeah, sure. I wanted to talk to you about that job anyway."

"What about it?"

"I think you can do better. I mean, cleaning rooms is fine, but it isn't something you're gonna want to do for the rest of your life."

At first, Rainey's skin prickled. She didn't want him deciding whether her job was good for her or not; that was her choice. Besides, that's where she saw Winnie. But she told herself to hear him out. "Maybe you're right, but I'm not quitting unless I find something better."

He slurped coffee from his mug. "I think you'd be good at one of those township jobs. There's an opening at the North Philly Municipal Building. They pay good, and you'd get to be around some of those bigwigs that enforce all the laws around here."

Rainey placed her coffee mug on the counter and faced him, instinctively knowing there was something else behind this, something that would benefit the club. "Oh, yeah? And how am I supposed to get a job there?"

"The club knows a few people. All you need to do is go and apply."

"What's the job?" she asked cautiously. She wasn't sure she liked what Stoker was implying, but if it meant making more money, she might be interested.

"Not sure. Some kind of secretary or customer service type thing."

"How did you hear about it?"

Stoker looked up from his coffee. "There are lots of things I hear about, and if they're better for you that's all that matters."

Rainey flinched. "Did someone tell you to make me apply?"

Stoker slammed his hand on the table. "I said I think it would be good for you. Now, take a shower and I'll drive you over. You can see if you like it. That's all there is to it."

Rainey was annoyed by his demanding tone. "I'll be late for work," she said trying to come up with an excuse.

"So what?" Stoker said, holding his cup out to her for a refill.

Rainey grabbed the coffeepot and poured its contents into his mug. "Fine," she stated, letting out a loud breath. "But I'm only going there to make you happy. I'm going to get a load of shit for being late."

Hearing the distress in her voice, Stoker softened. He stood and took her into his arms. "I'm sorry I got all worked up. You have to understand that when I tell you to do stuff, there's a reason. Okay?"

Rainey tilted her head. She thought about arguing with him. She didn't like him telling her what to do, but he did just apologize, she reasoned. She decided to go check out the job, and she would deal with Titus once she got to the motel.

***

Rainey read the nameplate on the receptionist desk. MARIE SIERNEY. "Hi, Marie. I'm here to apply for the open position."

Marie looked her up and down. "The records clerk position?"

Rainey bit her lower lip, remembering she didn't know. "Is that the only job there is?"

Marie pursed her lips. "Yeah, at this time. That's right."

"Then, yes. I want to apply for the records clerk job."

Marie sighed, pulled out a clipboard, and handed it to her. "Fill this out and bring it back to me."

As she was filling out the form, a tall, thin man dressed in black pants and a blue button-down shirt approached the reception desk. She didn't pay much attention until she noticed them whispering and then Marie pointed at her. Rainey's pulse quickened as the man approached, wondering who he was, and worried he'd ask questions that she wouldn't be able to answer.

"Hi," he said, stepping up to her. "Do you know Boulder?"

She hesitated, unsure how to answer.

"Are you Rainey?" he asked.

She nodded.

"Boulder mentioned you would be coming in. I'm David," he said, holding out his hand. "Why don't we go into my office and we can talk?"

She shook his hand. "I . . . I . . . I didn't finish the application yet."

He flicked his hand. "You can finish doing that in my office."

Following David, she glanced at Marie, who was glaring back at her. Rainey gave her an uneasy smile as she walked by. Inside the office, he told her about the job responsibilities.

"How much does this job pay?" Rainey asked timidly.

"Twelve an hour," he said.

"I don't really know how to type."

He smirked. "You can learn, right?"

Rainey nodded, happy that he gave her an out.

"Then you'll learn. Any other questions?"

She shook her head. Then said, "Wait! When can I start?"

"How does Monday sound?"

Rainey breathed a sigh of relief; she had just gotten her first real office job. "Yeah, that would be great."

Everything happened so fast, and even though she knew she was only getting the job because of Boulder, it still felt like an achievement.

Outside, she ran to Stoker. "I got the job. They're going to pay me twelve bucks an hour. Can you believe it?"

Stoker kissed her tenderly. "Yeah, I believe it. You're going to do all kinds of great things."

"Well, I didn't exactly do it all on my own. David said he knew Boulder."

Stoker nodded. "Yeah, he does. We knew you'd be perfect for the job. You have that subtle charm and you're hot."

Rainey pushed on his chest gently. "Stop it. You know I have a record. Do you think that's going to be a problem?"

Stoker looked past her. "Boulder took care of all that. There's nothing to worry about."

Boulder took care of all that rang in Rainey's ears. She didn't like Boulder doing things for her without her knowing.

Interrupting her thoughts, he added, "This is going to be a big help to the club. I'm so proud of you."

Concern replaced her excitement. She knew there was more to this than he was admitting and, on the first day living with him, she was already getting herself in deeper with the club.

"How is me having a job here going to help the club?"

Stoker straddled his motorcycle. "Because these townships have a lot of power and we need some of that right now."

Rainey climbed on Stoker's bike and held onto him, regretting that she'd ever agreed to meet with David and having accepted the position. "I don't want any trouble," she said.

"Who said anything about trouble?"

Chapter Thirty-Two

An hour later, at the Drop Inn, Winnie slammed her mop handle to the floor when Rainey told her about the new job. "Wait! You moved out yesterday and today you got a job somewhere else?" she said, stunned. "I knew this would happen. I'm never going to see you anymore."

Rainey, shaken by her friend's reaction, rushed to her. "That's not true. Look, it's a better job and it pays a lot more money. Besides, other than chipping in for food it doesn't cost me anything to live with Stoker. I'm gonna be able to save more money now so I can take care of Ivy when I get her."

Winnie's shoulders rolled forward. "I know, but I can't help it. I liked you living with us. It all happened too fast . . . you and Stoker and moving out."

She grabbed her friend's hand. "He's my boyfriend, but you'll always be one of my best friends. Always."

Winnie cocked her head and grinned. "Fine, but I'm telling you if things get weird you have to promise to let me know so I can talk to Stoker," she said.

She raised her right hand into the air. "Promise."

"What are you gonna tell Titus?"

Rainey shrugged. "That I got another job and I can't work here after this week."

***

On Rainey's last day at the Drop Inn Motel, Stoker was waiting for her outside. He was leaning on the seat of his motorcycle and holding a single rose.

Rainey ran to him. "What's going on?" she asked, grinning.

He handed the rose to her. "Oh, nothing," he said, pulling her in for a kiss. "I have a surprise for you."

"Oh, yay! What is it?"

He shook his index finger at her. "It's a surprise to celebrate your new job. Climb on, we have to go."

Giddy with excitement, Rainey got on the back of the bike, wondering what Stoker had in store for her. When he parked, it was in front of a pizzeria.

"Here we are," he said, grinning.

Rainey didn't care where he took her. She was thrilled that he wanted to celebrate something good that had happened for her. She looked at him. "This is great. I love pizza." She got off the bike and followed him into the restaurant.

"Let's sit back there," he said, pointing deeper into the restaurant, where only one booth was occupied. As they got closer to the table she squinted in the poor lighting and her heart quickened.

"Ivy?" she mumbled.

Her now nine-year-old sister looked up at her and rolled her eyes. "Oh, hi."

Looking at her sister and the woman sitting across from her, Rainey slid into the booth next to Ivy. Putting her arms up, she wrapped them around her sister's shoulders, but Ivy pulled away. Her sister's reaction was unsettling, and with a broken heart, she collected herself. But still, the tension was thick. "How have you been?" she asked, keeping her voice bright.

"Fine," Ivy remarked, with her eyes fixed on the slice of pizza in front of her.

"How's the pizza here?"

Ivy rolled her eyes again. "Fine. And, if you stop talking to me, I can eat it."

Rainey looked across the table at the woman who had been sitting there quietly watching. Noticing, Stoker pointed to the woman, "This is Janis," he said, and Rainey gave her a quick smile.

Stoker put his hand out for Janis and pulled her to her feet. "We're gonna go down the block and throw back a few beers so you and your sister can talk. We'll be back in a while and Janis will take her home."

Rainey nodded, more interested in connecting with Ivy than anything else. When they were gone, she turned to her sister. "How do you know Janis?"

Ivy shrugged and took a bite of her pizza. "She hangs out at my house."

"Oh, yeah? How long has she been around?"

The girl shrugged. "I don't know. Since like a month ago. Why?"

Rainey shook her head. "No reason, I was just curious. Is she nice to you?"

Ivy nodded. "Yeah, she's very nice. I don't think she'll leave me like you did," she said in a flat voice.

"Hey," she said, turning to face Ivy, "I didn't leave you on purpose. Every single day I wish you and me were living together."

"Okay," Ivy said dismissively, avoiding her sister's eyes.

"Can you look at me?"

She turned and stared into Rainey's eyes, but her forehead was scrunched and her lips were pinched. "What do you want from me? Huh?"

"I don't want anything from you, Ivy. I want to help you."

"Yeah, well, it's too late."

"What does that mean? Did someone hurt you?"

Ivy pointed her finger at Rainey's face. "What do you care? What are you gonna do if someone hurts me? Kick their ass? Tell your dumb boyfriend? Just go away and leave me alone."

Rainey was rattled as she reached into her pocket and pulled out a twenty-dollar bill. "Here, take this. So you can buy some food."

Ivy pushed her hand away. "I don't want your money. I don't want anything from you."

"Why are you mad at me?" Rainey asked in a shaking voice, trying hard to keep her emotions in check.

Ivy crossed her arms over her chest. "Because when you left me, you ruined my life."

Rainey's eyes widened. "I didn't leave you and I need you to understand that. Everything Mom and Dad have told you about me is a lie."

"I wanna go home," Ivy said, sliding out of the booth.

Holding back tears, Rainey followed. "I'll go with you to find Janis. She'll walk you home."

"I'm not a baby. I can walk home by myself."

Rainey gently grabbed her arm, unable to bear the thought of Ivy walking away from her. "No, let's get Janis. It's not safe for you to walk through Kensington on your own."

Ivy spun on her. "It's not safe to live at my house either, but you don't care about that, do you?" She pulled her arm away from her sister and ran toward the door.

Chapter Thirty-Three

Rainey ran after her sister, took hold of her arm, and spun her around. "If you remember, I did come back for you right after I got out of jail," she said, unable to hold back her anger. "Dad punched me in the face and I woke up in an alley. I tried, but they won't let me see you."

Instead of hearing what Rainey had said, Ivy screamed, "Get away from me! Help! Somebody help me!"

A heavyset woman dressed in a fast-food-restaurant uniform rushed up to them. "What's wrong, honey? She bothering you?" she spat, glaring at Rainey.

"Yeah," Ivy said, pouting and fake sniffling. "She keeps trying to get me to go with her."

"Is that so?" fast-food woman asked.

Rainey shook her head. "She's my little sister and we're having an argument, that's all."

"She's a liar," Ivy protested. "She left me and I haven't seen her in a long, long time."

Fast-food woman bent down. "Sweetheart, you wouldn't be fibbing me now, would you?"

Ivy shook her head.

The woman looked at Rainey, who was visibly distraught, and back to Ivy. "Where you live, baby? I got my car over there and I'll get you back home."

"No, you won't," Rainey said, stepping in front of her sister. "She's not getting in a car with a stranger. Thank you, but we're fine."

Just then, to Rainey's relief, Stoker and Janis approached.

"What's going on here?" Janis asked, and Ivy threw her arms around her waist.

Fast-food woman said, "This little girl told me this lady is bothering her. Now, this one," she said, pointing at Rainey, "claims they're sisters and the little one says they ain't."

Janis gave the woman a polite smile. "It's fine. She's with me. I'll get her home."

Ivy smiled, too. "Thank you," she said as she walked away with Janis.

Annoyed and confused, Rainey watched them walk off, then she turned to Stoker. "What the fuck?"

"What happened?" he asked, looking at her with concern.

Rubbing her forehead, Rainey walked toward the motorcycle. Then she turned and looked at him straight on, "I have to get her out of that house. We need to figure out a way for her to live with us."

Stoker shook his head. "We already talked about this. Did you forget about Jiggy?"

She blew out a long breath. "No. How could I ever forget about him? I went to juvie because of him. I can't live with myself seeing her like this. You don't know Ivy, she used to be sweet, so loving. Now she's angry and hates everything and everybody, especially me."

"I think you're overreacting."

She glared at him. "Don't do that to me. I need you to have my back."

"All right," Stoker said. "How about this . . . I'll get Janis to talk to your sister to smooth things over and try to make the kid feel better."

"You will?" Rainey asked, allowing herself to feel hopeful.

"Yeah, let's get going. I need to get back to the club for a meeting."

***

When Stoker got home from his meeting that night, Rainey was lying in bed, listening to music. He walked into the bedroom and kissed her on the neck.

"I've decided to stay at the Drop Inn," she said nervously. "I called Titus and he said I can have my job back."

Stoker pulled his shirt over his head and glared at her. "Why?"

Rainey cringed at the sharpness of his tone. She knew he wasn't going to be happy about her decision and was hoping to avoid a long, drawn-out argument. She had a lot of time to think and knew it would be better for her to stay at the Drop Inn.

Looking into his eyes, she took in a breath through her nose to calm her nerves. "The thing is, what happened with Ivy really turned my world upside down. Winnie is like another sister to me and right now I need to be close to her. If I stay at the Drop Inn, I'll get to be with Winnie every day." She rolled on her side and bunched the pillow under her head, avoiding Stoker's eyes, "I'm sorry and I hope you're not mad at me. I know how much you wanted me to take the job."

He sighed. "This is going to cause a problem," he said, crossing the room. "I told Boulder you were starting the township job on Monday. He'll be disappointed. He called in a favor with David."

Rainey leaned up on her elbows. "No, Boulder called in a favor so I could spy on the people who work there. Isn't that what he really wanted me to do? The job was never about helping me."

Stoker sat on the bed next to her. "That's true. He does have other motives but you were happy with the offer. Remember the twelve bucks an hour?"

"I do. But money doesn't help if Ivy won't talk to me. Besides, you told me she can't live with us. I feel like I'm losing too many people in my life. This way I can still be with Winnie every day and give money to Janis for Ivy, so she can eat."

Stoker looked down and shook his head. "Well, I'll let Boulder know that you're turning down the job."

"Are you mad at me?" she asked, seeing his disappointment.

He gave her a half smile. "I'm frustrated that you're not taking the job. And I think it's a mistake on your end, but hey, you're old enough to figure out what you want to do. Just don't expect Boulder to call in any more favors for you."

The sharpness of his tone cut her at the core, and Rainey's stomach flip-flopped. She had struggled over what to do, and now she was realizing the depth of her decision. "It sounds like I'm being punished."

"Yeah, you will be. See, the club is all about loyalty and trust. Boulder put himself out there for you, and you're letting him down. He'll be disappointed. We'll both pay for this."

Rainey froze. She hadn't considered that Stoker would get heat for her decision. "He's not going to kill us, is he?"

"No," Stoker assured her, "nothing that drastic."

"Do you hate me?" she asked, finding it hard to meet his eyes.

"Nah," he said, running his hand over her hair, "I still love you. But you and me have to get on the same page. You're my ol' lady, so Boulder will get over your decision at some point. But going forward, you can't say one thing and do another. I'll be on the hook for this one and so will you."

Rainey felt immense love for Stoker at that moment. That he was willing to take a hit for her, that he'd brought Ivy to see her, and it was clear he was committed to her. She pulled Stoker down and laid on top of him. "I'm sorry I made things hard for you with Boulder," she said, kissing him on the mouth.

Stoker kissed her back, but he was distracted with the price Boulder would make them pay for Rainey going back on her word.

Chapter Thirty-Four

Two weeks later, on a Saturday night, Winnie visited Rainey in the row home she and Stoker had been given to live in.

"This is nice," she said, looking around the living room as Rainey held her breath, desperate for Winnie's approval.

"Yeah, the furniture's beat and the walls need painting, but at least the club is paying for it." Rainey looked around the space, taking it in. She didn't love it, if she was being honest, but it was hers and Stoker's and that made it special.

"How are things going with Ivy? Have you seen her again?"

Rainey shook her head. Over the past couple of weeks, she'd asked Stoker almost every day if he'd talked to Janis. Rainey had been venting to Winnie about how difficult it had been to get even a scrap of news.

"I asked Stoker to have Janis meet us tomorrow so I can try to talk to Ivy again. I'm hoping to find something out soon. Anyway, the club is having a party tonight and Stoker said you can come with me."

Winnie squinted at her. "Yuck. Really? Their parties are so dull. It's all about the bikers, and all the girls do is hang around and fight with each other."

Rainey winced. Winnie was right, their parties were boring and when she had to go, she hated it. "That's exactly why I need you to come with me. I don't fit in with the other girls. Please?"

"Oh, I don't know."

"Oh, really?" Rainey said, trying to convince her. "Don't you remember a certain someone turned down a better-paying job so she could see you every day?"

Winnie rolled her eyes and smiled. "You're a pest. Okay, fine. I'll go with you, but I don't have to like it."

***

Later that night, Rainey and Winnie were sitting at the bar in the basement with a few of the girls while the men played pool. The night had been going well, and having Winnie there made it better until Kiki stood on the other side of the bar and scowled at Rainey.

Kiki's upper lip curled, "I heard you made my ol' man look like an asshole. He went out of his way to get you that job and you turned around and quit before you even got started. You're one fucked-up bitch."

Alarmed by Kiki's intensity and her accusation, Rainey's eyes grew wide. "I didn't mean to insult Boulder," she said seriously, her voice cracking as her nerves took over. "I wanted to stay at the motel. It was nothing personal."

Kiki pushed on Rainey's shoulder. "Then you should've thought about that before my ol' man went through all the trouble to get you hooked up. Maybe you need to start selling that skinny ass of yours to the men in that motel, like your friend here," she said, gesturing to Winnie.

"Shut up, Kiki. How about if you mind your own business?" Rainey hissed.

All of a sudden, Kiki threw her head forward and head-butted Rainey. Dazed, her knees buckled but she caught herself on the edge of the bar before hitting the floor. She sprung forward and punched the older girl right between her eyes.

Falling backward, Kiki smashed into bottles of liquor on the table behind her. She lurched forward and growled at Rainey as she jumped over the bar and her fists flew.

The two women fought, punching and kicking each other until Boulder ripped them apart, yelling, "That's enough!" making the entire basement go quiet. "You both got your licks in and that's all I want to see for tonight."

Rainey was panting when she looked over to find Stoker watching from across the room. Unable to face any of them, she grabbed Winnie's hand and pulled her out of the basement.

"What was that?" Winnie shrieked once they were away from the crowd.

"That's because I decided to turn down that dumb job Boulder wanted me to take. Kiki's a bitch. I hate her. Come on, let's get out of here."

***

Back at Rainey's, the girls were sitting in the kitchen, Winnie was still wide-eyed. "So Boulder got you that job?" she asked.

With a paper towel, Rainey dabbed at the blood coming from her nose. "Yeah, he called in a favor to some guy named David, who works at the township."

"Holy shit," Winnie breathed. "You didn't tell me all of that."

"Why? What difference does it make?"

"Jesus, Rainey. The Devils Angels are all about doing what you're told. Not just the members but the women, too. You can't just change your mind once you said you'll do something."

"Well, I did. I know that it was crappy, but I wanted to be able to see you every day," Rainey paused, trying to calm herself down. "Besides, I was worried about getting caught up in too much club stuff," she admitted. "I know what prison is like and I never wanna go back."

"That's great, but you have to do something to make it up to Boulder," Winnie said.

"Like what?" Winnie's reaction was making her realize the impact of what she'd just done.

"Like, I don't know." Winnie's eyes grew larger. "Listen to me, Stoker is gonna pay a price for what you've done. Things like this don't go unpunished."

Rainey tipped her head back and squeezed the bridge of her nose to stop the bleeding. "Maybe Boulder is okay with it. It's been two weeks since I turned down the job. Don't you think he would've said something by now?" Even as Rainey said it, she had a sweeping sense of uneasiness.

"Listen, you don't want to be on the wrong side of Boulder. He's the boss of all these guys, including Stoker. He can make your life hell," Winnie warned.

"Are you serious? Remember, Stoker is his second in charge."

Winnie nodded. "I'm dead serious. I've been around these guys for a long time. What you did was bad and you need to make this right. If not for you, then for your boyfriend. I'm sure Stoker took a lot of crap for this already. You have no idea how bad things can get when the president of the Devils Angels thinks you screwed him over."

Rainey grew light-headed, her vision blurring and her nose throbbing with pain. "I made a huge mistake," she said.

Chapter Thirty-Five

When Stoker returned home that night, Rainey was sitting on the sofa in the dark.

"Hey," she breathed, as he threw his leather vest on a chair and turned on a light.

"Hey," he said tersely. "That was some messed-up shit at the club tonight."

"I was defending myself. She head-butted me, and I wasn't gonna let her get away with it."

Stoker sat and put his hand on her leg. "Look, after you left, Boulder talked to me about what the consequences will be for turning down the job."

Fear mounted in her belly by the seriousness of his tone. "What did he say?"

"Well, first he explained that David was surprised and annoyed that Boulder had wasted his time. Of course, Boulder is embarrassed and worried about our homes. You don't fuck with the township people after calling in a favor. The township can make our lives hell, we own most of the houses on this block, and not everything is exactly up to code."

"I know he's mad at me. Is he mad at you too?"

Stoker nodded. "I expected him to be pissed, but I've never seen him like this, and that thing with Kiki tonight set him off."

Rainey flinched. "So what do I need to do? How can I make it better?"

Stoker hesitated before letting out a long breath. "You're gonna have to sleep with Boulder. That's how he's going to make us both suffer."

Gripped by remorse, Rainey jumped to her feet and paced, picturing Boulder's hands touching her and forcing her to do whatever he wanted.

Almost as worrisome was the image of Kiki rising to her mind. No way would she let it slide that Rainey had slept with her man.

"What?" she shouted. "Ew, no, I'm not having sex with him. There's no way, Stoker. This is ridiculous."

He raised his eyebrows. "It's better than the alternative."

"What alternative?" Rainey asked, hating how her voice shook.

"If you don't sleep with him, he'll come down hard on you . . . physically. And I'll be forced to ditch you as my ol' lady and you'll be up for grabs by whoever, whenever."

Panicking, Rainey grabbed his arm. Regretting having ever moved in with Stoker and wishing she had stayed with Winnie, where she had been safe. "You need to tell him no. You need to make him stop. Tell him I'm sorry or something."

Stoker shook his head. "I wish there was a way, but my loyalty is to the club first." He put his hand on the back of her head and pulled her to him. "I love you and I don't wanna lose you. I need you to do this for me, for both of us."

Rainey shook uncontrollably. "I can't do it. I mean, how can you even let me? And what about Kiki? She'd probably kill me if she found out."

"Kiki will do as she's told. You'll have sex with Boulder. She'll be jealous and will probably ride your ass for a while, but it'll eventually blow over."

Rainey paced the living room again, wishing she'd just taken that stupid township job, wishing she'd never moved in with Stoker, and wishing she'd listened to Winnie's warnings about the club. "And what about you? Are you going to be jealous?"

"Well, I ain't gonna like it, but that's just how it goes. If you fuck up, there's a price to pay. I wanted to let you make your own decisions, and this is the result. It's not that complicated."

Rainey fell to her knees in front of him. "Please, Stoker," she begged, openly crying. "You have to think of something. I'll . . . I'll work for the township. Okay? Tell him I'll do it."

Stoker gently grabbed her by the shoulders. "It's too late. I thought about the same thing, so I called David. They already filled the position."

Rainey laid her head in his lap. "I'll move back with Winnie."

"That won't matter."

Her heart raced. It was as though there was always something bad waiting for her. Rainey wished she'd never gotten involved with Stoker. Yes, she loved him, but she wasn't certain that being in love with him was in her

best interests anymore. She'd caused them pain and now she was forced to be used by a man that made her flesh crawl.

***

She and Stoker sat in the living room together until they both fell asleep. When they woke the next morning, Rainey was refreshed until she remembered what they'd discussed the night before.

"Is there any other way?" she asked, turning to him.

Stoker, still wiping sleep from his eyes, fumbled for his words. "I'm afraid there isn't. You're gonna have to accept it, get it done, and then we can put this behind us."

She gazed at him, wondering how he could be so casual regarding her having sex with his boss. If it were her, she'd fight to the death, but it was him, and the Devils Angels came before all others.

Chapter Thirty-Six

"All right," Stoker said later that morning, "let's get this over with."

Rainey's shoulders were hunched and she gave him a blank stare. The past few hours had been hell, filled with raunchy visions of being with Boulder. She couldn't help but think of the way Freddy had hurt her and now she was scared Boulder would hurt her too.

"I don't wanna go," Rainey whispered.

"Come on. We already talked about this. I'm dreading this as much as you are."

"That's impossible." She let out a groan. "I'm so freaked out. What if he hurts me?"

Stoker patted her shoulder. "He's not going to hurt you and he won't do nothing weird; he gave me his word. We have to go. I need to bring you over there and you don't wanna be late."

"Are you staying the whole time?" Rainey asked, unsure whether she would be more uncomfortable if he stayed or left.

Stoker shook his head. "Kiki and me have to go to the club and wait. He told me the next time my ol' lady breaks a promise that I should think about the consequences real hard. And believe me, if it happens again, I will."

Rainey's stomach dropped and she broke into a sweat from the waves of nausea that swept through her. Stoker grabbed her shaky hand and held it tightly. Rainey's knees wobbled as they walked to the end of the block where Boulder and Kiki lived. Feeling cheap and dirty, Rainey stood on the porch next to Stoker for a moment before he knocked on the door.

Kiki opened the door and took in Rainey with deadpan eyes. Then she shifted her focus to Stoker, and her demeanor lightened. "He's waiting. He's in the kitchen having a drink."

Stoker nodded and grabbed Rainey's hand, leading her into the house. Boulder met them in the dining room and looked Rainey up and down. She was creeped out, and goose bumps rose on her flesh. He turned to Kiki. "Go get her those pink underwear you got. You know, the ones I like. And I want her to wear those high-heel shoes too."

Rainey gasped and looked at Stoker, but he didn't meet her gaze. Instead he let go of her hand and took a seat at the dining room table. It seemed to her like she was sinking to the bottom of the ocean and just out of reach of a life preserver.

"Move it," Kiki ordered, grabbing Rainey's attention.

Rainey followed Kiki upstairs. Once inside the bedroom she said, "Please, Kiki. I'm sorry about the fight we had the other night. Isn't there anything I can do so that Boulder doesn't want to . . . to—"

"Fuck you?" Kiki said, watching her with steely eyes.

Rainey looked at her feet. "Yeah. I'll do anything you want."

"Too late. He's already made his decision."

Kiki opened the top dresser drawer and pulled out a pink lace bra with a matching thong. "Put these on. The bra will probably be too big, given you ain't got no tits, but the thong will fit."

She moved to her closet and pulled out a pair of six-inch stripper heels. "We look about the same shoe size," she said, tossing them at her. "I'm gonna go to the club with Stoker while you screw my ol' man. I won't ever forget it either, you can count on that. But it's what Boulder wants and so he'll get to bang your nasty ass." Kiki turned to leave the bedroom. "Boulder will be in soon. Get yourself ready."

Rainey's hands shook as she changed, then sat on the bed, scantily dressed, and waited. After what seemed like an eternity, Boulder opened the door and stepped inside the bedroom.

He threw back the whiskey left in his glass and leered at her. "Come on. Stand up. Let me see you."

Rainey stood with her arms crossed over her chest, holding the too-large bra against herself. She kept her shoulders hunched forward and her knees bent as she tried in vain to hide her body from him.

Boulder approached her and smoothed her hair. "Straighten up," he barked.

Immediately, Rainey did as she was told.

She stood stiff as a statue while he circled her. "Goddamn, you're hot. The minute I laid eyes on you I knew Stoker was a lucky man. Now I'm lucky too."

Rainey watched him intently, realizing she'd never really taken him in before. He was stocky with a wide chest, thick biceps, and his waist tapered into a V above his hip bones. He had thick black hair, a bushy mustache, and a goatee with a thick stripe of hair from his lower lip to his chin. Underneath the tire mark tattoos, his right forearm was tattooed with the word "Devils" and his left with "Angels." He had so many tattoos they became indistinguishable.

She watched him remove all of his clothes, and even though she tried to remain silent, she gasped at his naked body. She hadn't realized that he was pure muscle. He had hard abs and thick, tight thigh muscles. The more she took in, the quicker her heart raced.

Naked, he sauntered up behind her, locked his hands around her waist, and pulled her into him. Feeling his erection on her lower back, she tried to pull away, but he held her closely.

"I'm not gonna hurt you," he whispered in her ear. "I promised Stoker I'd be gentle."

Then he turned her around to face him and placed his lips over her mouth. He kissed her softly, slowly working his tongue into her mouth. After a moment she closed her eyes and gave in to it, returning a passionate kiss. When he slid his hand under her thong and caressed her, she threw her head back and let out a soft moan. He unfastened the bra and took one of her breasts into his mouth. Then suddenly he stopped.

Surprised, she opened her eyes and looked at him. That seemed to be what he was waiting for, because he gave her a sexy grin and slid the thong all the way off. After she stepped out of it, he laid her on the bed and pressed her thighs down. His tongue danced between her legs and she couldn't hold back her sexual desire. She pulled him to her, forgetting about everything else and being present in that moment as Boulder slipped inside her. They moved together in an effortless rhythm. As he made love to her, he reached between her legs to caress that magical spot until they both burst with pleasure.

Afterward, they lay together in each other's arms. It was then that guilt consumed her and Rainey couldn't make eye contact with him.

"You like that?" he rumbled after a moment.

Feeling oddly enthralled by him, Rainey shyly nodded.

"I want to hear you say it," he insisted.

"I liked that," she whispered.

He kissed the tip of her nose. "Yeah, I liked that too. Maybe I should punish you again," he said, reaching between her legs.

Giving herself over, Rainey leaned into him. Boulder made her body sing. Yes, she loved Stoker, but Boulder's hands and mouth were built for her body. When they were done the second time, Rainey sat up and grabbed for her clothes, her face flaming. That wasn't what was supposed to happen. She wasn't supposed to have enjoyed it.

"Hold on. You're leaving so soon, are you?" he asked.

"Stoker's waiting for me."

"So what?"

Rainey tilted her head, and her long blond hair fell to one side, giving Boulder a lustful stir in his groin.

"It's not right," she said. "I did what you wanted me to do."

He lifted his eyebrows. "Did I say your punishment was over?"

Her skin prickled with both guilt and excitement. "No," she said, a smile tugging at the corners of her mouth. Rainey convinced herself that she wasn't making the choices, she had to do what Boulder wanted, and this alleviated some of the guilt that had consumed her a moment earlier.

"That's right. I never said I was finished." He reached for her head and gently pushed it toward his groin as she willingly fulfilled his desire.

***

Rainey woke and for a moment forgot where she was. Looking over, she was disturbed to see Boulder's sleeping next to her. Then it all flooded her consciousness.

"Oh, shit," she said, nudging him. "Wake up. We have to get outta here. They're waiting for us."

Boulder scratched his head and nodded. "All right. We'll get dressed and get outta here." As he stood over the bed his eyes met Rainey's and he grinned. "You tasted as sweet as I'd imagined."

She blushed. "Um, I'm not sure what to say."

"Really?" he mumbled in her ear. "I know you feel the same about me."

She shook her head, feeling a rush of sexual tension between them again. "I turned down the job, I took my punishment, and now we're even. Okay?"

He chuckled. "Okay, if you say so. But don't be surprised when you're thinking about me when you're making love to your boyfriend."

"I doubt that," Rainey said, though part of her knew Boulder was right.

Because even at that moment, she couldn't push aside her lust for him. She had never expected it to happen, to like him, to want him, but she did, and now she had to figure out how she'd go back to her life with Stoker and leave her thoughts of Boulder behind.

Chapter Thirty-Seven

When Rainey walked into the basement of the club behind Boulder, all eyes were on her.

"Whore," one girl said through a cough as they passed.

Boulder spun on the group of mamas. "I don't wanna hear another word out of you bitches. You understand me?"

Rainey's mouth fell open and she shuffled back a few steps at his outburst.

The girls nodded, but she noticed that Kiki stared at him, jealousy oozing from her hard glare. Boulder met her eyes for a second before moving across the room to where his members were waiting.

Rainey joined the women and stood awkwardly and was thrilled when Taz walked down the basement stairs.

"Hey, girl," Taz said, hugging her, "what's going on?"

"Oh, just another day in paradise," Rainey said, trying to brush off all the mixed emotions flowing through her.

"How did everything go?" Taz whispered, leaning in.

Rainey fidgeted but then decided that talking to Taz about it would be good practice for telling Stoker about it later.

"It was fine." She shrugged. "I mean, it was something that had to be done. He wasn't mean or anything."

Taz grinned. "Nah, Boulder is great in bed."

Rainey's eyes bulged. "You've slept with him?"

Taz's eyebrows bounced and she nodded.

"When?"

"Let's see. It was about seven years ago, before he took Kiki as his ol' lady. I had just turned eighteen and I thought he was gonna pick me, but he chose Kiki. She was also screwing him at that time. It was a weird thing to

go through, two chicks vying for one man's attention. He was totally into it, but after a while it turned me off."

Rainey leaned in, dying to hear more of the story. "Why did he pick her?"

Taz giggled. "I have no idea, but the girls all agree she must give good head, 'cause she can be nasty." She looked at Kiki. "I mean, she's really pretty, I guess, with her black hair and those blue eyes. She has a hot bod too."

Rainey glanced over. "Yeah, but she's crazy. If Stoker were the boss, I'd never let him sleep with another girl."

"Yeah," Taz said, shifting uncomfortably, "about sleeping with Kiki's man . . . you need to watch your back with her. The last time Boulder slept with a girl for a punishment, she made him kick her outta here. She wasn't nobody's ol' lady, though, so at least you have that. She works on Kensington Avenue now."

Rainey watched Kiki slam back a shot with three of the other girls, then said, "Let me know if you hear anything, okay?"

"Yeah, sure. I'll help you out. And, um, you'll let Stoker know that I'm on your side?"

"On my side for what?"

"For whatever you need." She leaned closer and whispered, "I've been spending like all of my nights in Andrew's bed. You know, Stoker's ex-roommate? Anyhow, I think he's gonna ask me to be his ol' lady. I know he'll want Stoker's opinion, so—"

Rainey grinned, pleased that Taz was confiding in her and happy to be in a position to help. "You like him a lot, huh?"

"Yeah," she said with a smile. "He's a nice guy and I think he'll take good care of me. I mean, I'll still have to work and all, but at least I'll have a man of my own."

"And you won't have to sleep with the other guys," Rainey added.

"Nope, not after I'm officially his ol' lady." She reached her arms out to her sides, "Huge benefit. Anyway, will you say something to Stoker?"

"Of course I will. Andrew would be lucky to have you."

As Taz excitedly talked about what it would be like to be an ol' lady, Rainey's mind wandered to Boulder. She looked across the room and Boulder met her eyes. Wincing, she quickly averted her gaze to her boyfriend and when Stoker gave her an air kiss, her stomach went sour.

Later that night, as Rainey and Stoker laid in bed, he rolled onto his side and looked at her. "How did everything go?"

Rainey looked away, clearing her throat and trying to steady her nervous voice. “It was fine. Please don’t ask me about it. I did what you wanted me to do and it’s over. Okay?”

Stoker wanted more, but he let it drop. He had picked up a strangeness in her voice. He pushed his ego aside, knowing it wasn’t fair to make her talk about sleeping with Boulder. He reminded himself that Rainey wasn’t like the other girls who hung around the club hoping to become an ol’ lady. “Yeah, that’s okay,” he said, nodding. “You’re right, it’s a bad idea. We don’t have to talk about it.”

Rainey pulled the blanket up to her chin. “Good night.”

He leaned over and kissed her on the lips. “I’ll see you in the morning.”

Rainey rolled away from Stoker and pressed her fingers against her lips, but all she could taste were remnants of Boulder.

***

The next morning, Rainey called a taxi to take her to work. She’d nearly made it out the door when Stoker caught up to her.

“What the fuck is this?” he asked, confused.

“Yeah,” Rainey said, not meeting his gaze, “I called a taxi to take me to work today.”

“Why would you do that?”

“I need a little time to myself.” She approached him and put her arms around his neck. “I need time to clear my head.”

Stoker watched her carefully, and under his scrutiny a thin veil of sweat formed above her upper lip.

“Oh, yeah?” he said. “Are you sure about that?”

She gave him what she hoped was a charming and genuine-looking smile. “Yes, I’m sure. But you’ll pick me up from the motel later?”

“Yeah, I’ll be there.”

Rainey pulled the front door closed behind her and raced down the steps to the waiting taxi, trying to keep her mind from wandering to Boulder, again.

Chapter Thirty-Eight

As soon as Rainey got to work that morning, she found Winnie. Desperate to tell her the truth about Boulder, she shut and locked the motel room door. She grabbed Winnie by the hand and led her over to the bed.

"What's going on? Everything okay?" Winnie asked, her eyes searching Rainey's face.

Rainey shook her head, barely able to hold back the tears. "Nothing is okay."

"Did something happen after I left Saturday night?"

"Yes. You told me I'd be punished for not taking that stupid job. So when Stoker came home from the party, he told me I had to sleep with Boulder."

Winnie's hand flew to her mouth. "Oh, shit. I knew something bad would happen."

"Well it did and now everything is totally messed up." Rainey closed her eyes and took a few calming breaths. She needed to get this out. "So yesterday Stoker took me to Boulder's and I had sex with him."

"Oh, man. That's tough, but Stoker knows it isn't your fault. He won't hold it against you."

Rainey ran her hand over her hair. "No, you don't understand. I had sex with Boulder three times."

"Okay," Winnie's brow pulled together. "He's the boss. If he wanted you to do that, you had to. What's the problem?"

Ashamed, Rainey put her hands over her face. "I liked it." She looked up, "Actually, I loved it. I wanted him and now I have all this guilt. I could barely look at Stoker last night."

"Wait, what? Are you telling me you're into Boulder now?" Winnie screeched.

"No. Yes? I don't know. I didn't expect to feel this way. I thought I was gonna throw up on the way to his house. Then he comes into the bedroom and . . . and . . . he was kind and gentle and he made me feel wanted. I mean, it was so intense between us. His hands and mouth . . . and everything about the way he moved was sexy. It's hard to describe how he made me feel. I don't even understand it myself. There was a quiet power about him that was a big turn-on."

Winnie put her hand on Rainey's back. "Fuck, girl! Really?"

At a loss, Rainey threw her hands in the air. "I never expected to like being with him. On my way to his house, I hated him so much. I still hate him, I think. I'm confused."

"No, Rainey, you need to see this for what it is. The two of you shared a moment of hot sex. Boulder is that kind of guy. Lots of us have slept with him. His power in the club is a big part of his sex appeal. Same with Stoker. You understand what I'm saying?"

"Yeah, I guess. All that power did make him a lot hotter," she said thoughtfully.

"Exactly. That's why Kiki went after him so hard. Oh, damn," Winnie whispered, "Kiki."

Panic filled Rainey again at the mention of the woman's name. "I know," she groaned. "Do you see how screwed I am? Stoker would never forgive me if he knew I enjoyed it and I'm sure Kiki wants to kill me right about now."

"Okay, try to relax." Winnie put her hand on Rainey's cheek. "None of it matters because it's Boulder. He gets to make the decisions, not Kiki and not Stoker. You can't be worried. You did what you had to do."

"Maybe I can move back in with you?" Rainey asked.

"You're always welcome, but it's not that simple now. Stoker isn't going to let you move out after this. He'll know something is wrong and then that'll put him in a bad place with Boulder."

"Do you think I should come clean with Stoker?"

"No! I think you should keep your mouth shut. This is all Boulder's fault."

Rainey stood and walked to the door, shaking her head. "I don't know how I can live with myself. I have to figure something out. I've betrayed the person I love."

"Didn't Stoker tell you to have sex with him?"

"That's exactly it!" Rainey jabbed her finger in Winnie's direction. "My boyfriend, the man who supposedly loves me, talked me into sleeping with his boss. It's weak and annoying and now I'm afraid he won't stand up for me."

Rainey understood what had really been plaguing her, the fear that if push came to shove, Stoker wouldn't have her back. Not against Boulder, and never against the club.

Winnie rushed over and hugged her. "Everything will be fine. Give it some time, think things over. Don't make any dumb decisions. It doesn't matter how much guilt you have about Boulder or resentment toward Stoker. They'll always be loyal to the club first. Period."

"I'm learning what that means every day." Rainey grabbed the doorknob and turned back to her friend. "But one thing is for sure, the Devils Angels don't own me and not one bit of me is dedicated to them."

Rainey pulled the door open and stepped into the hallway. As she went about her work, she thought about what would happen if Stoker knew the truth. Would Stoker want to kill Boulder or would he blame her? She wasn't sure how he'd react, and that bothered her. Stoker had been adamant about his loyalty to the Devils Angels. He didn't fight to take Ivy in, and he'd urged her to sleep with Boulder. Winnie was right, Stoker had played a big part in what had happened.

She couldn't let go of her disappointment that her boyfriend had willingly let her pay with her body. She wondered what else he might want her to do if things didn't go well. By the end of her shift, she'd decided. She had to talk to Stoker. She needed to tell him what happened in that bedroom. It didn't matter if he didn't love her anymore; it was the only way she could live with herself.

Chapter Thirty-Nine

After work, Rainey met Stoker out front. She leaned in and gave him a quick hug without saying anything.

He looked at her with concern. "I thought we'd grab dinner tonight. You know, head into the city and go to the Oregon Diner. I know you love that place."

She gave him a quick smile. "That sounds great. You can be very thoughtful when you wanna be."

At the diner, Rainey picked the table where she used to sit with her aunt. Images of Sophie's face swam through her mind, and bittersweet memories of the last time she'd visited with Ivy coursed through her.

"I wanted to come here so that we can talk," Stoker said.

Rainey looked at him. His handsome face was lined with worry. Her stomach churned, guessing that either he regretted what he had made her do or Boulder had told him everything. She had resigned herself to telling the truth, that everything should be out in the open if they were going to stay in a relationship.

"Sure. What's up?" she asked.

"I need to discuss what happened with you and Boulder."

Rainey inhaled sharply, then forced herself to breathe more deeply. Calm down, she told herself. You wanted to tell him the truth and now is your chance. Breathe.

"Okay," she said, in what she hoped was a soothing voice, "let's talk about it. I'll tell you everything that happened."

Stoker held his hands up. "Whoa. I don't want you to tell me anything. I want to tell you something."

Rainey's shoulders fell with relief. "Oh, okay."

"I'm sorry that I made you go through with that. I should've pressed harder on Boulder. The thing is, when I tell one of the members what to do, I expect them to do it, without question. My boss expects the same of me. It was a big price for you to pay, though, especially since I brought you into this club. You weren't one of the chicks hanging out waiting to be made an ol' lady. Anyway, I want you to know that I'm sorry I didn't push back harder. I blame myself for what happened."

At this, Rainey's heart grew, feeling his love for her. "Thank you," she said, grabbing his hand and bringing it up to her cheek.

"You forgive me?" he asked, looking at her expectantly.

She squeezed her eyes shut for a moment, blocking out the pain of guilt and regret. "Yeah, I forgive you. But you know, I have guilt about the whole thing that happened."

"You mean not taking the job?" Stoker asked, looking confused.

She shook her head.

"Oh. I don't wanna know what happened in that bedroom. I think it'll be better for both of us. The only thing I need to know is that he didn't hurt you."

Rainey pinched the bridge of her nose, giving herself a second to think. "No, he didn't hurt me."

"Okay, good. That's important."

A moment passed as Rainey wrestled with her conscience. "Are you being honest that you don't want to know what happened?" she asked, thinking that if Stoker really didn't want to know, it was okay not to tell him. It wasn't betraying him.

He nodded.

"The whole thing makes me feel like shit," she confessed.

"Well, don't do that to yourself. Let it go."

"I think this is going to make things a lot harder between me and Kiki."

Stoker shook his head. "You don't need to worry about Kiki. I'll talk to her. I'll let her know that I don't want her fucking around with you."

"Great," she breathed, though she wasn't sure how much it would help.

"When we go home, I want us to try to pick up where we left off," Stoker said.

"Yeah, me too," she responded in a quiet voice, hoping that was possible after all that had happened.

***

Stoker moved closer to her in bed that night. He placed his arm over her waist and kissed her neck, his lips steadily moving to her breast. Rainey didn't protest or try to stop him. But when he was making love to her, her eyes were open and her body was numb. She tried to focus on what they were doing, to find her groove and show Stoker the love she had for him, but nothing surfaced. All she could think about was what she had done with Boulder, what Stoker had let her do.

She saw herself as dirty and used, a cheap roll in the hay. As her mind spun, her hate for Boulder grew, but so did her lust for him. She'd finally found some happiness with Stoker, and Boulder had stolen it from her.

After they finished, Rainey laid wrapped in Stoker's arms, feeling more resolve than she had in a while. "If anything like that ever happens to me again because of the club I'll leave and you'll never find me," she said firmly.

Stoker opened his eyes and took long, slow blinks before speaking. He wanted to tell her that nothing bad would ever happen to her again. But he knew that was a promise he couldn't keep. So he said the only thing he knew to be true. "I'll fight to my death for you. I'll protect you until the day I die," he vowed.

She slid her body against his and closed her arms around his waist, wanting to believe him but remembering he'd always protect the club first. "I'm sorry for what happened. I'm sorry that I didn't take that stupid job. I'm sorry for everything."

She closed her eyes and listened to the steady beat of his heart. For several minutes she fought the nausea that had crept into her belly; then she drifted to sleep. Hearing the sounds of her steady breathing and knowing she was asleep, Stoker whispered, "Everything will be better in the morning, each day will get better. I promise."

Chapter Forty

The next day, Rainey was home alone watching television while Stoker was out having drinks with Andrew when there was a knock on the door.

She looked through the peephole and froze. She pulled the door open a crack, "Stoker's out," she said.

Boulder shrugged. "Okay. Are you gonna let me in?"

Hesitantly, Rainey pulled the door open and he brushed past her to the kitchen, where he opened the refrigerator and pulled out a beer. After twisting off the cap he flung it into the sink and took a few gulps.

"You want some?" he asked, pushing the beer bottle toward her.

"No, I'm good. Stoker went to the Dive Bar with Andrew for a few drinks. He'll be back later and I can tell him you want to talk to him."

He looked at the label on his beer bottle and up at her. "I didn't come here to talk to Stoker, I came to talk to you."

Rainey zipped her hooded sweatshirt and crossed her arms over her chest. "Okay. What?"

"About the other day . . . that was some good sex we had."

She gave him a hard stare at a loss for words. A dribble of sweat rolled down her spine.

"Anyway, I didn't want things to be weird between me and Stoker. He understands that sometimes we all gotta do things we don't wanna do. Thing is, Kiki has been a bitch ever since then and I can't get you outta my mind."

"Look, Boulder," Rainey said, finding her words, "what happened wasn't right. I love Stoker. I did what you wanted, and that's it. It wasn't some great love affair that happened between us. You chose the punishment, remember? If it wasn't for you making me do it, you and

me," she said, waving her hand between them, "never would've happened. Stoker and me are happy together."

Boulder held his palm up, facing her. "I get it. I understand. Look, I love Stoker too. He's my brother, and I'd never do anything to hurt him."

Rainey placed her hands firmly on her hips. "You mean like sleep with his girlfriend?"

"Yeah, you could say that. It was stupid. The thing is Stoker never had a dame he was nuts about like you and I needed to test his loyalty to me and the club. And you're right, it's over. It was a one-time thing and I can admit I may have taken shit too far. But I don't regret spending that afternoon with you. It was fucking fantastic and I'll never forget it. I know why he's in love with you. That's it. That's all I have left to say."

He walked out of the kitchen and she followed him. When he got to the front door, he put his hand on the knob and turned to her. "This conversation stays between the two of us," he said.

"Fine with me."

"You don't have to avoid me either. I'm not gonna hurt you. Now, Kiki, on the other hand, she's still mad as hell so you may get some crap coming your way. I'll do my best to keep her and the other girls in control if I'm around and I see it. It's the least I can do."

"I'm not afraid of Kiki or any of the other girls. I don't care what they think about me, and if any of them come at me, I'll do what I need to do. I don't need you to protect me."

Boulder grinned. "Yeah, that confidence you got there will help you out your whole life."

When he was gone Rainey leaned against the wall and held her stomach, hoping that would be the last time she ever had to talk to Boulder about what happened between them that day.

***

Rainey was in the kitchen pouring herself a bowl of cereal when Stoker came home a few hours later.

"Aw, you've cooked for us," he teased.

"No, I've cooked for me," she giggled, amazed at how much lighter life seemed, choosing to believe everything that happened between her and Boulder was behind them.

"You seem better," he said.

"I am. How did things go with Andrew?"

"Oh, just like you said, he wants to ask Taz to be his ol' lady."

"What did you tell him?"

"I told him I thought it was a good idea. Isn't that what you told me to say?"

She smiled. "Yep. So is he going to ask her?"

He nodded. "I told him we would have them over for dinner."

Rainey stopped dead and her eyes widened. "You know I can't cook."

"Well, you'll get with Taz. She'll teach you. That bitch can cook up a storm."

"So Taz has cooked for you before?" she sang playfully, wanting to know more.

He bent down and nibbled her earlobe. "It wasn't nothing like what you're thinking. She cooks for the holidays. The other girls help, but she's the one who does all the fancy work."

"I do my fancy work when I fight," Rainey said, playfully raising her fists.

Stoker laughed. "I see. You're fancy with your fists. There's something to be said about watching two chicks scratching and clawing and pulling hair."

"No, I know how to fight," Rainey protested.

"Yeah, I've seen you. You some big badass now?" he teased.

"Something like that. I learned how to fight in juvie, and when I say fight, I mean I might even be able to kick your ass," she kidded.

Stoker broke into a hearty laugh. Then he stopped and looked her in the eyes. "You want to fight me now?"

She grinned, pulled her shirt off and tossed it to the floor.

Stoker took off his shirt and jeans. Then he took off the rest of her clothes and pushed everything off of the kitchen table. He laid her down, kissing her neck, working his way down until Rainey could only think of him.

Chapter Forty-One

In the evening, while Stoker was meeting with Boulder, Rainey took the bus to Kensington. She wore jeans and a baggy sweatshirt and her hair was in a bun and tucked up under a baseball cap. She hadn't told Stoker her plans, but she was going to stake out her old house, hoping to see Ivy.

Rainey walked quickly through the darkened, familiar streets. When she reached her old house a small group of people were standing on the porch and a wave of relief crashed over her. I can hide in the crowd, she thought. Rainey watched closely to make sure none of them were Miranda or Peter before she crossed the street and joined the small group.

She approached one of the guys. "Hey, so I'm looking for a place to stay tonight and heard about this place. Are they taking any more people in tonight?"

The guy blew out his cigarette smoke. "Those two losers would never turn anyone away. It don't matter if we're all sleeping on top of each other. I'm Mason, by the way."

Rainey smiled at him. "I'm Mary."

Mason looked her up and down. "Mary, huh? You don't look like a Mary."

She turned on her fake flirt. "Oh, no? Who do I look like then?"

"I'd say a Lola or something more exotic."

She forced out a giggle. "I was thinking about staying here tonight. Maybe you and me can hang out."

He pushed his hips forward and rocked them from side to side. "Yeah, we can hang out. That would be cool. Let's go inside and get us a spot. You got money?"

Rainey nodded. "How much is it to stay?"

"Twenty bucks."

"Shit, with all these people here? They're making a fortune. What are their names, anyway?" she asked, staying in her role.

Mason chuckled. "I know the guy's name is Peter but I ain't sure about the chick."

"Well, let's go and get a spot then," she said.

Mason put his arm over her shoulder and she latched onto his waist. Once inside, she kept her head down to hide her face.

"There's Peter over there let's go give him your twenty."

Rainey had planned for this moment, but still, being so close to her father rattled her. Gathering herself, she put her hands between her legs and bounced. "I have to pee so bad I'm going to burst." She handed Mason a twenty-dollar bill. "Will you give this to him so I can go to the bathroom?"

Mason took the money. "Sure. There's a bathroom in the back," he said, pointing toward the kitchen.

Rainey headed in that direction, then milled around until she saw Mason coming back toward her. "We all good?" she asked.

"Yep. Let's go find our place," he said, leading her toward the dining room.

She pulled on his hand. "There are already a lot of people in here. How about upstairs? Can we go up there?"

He nodded. "I always forget about the upstairs. A while back they moved their kid out of the bedroom and opened it up for us."

"Oh, that's weird," Rainey said, using all of her energy to keep her voice neutral. "Where does their kid sleep?"

Mason shrugged. "I heard they made a room in the basement for her. I've never seen the kid."

Rainey widened her eyes and gave him a sly smile. "Well, let's look for her. Don't you think that would be fun?"

"Fun? No. Why would that be fun?"

"I don't know. I guess maybe because I miss my little sister. She died in a car accident last year," she said, pouting, spinning a story in hopes of getting his sympathy.

"That sucks," he mumbled.

"Then can we look for her?" she asked. "It would make me happy."

Instead of answering, Mason leaned in and kissed her. Rainey let it go on for a moment, then gently pushed him away. "Shit, Mason. I barely know you yet."

Mason shimmied closer. "Okay, sure, why not? Let's go find the kid, then the two of us can head upstairs."

Not wasting a moment, Rainey walked toward the kitchen and out through the back door. Buried under an old mattress were two metal doors coming from the ground. She pulled one open and looked down into the blackness.

"How did you know this was here?"

Rainey paused. She hadn't banked on this question, though she realized she should have. "Oh, I grew up around here and all of the row homes have them."

"Gotcha." Mason nodded and she breathed a sigh of relief. "You want me to go first?" he asked, looking into the pitch blackness of the basement.

She shook her head. "No, I'll go down. You stay here and stand watch. If anyone comes outside you need to distract them. Okay?"

He pulled a joint from his cigarette pack and lit it. "You want a hit before you go?"

She forced a smile, playing the part. "Nah, I'll have a hit when I come back up. I don't think I need to be smoking pot when I'm about to enter the black hole of hell," she joked, pointing into the darkness.

She turned and descended the steps, brushing away cobwebs. After taking a few more steps down, she glanced over her shoulder, satisfied to see that Mason was no longer paying attention to her.

Inside the basement, her nose immediately filled with the smell of sewage and mold. Rainey took out the small flashlight she'd brought with her and the beam lit up the eerie surroundings. There were old boxes and pieces of broken furniture stored against the walls. Dust and dirt occupied every space. Her bike lay with missing tires and the old board games that her Aunt Sophie had given her were scattered over the floor.

She stepped gingerly, careful not to trip on the old kitchen cabinet fronts discarded throughout. She ran her flashlight around. In the far corner was an old kitchen chair and next to it was a bucket. She moved the light farther to the right and it bounced off a gray mound on top of flattened cardboard boxes. Rainey's breath hitched and she approached cautiously.

Anxiety built with every step as she inched her way deeper into the decaying cavity of the home. Her concern over Ivy's well-being swelled. Her parents were cruel, thoughtless, and irresponsible people who wouldn't know if Ivy was alive or dead.

She stood over the small form, trying to steady her breathing, as the smell of feces filled her sinuses. Rainey pulled air into her lungs and closed her eyes as she pulled the blanket back.

Chapter Forty-Two

Rainey lifted the blanket, peering underneath, and gasped for air. Ivy was on her back. Her hair was tangled around her face. She put her ear on the child's chest but her own heartbeat was booming so loudly that she could hear nothing else.

"Ivy! Ivy!" she screamed, panic-stricken. Rainey lifted the girl's shoulders and shook her. Her mind was racing. Is she dead?

Ivy's eyes popped open and she sucked in a sharp breath.

"O my God. Ivy! Are you okay? Are you okay?" Rainey gushed, breathing heavily.

Ivy just stared up at her with bloodshot eyes and drooping eyelids.

"Ivy?" Rainey asked, leaning over her.

"Get offa me," Ivy slurred.

Rainey pulled her closer and sniffed, repulsed from the smell of alcohol. "You're drunk!"

Ivy's eyes rolled. "Get away from me. I already told you I hate your guts. Whadda you care if I'm drunk? It's none of your bizness."

Rainey pushed her sister's hair back from her face. "You're only ten. You can kill yourself by drinking too much alcohol."

The child threw her hands up. "Well, when I ain't got nothin' to eat or drink I'll take whatever my friends are willing to give me."

"What friends? Those idiots upstairs aren't your friends."

"Hey!" Ivy screamed, pointing her finger in Rainey's face. "Don't call my friends idiots. At least they care about me."

"Come on. I'm taking you out of here," Rainey said, lifting her to her feet.

"I'm not going with you."

"Yeah, you are."

As Ivy's limbs went limp, Rainey lifted her into her arms. She carried her sister's slight body up the steps and came face-to-face with a surprised Mason.

"What the hell?"

"Do you have a car?" she asked, dropping the act.

"What? Are you crazy?"

"Hey," she growled, baring her teeth. "If we don't help this kid she could die. Do you want to go to jail if she dies?"

Mason threw his half-empty beer can on the lawn. "Fuck, man. I don't need to get involved in this shit."

She looked at him dead in the face. "I swear, I'll keep you out of it. Just give me a ride and I'll take care of everything. We'll pretend we never met."

They were two blocks from the hospital when Rainey ordered him to pull over.

"We'll get out here. It's not too far to walk."

Mason turned and looked at her in the backseat, Ivy on her lap.

"You sure?"

She nodded. "Thank you for driving us."

Rainey carried Ivy out of the car and watched as Mason drove away. She stood on the curb long enough for his taillights to be out of sight before she flagged down a taxi and directed the driver back to her house.

***

When they arrived in North Philly the taxi driver turned to look at Rainey in the backseat. "Listen, young lady, this isn't a place I usually drive my cab. I can't wait here for long."

"No, you'll be fine. I swear. I'm gonna go inside and my boyfriend will come out and pay the fare. If anyone comes to the car tell them you're with Rainey."

He sighed, but gave her a quick nod.

Rainey thanked him and stepped out of the taxi. Peering back at the older, balding man through the window, she said, "He'll be right out. His name is Stoker. Two minutes."

Carrying Ivy, she rushed up the steps, and flung the front door open. Startled by the loud bang, Stoker jumped to his feet and grabbed the gun he had strapped to his leg.

"What the fuck, Rainey," he breathed. "Don't barge in like that it could get you killed."

She gave him a bewildered look; he had startled her as much as she shook him. "There's a taxi outside. I didn't have any money to pay him. I told him you'd pay the fare."

Stoker pulled the curtain back. "What did you do?" he asked, looking at the child she placed on their sofa.

"Please, just pay the taxi driver and then I'll explain. He's an old guy and he's worried about the neighborhood," she pleaded and pointed at the front door.

Stoker grumbled incoherently but made his way outside. When he returned, Rainey was in the kitchen, filling a glass with water.

"So you want to tell me what's going on now?" he asked.

She blew out a breath. "I went to my house. I had to see Ivy; it's been eight months since I've seen her. I know Janis has been checking in on her, but I had to see for myself. And I'm happy I did. Look at her."

Stoker crossed his arms, looking at Ivy, and trying not to let the shock of her condition show on his face.

"She's drunk, Stoker. She's ten years old and she's drunk," Rainey pointed out, desperate for him to understand why she brought Ivy home with her.

"Okay. In case you hadn't noticed, there are a lot of fucked-up kids in North Philly. What do you expect? They're everywhere. Tell me what you're thinking here."

Rainey went over to him. "I was thinking she could stay here for a few days. Until we can get her sober and fed. You know, give her a little time to catch her breath."

"What about when those fucked-up parents of yours notice her missing and tell Jiggy about it?"

"They won't notice her missing for a few days," Rainey said, shaking her head. "They never checked on us."

Stoker still had his arms crossed, but she wedged them open, wrapping her arms around his waist. "Pleeeeease. I swear, she won't be any problem at all and I'll take care of her. You don't have to do anything. I need you to give me a few days with her," she begged.

Stoker looked into her eyes and she thought she saw a flicker of sympathy pass through them. Finally, he sighed. "I'll talk to Boulder in case that douchebag Jiggy calls him. A few days. That's it."

"Thank you, thank you, thank you," Rainey said. "I have to call Winnie and let her know I won't be at work for the next several days so she can cover for me with Titus."

"A few days, not several," he reiterated and lit a cigarette. "This isn't a game, Rainey. There are high stakes here for everyone involved."

Rainey raced off to the living room to bring Ivy the water. She was ecstatic to have her little sister with her. She planned to show Ivy love, let the child know how much she cared; this was finally her chance. She pushed away the nagging thought that it would be hard to connect with her sister. After all, Ivy had told her more than once that she hated her. Of course, this broke Rainey's heart and she told herself Ivy felt that way because their parents had poisoned her sister against her. Since her release from juvie, trying to make Ivy love her again had become troubling. But that wasn't going to keep Rainey from loving the child, and maybe having a few days with her sister would help mend both of their hearts.

Chapter Forty-Three

When Ivy woke on the sofa the next morning, Rainey was already up, sipping a cup of coffee and watching her.

"Where am I?"

Rainey smiled, hoping desperately that Ivy would smile back. "You're at my house. I brought you home last night when I found you in the basement."

The child rubbed her eyes. "Do you got any food?"

She nodded and led her to the kitchen. "I have cereal, toast, or frozen waffles."

Ivy shrugged. "I'll have waffles."

She sat at the kitchen table while Rainey flitted around, getting her breakfast. She laid the plate down and sat across from her sister, watching as she picked up a waffle, folded it in half, and took an enormous bite. Rainey's heart was breaking, realizing that once upon a time she'd also eaten with the grace of a grizzly bear.

"So," she said, clearing her throat, "when you're done here you can take a shower and I'll find you something clean to wear."

Ivy glanced up, her eyes piercing. "All of a sudden you care 'bout me?"

Rainey, insulted and resisting the urge to argue with the child, said, "I've always cared about you."

Ivy glanced at the refrigerator. "What else you got to eat?"

Rainey placed a bowl of cereal down and Ivy shoveled it into her mouth. When she finished, she lifted the bowl and drank the milk. Meanwhile, Rainey looked around the kitchen, trying to think of something to talk to her about.

"So how have you been?" she asked, hating her own awkward question. She and Ivy had once been so close, though that was a whole lifetime ago.

They were both so young back then . . . before she was sent away to juvie and Ivy was left on her own.

Ivy glanced up through her tangled hair. "I've been like shit. What? Are ya stupid?"

Heat rushed to Rainey's face. "Hey, don't talk to me that way. I'm trying to help you."

Ivy blushed, and Rainey softened. She understood her sister's anger, but she wasn't about to be Ivy's punching bag.

"You're ten. You shouldn't talk like that anyway."

The child shrugged. "Everybody I know talks like that. All the kids at school and all the people at my house. So what?"

"So it's not nice. It's rude to call people stupid. Besides, I know you're better than that."

Ivy got up and pulled the refrigerator open. "You don't even got no soda in here?"

Frustrated and disappointed that Ivy wouldn't even try to engage with her, Rainey stood abruptly. "Let's go. I'll show you the bathroom so you can shower."

Ivy avoided making eye contact as she adjusted her shirt. Then she followed Rainey to the second floor. Up in the bathroom, Ivy undressed down to her dingy, worn underwear. She turned to Rainey, covering herself with her hands. "I can take a shower by myself."

Rainey nodded, snatching her clothes from the floor and stepping into the hallway. The clothes smelled of sweat and urine. She held them at arm's length, walking down to the kitchen, then she lifted the lid on the trashcan. As she was about to throw the clothes away, her fingers brushed on something in a pant pocket. She reached in and pulled out a small pipe. She stared at it for a prolonged second, then turned it over in her hands. She studied it closely and kept wishing it would disappear. Her stomach tightened. She wanted the pipe to be a big mistake, a misunderstanding that could be explained. Her instinct was to pretend like she hadn't found it, but her mind knew that was the wrong thing to do. *This can't be happening*, she thought.

Rainey rushed back upstairs and barged into the spare bedroom her sister was using. Ivy was standing with a towel wrapped around her, and she held onto it tighter.

"What?" Ivy asked, cowering under Rainey's glare.

Rainey was scowling at her with her arms crossed tightly over her chest. "This is what," she said, tossing the glass pipe on the bed.

Ivy turned and grabbed it. "So what? It ain't mine," she said without hesitation but wouldn't make eye contact.

Rainey wanted to believe Ivy's lie more than she wanted to take her next breath. She had learned there were moments when the lies she told herself were the only reasons she could wake up and face each day. These lies allowed her to keep moving forward and hanging onto her sanity by a small thread. This was one of those moments.

At a loss, Rainey's arms dropped to her sides. "Then who does it belong to?"

"Some girl named Wendy. Sometimes she asks me to keep her pipe or a bag of weed for her. She gets pretty messed up and then her boyfriend steals stuff from her pockets. Wendy sleeps with me sometimes when I get nervous." Ivy pivoted, not wanting to tell her too much. "Are you gonna give me something to wear or what?"

Rainey pointed to the clothes on the bed. "Some leggings and a T-shirt. They're gonna be big but you ain't going anywhere so it doesn't matter."

The sisters spent the rest of the day hanging around the house. Rainey kept trying to start up a conversation, while Ivy gave her one-word answers. While it wasn't what Rainey had expected it to be, it made her content to have these moments with her little sister. Throughout the day, Rainey wished that they'd never been separated. So much had been lost between them in those three years.

By the time Stoker arrived home that evening, Rainey had just finished making fish sticks and boxed macaroni and cheese for dinner.

He strutted into the kitchen. "Holy shit. You made dinner?" Stoker asked, smiling and pulling her into a kiss as Ivy sat at the table and watched.

"Yes, I did," she sang, happy he was home and could help get her sister to talk. "Ivy, this is Stoker, Stoker, this is Ivy."

He swaggered over to the young girl. "Well," he said, turning to Ivy at the table, "Rainey told me you were pretty, and she was right—you're a beauty. How are you feeling?"

Ivy, mesmerized by him, stuttered, "F . . . f . . . fine." Her eyes were wide and glued on him.

Stoker glanced at Rainey and she suppressed a grin. He often got that same reaction from women but never from the little sister of his ol' lady, and he couldn't help but chuckle.

"What's funny?" Ivy asked.

"Oh, uh, nothing. I just can't believe how much you and Rainey look alike. You're a younger version of her but with brown hair and brown eyes," Stoker explained.

"Ew," she mumbled.

"Ew? What are you blind or something? She's gorgeous and so are you."

Ivy smiled, and Rainey allowed herself to relax. Her little sister seemed happier now than she had been all day.

After dinner, the three sat on the sofa. Ivy chose the seat next to Stoker, and when she did Rainey's stomach panged, disappointment hitting her again. Noticing her demeanor change, Stoker patted Rainey's leg and the three watched a show on television before they went to bed.

Later, lying in bed, Stoker turned to Rainey. "How did it go with her today?"

"It was awful. She barely talks to me, and when she does, it's mostly hateful. My parents have really screwed her up. She was too little to be left alone with them. She's cursing and drinking already. And," she hesitated, not wanting to say the words out loud, "I found a crack pipe in her pocket, but she denied it was hers."

"Oh," he breathed, looking away. "Do you believe her?"

"I want to, but my gut is telling me different."

"I'm sorry, babe," he said. Then, trying to be optimistic he added, "Would it make you feel any better if I told you I was drinking beer at ten?"

Rainey shook her head. "Um, no, it wouldn't. That's messed up."

"Well," he said, tucking his hair behind his ear, "you know I was raised by my mom and all the men she brought home. We lived in a run-down home in West Philly and all the kids in the neighborhood drank. We'd steal beers from our refrigerators. It was no big deal."

She side-eyed him. "I see, and look how you turned out. Is that what you're gonna say?"

He plastered several kisses in the space between her chin and chest. "Well, yes, I was. Look," he said, getting serious, "she seemed okay tonight."

Rainey sighed. "Yeah, once you came home. She got one look at you and her heart melted." She smiled at the thought. "At least I know she's got good taste in men."

Stoker put his arm around her waist. "Ivy can stay one more night, but after that, she's gotta go home."

"I know. I just wish I had more time with her. I wish I had forever," she mumbled. Rainey pressed her forehead into his chest; her bitter sadness was suffocating.

Chapter Forty-Four

Two days later, Rainey guided Ivy onto the back of Stoker's motorcycle. The second day had been no better than the first, and in fact Ivy had made it a point to stay in the guest bedroom most of the day and only went downstairs when Stoker got home. As she stood on the sidewalk watching Ivy, anger and sadness competed for Rainey's attention.

"I'll see you soon," Rainey told her sister, trying to part on a note of hope.

Ivy looked away. "Whatever."

Stoker twisted his head back toward her. "Don't you want to thank your big sis for coming to get you? She put herself in danger to do that."

Ivy glanced at her sister for a second, but her eyes were flat. "Thanks," she mumbled without emotion.

Stoker met Rainey's eyes and shook his head softly. He understood that she was suffering and that she only wanted to help her sister.

Rainey leaned in and kissed her on the cheek. "I love you, Ivy."

"Yeah, sure," she responded, causing Stoker to tightly clench his jaw before he drove off.

A few blocks from Ivy's home, Stoker pulled next to a curb. The young girl stood next to the bike. "Thanks for driving me," she said.

Stoker shut off his motorcycle. "You know, Ivy, your sister has been fighting for you since I met her. It wouldn't have killed you to be nicer to her." Without waiting for an answer, he started his bike, took one last look at her, and said, "Take care of yourself."

***

That night, sitting at the kitchen table with Stoker and Boulder, Rainey rubbed her temples, trying to relieve the stress that had built up over the past two days. By this point her anger at what had become of Ivy had won out over her sadness.

"Anyway," Boulder was saying, "when Jiggy called today, he told me if the kid splits again he'll be coming after one of our girls." He paused, and looked directly at Rainey.

Stoker broke in. "Yeah, man. I got it. Won't happen again."

Rainey leaned up on her elbows and looked from one man to the other. "What? Are you two afraid of some piece of shit like Jiggy?"

Boulder let out a hearty laugh. "No, we ain't afraid. But like we already told you, the club needs to keep things cool. How would it be if Jiggy came and took you, for example? I'll tell you how it would be—it would be an all-out war because nobody is gonna fuck with our women, especially one of our ol' ladies."

Deflated and oddly relieved to have Boulder make a statement of protection for her, she sat back in her chair. "Well, what about my sister? Am I supposed to leave her in that house? They're giving her alcohol already. Did Stoker tell you Ivy was drunk when I found her? Jiggy is an evil troll."

Boulder raised one eyebrow. "Evil?"

"Yes," Rainey said, looking into Boulder's eyes. "Jiggy is evil. He's a rotten pig who doesn't care about anybody."

"Tell us something we don't know," Stoker commented.

Rainey stood and paced. "Come on, you guys. There's gotta be something we can do to help Ivy."

Boulder sat back in his chair and chugged his beer. "There is, and we're doing it. Janis has been going over to that shithole every week to keep an eye on her. That's it, Rainey. It's a big risk we're taking just sending her there." He leaned across the table and grabbed a pack of cigarettes. "Stoker and I are doing that thing with Janis for you. Because it's you. That's all I want to hear about this. Do you understand?"

Disappointed, Rainey took a quick look at Stoker, and he gave her a curt nod.

"Okay, fine, I'll drop it," she said, collapsing in a chair quietly to appease the men. But there wasn't a bone in her body that was willing to let it go. She'd keep trying until she figured out a way to help her sister.

She had agreed to avoid any more trouble with Stoker or Boulder; she had learned her lesson. There were so many words left in her just fighting to come out. She understood that lying is something people do all the time, something she had been doing a lot since she met Stoker, and she wasn't proud of it.

In her life before Stoker, she hated to lie because she believed it made her lose pieces of herself. Lies, as far as Rainey was concerned, were a coward's friend, and telling the truth was the existence of courage. But few people had the stomach for the truth. Why is it so much easier to lie? she thought.

When Boulder was gone, Rainey turned to Stoker. "How am I supposed to give up on my sister?"

Stoker stood and looked out the kitchen window, watching Boulder make his way down the street. "You don't need to give up on her," he said. "We're gonna keep an eye on things. Make sure she gets stuff she needs. I can't promise you everything will be perfect, but we're gonna try to make things better."

Her anguish bubbling over, Rainey cocked her head and looked into his face. "I appreciate what you're trying to do. But you don't know everything about my life before I met you, or Ivy's life now. Just because you were raised by a raging alcoholic doesn't mean we experienced the same things. So you go ahead and keep making your lame promises, but don't think I'm stupid enough to eat what you and Boulder are feeding me."

Stoker wasn't sure if he should be stunned at her disobedience or thrilled at her level of conviction. He admired that when she wanted something she went after it with her entire being. He hesitated for several moments as Rainey watched him wondering if she'd finally gotten him to understand her desperation.

"You're a strong woman. And, I know you're not happy right now."

"But," she said.

Stoker held up a hand to stop her from continuing. He leveled his voice, "I also know that you love me and you want to support me. The last time we went against the club, things didn't turn out too well. In this matter I won't go against the club. You're putting all of our members at risk. Jiggy has a lot of thugs, thieves, and pushers that he can call up in a second. They'll do whatever he wants them to do. Do you understand that?"

"Yeah, I understand perfectly. I know that's how he operates. And when Jiggy wanted Tootsie to cut my fucking pinky off," she screamed, holding up her hand with the stub finger, "she did it. And I let her do it. And do

you know why? Because sometimes we gotta do shit we don't like. It's the hard stuff we're forced to do that makes us human. It's easy for everyone to sit back and let Janis do the work. I never asked for anything to be easy, but now I'm asking for things to be fair and just and right. That's what I stand for and what I'll fight for."

Stoker took her hand and led her to the bedroom. He placed his gun on the dresser and turned to look at her. "You're feisty. That's one of the things I love about you. But hear me now, do not disappoint me."

Rainey heard him loud and clear, but she was torn between the man she loved and wanted to share her future with and the sister she loved who held her past.

Chapter Forty-Five

For the months that followed, Rainey kept her promise not to go back to see Ivy. But unable to take it anymore, she started scoping out her childhood home weekly, waiting for an opportunity to set eyes on her.

Seeing Ivy only a handful of times for a few seconds was torturous. At the same time, she resented the many sacrifices she was forced to make being with Stoker. Rainey was slowly losing pieces of herself as she kept sneaking away to see Ivy. Keeping everything secretive from Stoker and the club.

***

A year later, Rainey woke one morning and found Stoker sitting on the edge of their bed. His back was hunched and he held his face in his hands.

"What's wrong?" she asked, sitting up and putting her hand on his back.

He ran his fingers through his hair. "Nothing that you need to be concerned about."

She shimmied to the edge and sat next to him, her bare feet dangling off the side of the bed. "I hate it when you say that to me. Just tell me what's worrying you. Maybe I can help."

Stoker turned to face her, and the look on his face made her heart pause. He looked distraught and disheveled, like he'd been up all night. And her concern grew never having seen him like that before.

He sighed. "I've been waiting to let you know that I'll be gone a lot over the next couple of months. I'm opening up a shop for the club."

"What do you mean 'gone'?" she asked, not comprehending.

Stoker stood and crossed the room. "I mean leaving early and coming home late. Sometimes I'll be gone for a week or two. I'm not sure yet."

"When is this?"

"Starting today," he muttered.

Anger flared up in Rainey. "You didn't think to tell me before now?"

"Yeah, I did, but I knew you'd worry or be pissed off or both."

"Well, now it's both," she said. Then, knowing that attacking him would get her nowhere, she calmed herself down. "So what kind of shop is it?"

"Ah, a smoke shop. You know, expensive cigars and tobaccos, stuff like that."

"Who owns it?" she pressed.

"Too many questions. Okay?"

Incensed, she sprang to her feet, sick and tired of being told she asks too many questions. "No, not okay. I know the dumbass rule that you can't discuss club business with me, but from the looks of it, you need somebody to talk to."

"Nah, I'm good." He turned away from her and walked toward the bathroom as Rainey followed. She grabbed his hand and pulled him back toward the bed.

Her voice softened, wanting him to stay close to her. "So maybe I can work with you. I'm good at organizing. I could . . . I could help set up the shelves and stuff like that. I'll take care of the inventory and I can order products and stuff."

Stoker took both of her hands and squeezed them together. "You're not invited to help me. You need to stay here and take care of things."

She ripped her hands from his and spun away, insulted. "What things? What do I need to take care of here? I need to clean your house? Is that what you mean?"

He paused, considering her question. She wasn't easily silenced, like the other women of the club. Rainey wanted real answers that were logical and meaningful. But he had nothing he was able to share with her.

"Yeah, what's wrong with that?" he fired back. "You need something to do with your time. Why don't you go to a community college or volunteer somewhere? That would be good for you."

She narrowed her eyes. While both were good ideas, Rainey knew he was using it to get her off his back. "Why didn't you ever say that before?"

"There wasn't a reason before, but now it'll keep you occupied while I'm away."

"So what you're really telling me is that you're going to be away for a long time?"

He averted her gaze. "Yeah, maybe, probably."

Unable to control her anger and disappointment that she'd be left alone to deal with the Devils Angels, she turned and stormed off. She thumped down the steps into the kitchen and flopped in a chair. Almost an hour had passed before he came down showered and dressed. He grabbed the coffeepot, poured a cup, and leaned against the counter, looking at her.

"What?" she said.

He threw his mug into the sink. The coffee splattered everywhere, and the ceramic splintered into pieces. "I can't keep going over this with you. There's shit that's none of your business and when you want to know the details of everything I'm doing, it's annoying."

"Yeah, well, it's annoying not knowing if you're going to get yourself in trouble or, I don't know, killed. How do you think I feel? I'm not allowed to ask any questions and I have no idea where you are or how you earn your money. The only thing I know for sure is that you always have one or two guns on you at all times. I'm not stupid. I know you're doing stuff that I wouldn't like. I hope you're not doing anything with drugs."

"What are you talking about? When have you ever seen me high?"

"I'm talking about you selling them, not taking them. I don't know anything you do for the club; it's always a big secret."

His eyes scanned the splattered coffee all over the counter and backsplash. He wanted to be finished and leave. "I gotta go," he said and walked away.

***

An hour later, Stoker was sitting with Boulder as he received his final orders.

"Make sure your guys stay in line," Boulder stated.

"Yeah, I got this."

"You better got this. If this is successful, we'll be one of the largest weapons dealers in Philly. We'll have the mob and the gangs . . . they'll all be coming to us."

Stoker leaned against the doorframe. "I don't know about the mob. They seem to find their own way of getting guns."

Boulder bit into a jelly donut, and Stoker watched the dark red filling drip over his hand. Boulder slurped it off and said, "The mob will want them too, trust me. One other thing, did you take care of everything with your ol' lady?"

He shrugged. "Yeah, she knows what's expected. Look, I'm not gonna be around much and I need you to keep an eye on her. Don't go over to my house, she doesn't like that shit. Send Kiki over to talk to her a little. To help her understand that the women in our club show respect for what we're doing."

"Yeah, okay. I'll have Kiki stop by. Anything else?"

He nodded. "What have you heard from Janis? Everything going okay with Rainey's kid sister?"

Boulder looked away. "There's some fucked-up shit going on in that house. We ain't got the time to talk about it now. Catch me when I see you next week. We can talk then." He looked at the clock on the wall. "You need to hit it. Get this done right and make the club proud. Understand?"

Stoker nodded, a little worried about what information Boulder had on Ivy, but dropping the subject for now. The two men hugged and Stoker set off to take care of club business.

Chapter Forty-Six

Kiki was slamming dishes onto the kitchen table. “I can’t stand her, Boulder. I don’t want to go talk to the bitch. I hate that whore.”

“Is that right?” he said, glaring at her through narrowed eyes.

A prickle crawled up her spine when she saw the anger in his face. “I . . . um. . . I’ll think about it and let you know. But if I do, then don’t expect me to kiss her ass or nothing. I don’t care that she’s upset. She screwed my ol’ man,” Kiki seethed, trying to save face.

Boulder moved across the room in a swift motion and stood over her with a beet-red face and crazed eyes. “Come here, come here,” he said grabbing her by the shirt, dragging her into the living room, and dropping her on the floor.

Kiki rolled onto her side and put her hands up to protect her face, realizing too late she’d pushed him too far.

He leaned down and put his nose next to hers. “Don’t you ever tell me what you’re gonna do. You . . . you,” he screamed into her face, “will do whatever I tell you! And I don’t want to hear another word about me and her screwing. That was a long time ago. Now get dressed and march down to see that girl. I gave Stoker my word that you’d go.”

He stepped backward and Kiki bolted out of the room, afraid he would smack her around if she didn’t get out of sight quickly.

Thirty minutes later Kiki was knocking on Rainey’s door. Rainey crept to the front of the house and peeked through a window.

“Oh, man,” Rainey murmured, “just leave me alone.” She trudged over to the door and pulled it open. “Hey, what’s up?”

Kiki sneered at her. “What’s up? I came over to chat. You got coffee on?”

Confused, Rainey stepped aside and Kiki walked by her. Kiki had never come over before, and over the past year they’d avoided interacting with

one another as much as possible. Inside the kitchen, Rainey watched as Kiki opened a cabinet, then another.

"The coffee is on the counter in case you don't see it there in the pot," Rainey remarked sarcastically.

"Shut the hell up. I want something to go with the coffee, you idiot. You got any cereal bars or cookies or something?"

Rainey used all of her self-control to ignore Kiki's name calling, strode over to the refrigerator, and pulled out a loaf of white bread and a stick of butter. "We have toast."

Kiki scoffed.

"Why are you here?"

Kiki jabbed her finger in Rainey's face. "I don't want any shit from you. My ol' man made me come over here to tell you that you better settle the hell down before you find yourself floating in a river."

Rainey, already depressed about Stoker being away from home, had no patience left and wasn't about to be pushed around. She jutted out her hip and placed her hand on it. "You're so full of it. Boulder would never send you to deliver that message to me. So what else do you have?" she challenged.

Kiki pulled two slices of bread from the bag and shoved them in the toaster. "Okay, you want it straight . . . since your man can't control you, I'm here to tell you that you need to be more obedient. You're always whining and moaning and thinking that you're something special. So from now on listen to what Stoker tells you to do and stop talking back all the time."

Rainey forced a laugh filled with revulsion. "Just because you want to be bossed around by a man doesn't mean I want the same thing. The whining and moaning you mentioned, that's called asking questions and having a mind of my own, so get it straight. I want to be with Stoker, period. I don't need you coming over here telling me how to act. The thing is," she said, stepping into the woman's personal space, "you don't like me and I don't like you. So how about if we just stay out of each other's way?"

Rainey turned and walked away. A moment later, Kiki lifted a piece of toast and flung it at her back. Looking down, Rainey saw the toast on the floor and spun on her. "Are you out of your mind?" she yelled.

"I did what my ol' man wanted. That's all I needed to do."

Rainey stepped toward her again. "Well, you can go home and tell Boulder that you did your duty. And do yourself a favor, stop calling him your ol' man. You sound pathetic."

Kiki pushed her in the chest, and the girl stumbled back a few steps but caught herself before she fell.

Rainey smiled. "The last time you and me went at it, I promised Stoker I wouldn't kick your sorry ass. But just so you know, the day will come when I do. I know you think you're hardcore, but you're just another biker chick wannabe."

Kiki rolled her hands into fists and gritted her teeth. "You're a loser. You think you're so tough but you're nothing but a piece of trash. Just like your sister."

Rainey pounced on her, snatching her jacket collar and slamming her against the wall. She made a fist and pulled back her arm, but a conversation she had with Stoker the week prior surfaced.

He'd warned her not to fight with Kiki without witnesses. The other woman's story of the fight would carry more weight.

Boiling over with anger, Rainey looked into Kiki's face. Dropping her fist, Rainey stepped back, "You gotta leave. I have stuff to do. Thanks for stopping by. It's been lots of fun. Tell Boulder I'm doing fine and I don't need you to come here again."

Kiki turned on her heel. "I guess there's one thing you learned from Stoker."

"Oh, yeah? What's that?"

"Well, since I'm with Boulder you'll need to stand down. I can say or do whatever I want and you have to take it."

Rainey's anger flared again and, through clenched teeth, she said, "I don't have to take anything. And Kiki, if you ever talk about my sister again, I'll make sure it's the last time you do."

"Ohhhhh, big, bad Rainey," Kiki said, smiling and faking a shiver. "Get over yourself."

After she was gone, Rainey went upstairs and showered. She waited until dusk, and when the taxi arrived, she gave him the address for Winnie's house. She needed time to think. Time on her own. A friend she could count on. On the drive over, she thought about the things she'd say to her—things she hadn't dared to tell anyone.

Chapter Forty-Seven

Winnie pulled the door open and smiled at Rainey. "I'm so happy you came over. We hardly ever get a chance to talk at work," she said.

"I know. I'm sorry. I've been caught up with Stoker and everything . . ." she trailed off.

Winnie waved her off. "It's all good. What's going on?"

"I need to talk to someone, and you're the only person I can trust. I've been dealing with some stuff lately."

"Well, you came to the right person," she said. "You seem very serious. What happened?"

"Remember I told you I was forbidden by the club to go see Ivy?"

Winnie looked at her, confused. "Yeah, but that was like what? A year ago?"

"Ah-huh. Well, I haven't been very good at sticking to that promise."

Winnie sighed. "Rainey, what's wrong with you? You're putting yourself in a

bad place. You know that Stoker isn't playing with you about this. Aren't you scared he's gonna find out?"

She nodded. "Of course I'm scared, but I can't help myself. Nobody knows what I'm doing except for you. Promise you won't breathe a word."

Winnie twisted her thumb and index finger against her lips. "I'm a vault."

Rainey smiled. "I stayed away for the first three months, then I couldn't take it anymore. I've seen Ivy a few times without talking to her. I was scared that if I approached her, she'd say something to the girl that the club sends there to keep an eye on her, and Stoker would find out. I've been

going by the house for the past nine months to make sure she's alive. Last week I saw something that scared me. Stuff I'm really worried about."

"What?" Winnie whispered.

Rainey thought for a moment. "Well, you know Jiggy? He heads up Tootsie's gang, the Vamps."

Winnie's eyes widened with fear; she knew all about Jiggy from Tootsie. "What about him?"

"Well, I was looking into the kitchen window and he was inside with Ivy. I watched him put bags of dope into her pockets and send her out the front door. Obviously, I followed her. She walked to Kensington Avenue and a bunch of people, one after the other, gave her money and she handed them the bags of dope."

"Jesus, Rainey. She's like eleven."

"Yeah, no kidding. Anyway, I've been scoping the streets at night this past week and I see her out there. After she sells out, she runs off and jumps into Jiggy's car with him." Rainey's voice broke. "My little sister is selling dope for him and she probably doesn't understand what can happen to her if she gets caught."

Winnie gasped. "I don't know what to say. That's the most fucked-up thing I've heard in a long time."

"You can't tell Tootsie, okay? She'd be obligated to tell him that I know."

"I won't." Winnie shook her head hard.

Rainey sighed. "It's been so tough not to tell Stoker, but I know he'll lose his shit on me if he finds out what I've been doing." Her resentment for having to keep this a secret from him bubbled up. "I'm with a guy in a biker club that has a lot of power and won't use it to help me. And I hate that asshole Jiggy. My parents almost let him rape me, and now they are letting him use Ivy to move drugs." She collapsed on the sofa, feeling drained. She had kept the secret for so long, and was grateful to Winnie for listening to her. "I don't know what to do. I don't know how to help her."

Winnie sat down and put her hand on Rainey's arm. She leaned into Winnie for a moment, but at the sound of a toilet flushing, she jerked away.

"What was that?" she asked, her heart pounding. "Who's here?"

"It's just Leo. He took a few days off from work."

Rainey rushed to the bottom of the steps and listened, her heart still hammering. If Leo had overheard her, she was dead. She rushed back to her friend. "He works at night; that's why I waited all day to come to see you.

Why didn't you tell me he was here?" she whispered. "What if he heard what I told you?"

"He didn't hear you," she assured the girl. "He was in the shower."

Rainey closed her eyes and took in a calming breath. "I hope you're right."

"I am. Don't worry." Winnie paused long enough that Rainey turned to look at her. "So, um, this is really bad timing, but there's something I have to tell you too."

"Sure. What's going on?" she raised her eyebrows, interested.

"There's this guy that I've been seeing. I'm really into him and he's going to be a nurse. I've been with him at the motel and we were talking and I told him about always wanting to live in Florida someday. So then he tells me that he's moving to Florida, and I couldn't believe it. Anyway, he asked me to move there with him. Isn't that crazy?" she said, excitedly.

Rainey looked up at her in disbelief. "Wait. You're going to move to Florida with a guy you met at the motel and that you barely know?"

"I know what you're thinking," she said flatly, giving Rainey a cold stare. "Yes, I met him at the motel, but he doesn't pay me for sex. I mean, when I first met him, yeah, he paid me a couple of times, but once we got to know each other I stopped making him give me money. Then after spending time together we fell in love."

Rainey pressed her hands to her temples, she wanted to be supportive, but alarms were sounding in her head. It hadn't even entered her mind that he had paid Winnie for sex prior to dating him; now she was extremely concerned. "So then you stopped having sex with other guys?"

Winnie shook her head. "Henry, that's his name, he thought it would be good for me to keep making money so we can save it for our move, and I agreed."

"Henry, huh?" she asked thoughtfully, worried that if she reacted the way she wanted to, Winnie might shut her out and, she'd have no way of knowing if her friend was safe.

"Yeah, I know you'll like him. He's older and I kind of like that because he knows what he wants. He's really smart too."

Rainey's stomach was in knots, why didn't Winnie see something was wrong with the man she loved encouraging her to have sex with other men for money. "Where does Henry live?"

"Oh, he's in North Philly on Marshall Street, close to Temple University, it's not too far from here."

"So, did he go to the motel looking to . . ." Rainey trailed off, thinking about how best to ask the question without offending her friend. "Looking for someone to be with?"

Winnie nodded and looked at her thoughtfully. "Yeah, I guess he did. Like three or four months ago, he started coming to the motel. He said he was looking for a change of scenery, so he stayed there. You've probably seen him around. Tall, dark hair and long sideburns. He always carries one of those green, canvas army bags. Now he sleeps there at least one night a week." She smirked. "I stay at the motel overnight with him whenever he's there."

Rainey nodded, getting an image of Henry in her head, but nothing much stood out about him. "Then it shouldn't be hard for you to introduce me to him. I wanna meet him."

"Okay," Winnie agreed, then gave her a hard look. "But you have to be nice," she joked.

"Who, me? I'm always nice," she said, blinking her eyes innocently.

"Yeah, right. You're never nice to the guys that crash at the motel."

"Oh, well, now you're getting more specific. Yeah, I don't like most of those guys. I think they use women."

Winnie rolled her eyes. "No, they don't. The girls they pay to sleep with them are okay with what they're doing."

Rainey let out a nervous giggle Touché, she thought. My own boyfriend, whom I love, used to hang out with women there too. "I see your point; you're right."

"Besides," Winnie said, throwing her a playful look, "half the guys who go to the motel are nervous they're going to offend you or something. They all worry about what Stoker would do to them if you found a reason not to like them."

"That's so stupid," Rainey said. "I would never tell Stoker that someone at the motel annoyed me."

She went quiet, remembering when Winnie and Leo took her in. Rainey was so vulnerable when she first showed up on their doorstep. Through Winnie and later Stoker, her confidence had grown and she'd become more comfortable in her own skin, no longer afraid of everything and everyone. She gazed over at Winnie, thinking about how much she'd missed her friend since she'd moved in with Stoker. She loved both of them, but missed the closeness of having a friendship with another woman.

"I'm gonna miss you. If it weren't for you, I might still be living on the streets. I'll always be grateful that you were so kind to me," Rainey said, teary-eyed.

"Aw, girl. I'm gonna miss you too." She leaned in and whispered, "I think Leo is gonna be lost. I always figured he'd move outta here before me. He said something yesterday about our mom being gone and how I'm leaving now—he's feeling all alone."

"Don't worry," Rainey said. "I'll check in on him. He acts like I'm annoying, but I know he likes me."

Winnie grinned. "He does. You're like his other sister."

On her way home that night, Rainey thought about how lonely she would be once Winnie moved to Florida. She was the one steady person in her life and, had always known they could count on each other. Rainey wished she could make Winnie stay, but that wouldn't be right; after all, she was the one who moved out first to be with the man she loved.

Chapter Forty-Eight

Over the next week, Rainey and Stoker saw each other only a few times. Then on Saturday morning she moseyed downstairs and found him sitting in the kitchen.

"Hey, stranger," he purred. He moved to her, lifted her hair, and kissed her neck. His lips moved to her mouth and he kissed her passionately.

Her body woke with a sexual yearning for him.

When he pulled away Rainey smiled, feeling more relaxed than she had all week. "I'm so glad you're home. I've missed you."

"I know, I miss you too. I've been waiting for you to wake up."

She grinned, "Oh, yeah. Why?" she asked, with sex still on her mind.

Stoker averted her gaze and Rainey's grin faded.

"Oh," she said. "Did something bad happen?"

He offered her a weak smile. "No, nothing happened. But there's something I need to tell you." He paused and took her hands in his. Rainey took a deep breath to steady herself before he said, "I'm going to be away for a while."

"Okay," she said cautiously. "We knew this might happen. What's a while?"

"Probably three, four months? Maybe more."

"Wait. As in, you wouldn't be coming home at all?"

Stoker nodded. "Yeah. This shop is turning out to be a lot more than we thought. I'm meeting with a bunch of people all day and into the night. A couple of the guys from the club are going to stay too."

"Okay, that makes no sense," Rainey said, trying to work it out. "You're opening a business that's what? Forty-five minutes from here? But you can't come home at night?"

Stoker shrugged. "I don't know what to tell you. It'll just be easier."

Stoker couldn't tell her he would be traveling throughout Philadelphia, Camden, and Maryland to work with the various Devils Angels chapters. The goal was to open the smoke shop in North Philly and expand from there. Racketeering was what they did, and the chapters often came together to expand each other's businesses.

Rainey went to the sink and filled a glass with water. She knew there was something Stoker wasn't telling her, and had to try to get it out of him. She took a sip and kept her back to him. "I don't get it. I came here to live with you and you're out with your club almost every night. Now you're gonna be gone for who knows how long." She paused, and hated herself for what she was about to ask, but she had to. "Do you have another girlfriend?"

At this, Stoker rushed over to her and gently slid his hand over her cheek and through her hair. "Are you kidding?" he asked, deeply affected by her question. "I don't want anyone else. You're the only one I want; you have to know that by now. There are no other girls and I hate that you even thought that for a second. I'm sorry things have to be this way, but you know, we live in this house and don't worry about a mortgage or bills, right? Well, now I have to give back to the club."

A single tear slid down her face as she looked into his eyes.

"I know it's hard for you," he continued, "especially because you and Kiki don't get along. But I'm taking Andrew with me, so Taz will be in the same boat as you. Why don't you ask her to stay here with you while we're away?"

Rainey rested her forehead on his shoulder. "I don't know. I'll think about it. I found out that Winnie is moving to Florida, and now you're going to be gone. It took me forever to find people I want to be around and now everyone is leaving me. It's all falling apart."

"Nothing is falling apart. I'll be back as soon as I can. I promise. But tell me about Winnie. Why is she moving?"

Rainey shook her head. "She met some guy named Henry at the motel. I got a bad feeling about him. It sounds weird to me. First, he was paying her for sex but then they fell in love and I don't get the whole thing. All I know is that she'll probably move while you're gone and then I'll be all alone."

"I'm sorry," he said kissing the tip of her nose. "But how about this? When I get back, you and me are gonna take a little trip, just the two of us. Maybe we'll go to the beach. How's that sound?"

Rainey smiled and placed her hands on his chest. "It sounds wonderful, and also like a lifetime from now."

"How can I make it better for you?"

Rainey thought for a moment and wondered what she could ask for that would actually be helpful. Ivy's face flashed through her mind. "Well, there is one thing," she said, an idea forming. "I could use a car. I'm tired of taking the bus, so I've been blowing a lot of money on taxis."

Stoker nodded. "Done. I can get you a car today."

"Really?" she asked, a little nervous now, given that she had never driven before.

"Sure. The club has some cars we keep, and since you're my ol' lady you can use one."

"And you'll teach me how to drive it?" she giggled.

"Yeah, before I head out today. You'll be great; driving is easy."

She wrapped her arms tighter around his neck. "I might stay at Winnie's a couple of nights. You know, to help her pack and just spend time with her before she leaves. I don't want you to worry if you call here and I'm not home."

He watched her for a prolonged moment, and Rainey shrank under his gaze. "Okay, stay out of trouble."

"What does that mean?" she asked.

"You know exactly what it means. Don't take the car to see Ivy. Got it?"

Guilt heated her core, and she sighed. "I wouldn't," she fibbed. "Besides, I already told you I want to spend some time with Winnie. This might be the last chance I have. What if she moves to Florida and I never see her again?"

He chuckled. "You'll see her. Maybe we can even visit her once she's settled."

She smiled. "I would love that. I've never been to Florida . . . or anywhere."

Stoker grabbed his wallet and cigarettes and headed to the front door. "All right. I'm heading to the club. I have to talk some business with Boulder, then I'll bring a car back for you. Can you pack clothes for me? I'll be back in a couple of hours?"

Rainey's skin prickled. She hated it when he told her to do things the Devils Angels considered a girl's job.

"I guess," she said. "I don't know why you can't do it. Don't you want to make sure you pack everything you want?"

"I'm sure you can handle that for me. Just like I'm going to get a car for you. See how that works?"

She groaned, then cracked a smile. "Yeah, I see. Fine."

Alone in the house again, Rainey was already contemplating how lonely she would be. She loved Stoker and wanted to spend the rest of her life with him. As she packed his clothes her heart ached; she would miss him. She would miss Winnie too. So much loss was hard for her to handle.

***

Stoker stood next to Boulder at the bar in the club basement.

"Did you straighten out your house?" Boulder asked.

It was still early, but Stoker threw back a shot of whiskey. "Yeah, she's good. She knows what she has to do. She'll be fine. Hey, I forgot to ask you about her little sister, you mentioned something is going on there. What do you know?"

Boulder lit a cigarette and leaned his elbow on the bar. "Yeah, that kid's parents are some fucked-up people. The kid is running dope for Jiggy."

Stoker's eyes bulged. "Shit," he breathed.

"That ain't the worst of it. Janis saw Jiggy leaving one of the bedrooms, so she took a look inside after he was gone. The kid was on the floor, naked under a blanket. She had some bruises on her arms and face. Looks like the perv has gotten to her. You know, man, the one thing this club hates are pedophiles."

Stoker's eyes hardened and he held Boulder's gaze. In an unwavering voice he said, "I can't let that continue to happen. You knew when you told me about this, I was gonna have to do something about it. Nobody is gonna rape my ol' lady's sister."

Boulder blew out a fog of cigarette smoke. "Yeah, well, first get this done, and then we can talk about it. Right now, you stay back. And do not tell Rainey. Are we clear?"

Stoker pressed his lips together. "Yeah," he said without making eye contact, "We're clear." He pushed off of the bar and walked to the basement steps. "You make sure Janis keeps an eye on that kid. I want her there every night of the week now."

Boulder nodded. "I'll see what I can do."

After spending a few hours teaching Rainey how to drive, Stoker grabbed his bag and kissed her good-bye as he headed out to wheel and deal with other criminals from nearby states. He thought about when Ivy stayed at his house for those couple of nights. She was edgy and angry, but still an innocent kid. Now that he knew that she was being physically and sexually, assaulted he couldn't sit back and let it happen any longer. He was determined to break her free, to live up to his promises to Rainey, and to be a man that stands on the side of right.

Chapter Forty-Nine

Rainey was helping Winnie pack the last of her clothes into a cardboard box when there was a knock at the door. Winnie went to answer and left her upstairs alone. Several minutes later, Rainey wandered downstairs and found her friend in the kitchen with a man. At first sight, she vaguely remembered him from the motel. He was at least six feet tall and looked creepy the way his eyes bore into Winnie's back intensely without blinking, while she packed dishes and chatted.

"Hi, I'm Rainey," she said, entering the kitchen. "Winnie's best friend."

The man turned and looked her up and down. "Oh, yeah, she told me about you and I've seen you around the motel. I'm Henry."

She gave him a small smile. "Yeah, I figured as much." Rainey watched him closely. The first thing she noticed were his ocean blue eyes, so pale she could almost see through them. He fixed them on Rainey with a steady, scrutinizing gaze that made the skin on her arms prickle.

Henry straightened his back and pushed out his chest. "I dropped by to see if Winnie needed any help packing, but she said the two of you have it covered."

Rainey moved her eyes, taking in his average, almost boring face. He had a square jaw to match his square hairline . . . to match his square personality, she thought. His long, straight nose was camouflaged by his neatly trimmed mustache and beard.

"That's right. We have it covered," she said, nodding.

"Good, good," he said, never taking those haunting eyes off of her. "I'll come back tomorrow morning to pick up the boxes."

"No," Rainey said. "I have a car. We'll bring them to your house."

There was no way Rainey was letting her only girlfriend leave without seeing where he lived. Henry gave her the willies the way he stared at her,

then Winnie, like a hungry lion while he bit his fingernails. Then there was his odd tone, gloomy and without inflection, almost like he was reading from a scripted message he'd memorized. She wondered if he went out of his way to make his appearance somewhat normal but her gut was telling her he was not the guy you want your friend to settle down with.

"All right," he said, "I'll see both of you in the morning." He strode over to Winnie and gave her a peck on the cheek. Then he turned to Rainey with a tight-lipped smile and offered, "Looking forward to seeing you again tomorrow."

"Sure, see you then, Henry." She turned to Winnie and said, "We better get back to what we were doing."

Upstairs in the bedroom, Winnie spun on her friend. "What's wrong with you? I saw you staring at him. I can tell you don't like him."

Rainey crossed her arms over her chest, her doubts and instincts about Henry now more intense. "You're right, I don't like him. I'm not sure what it is, but he gives me the creeps." She moved closer and put her hand on Winnie's shoulder. "Please. Let Stoker meet him before you go to Florida with him."

She would say anything to stall for more time before Winnie left.

"Why? Does Stoker have some magical ability to see if Henry is a crazy maniac?"

Shit. Rainey didn't know how to respond. "No, it's not like that, it's just that I would feel better knowing my boyfriend met him, that's all. I just want to make sure you're going to be okay."

"Don't be weird, Rainey," Winnie said, giving her a lukewarm smile. "I know you're looking out for me, but you're seeing something that isn't there."

"Has Leo met him?" Rainey pressed.

Winnie shook her head. "But it's not because I don't want them to meet if that's what you're thinking. It's . . . you know, the whole working nights and sleeping all day."

Rainey furrowed her brow. "Isn't he worried about you running off with some guy he's never met?"

"What the hell?" Winnie said, wheeling on her. "I'm a grown woman. I don't need Leo's permission to do anything. Besides, Leo said he liked the fact that he'd have a place to stay in Florida when he visited."

"Well, Leo's a jerkoff and we both know it."

Winnie sighed and put her arms around Rainey's shoulders. "I know you're mad because you're going to miss me. I'm gonna miss you too, girl. The thing is, I'm happy to be going with Henry and I want you to be happy for me. You and me are gonna talk all the time on the phone. You and Stoker can come and visit, we'll go to the beach and do what people who live in Florida do. It's all going to work out. Okay?"

"Okay," she mumbled. Winnie was right: she was going to miss her and didn't want her to move away. But that didn't explain why she had an immediate dislike of Henry. Something wasn't right about him, and that feeling was buried deep in Rainey's bones.

***

The next morning, Rainey pulled up to Henry's brick house on North Marshall Street, a dumpy part of town. Henry's house was connected to another house on one side, and there was a small lot of grass and dirt on the other. The front windows were covered with bars, which wasn't unusual in bad neighborhoods, but Rainey noticed he had them on his second-floor windows too, which was odd. An old rusted chain-link fence surrounded the high, uncut grass on the side of the house.

Rainey looked at Winnie. "This place is disgusting. Have you been here before?"

Winnie looked at the house through the car window. She shook her head slowly. "Henry made it sound nicer," she said, sounding disappointed.

"Do you want me to take you home? You can just call the whole thing off."

At this, Winnie's head snapped around and she glared at her. "No, I want to be with him. And our house in Florida will be nicer because I'll take care of it."

"You keep making excuses."

"You know what?" Winnie said, staring through the front window. "When you decided to be with Stoker, did I tell you not to?"

"Actually, you did. You told me that he was my first boyfriend and it was too soon, but you know what? At least you knew him," she explained. "Do you remember how you interrogated Stoker the day he came to pick me up? I never stopped you. I let you say and think whatever you wanted

because I knew you had my best interests at heart, just like I have for you now."

Winnie lowered her head. "You're right, I did do all those things. But listen," she said, turning to face her, "I know what I'm doing. I understand that you don't know Henry, but I do and it's going to be fine."

Rainey banged her hands on the steering wheel. "I'm sorry. You might think I'm a jerk and I want to be supportive, but Henry gives me a bad feeling. Like the feeling I got from Jiggy. Like he's, you know, one of those guys who sees people not as people, but as objects, like a chair or a roll of paper towels. Do you have any idea what that does to me? It tears me up thinking that you might be going off with someone like that."

Winnie scoffed. "Okay, that's a weird thing to say. I know you care about me, but whatever you're feeling is wrong. You better adjust your creep detector. That's not Henry. He's sweet and loving and he wants to be with me. Now, are you going to help me with my boxes or not?"

They stepped out of the car. Figuring she had no choice, Rainey picked up a box and followed her to his front door.

Henry pulled the door open, stepped outside, and quickly closed it behind him. "You can leave all the boxes here," he said, pointing to the front of the house. "That'll make it easier for us to pack them into the moving truck."

Winnie turned to her friend and stretched her arms open. Holding back tears, Rainey stepped into her. They held each other in a tight embrace.

"I'm gonna miss you so much," Rainey whispered.

"Same here. I'll call you soon."

Rainey stepped back and nodded. Then she leaned in and whispered, "If things don't go well, call me, okay? Me and Stoker will come get you and bring you home."

Winnie gave her a sad smile. "I will."

Rainey slid behind the steering wheel of the car, looked at Winnie, and gave one last wave before she drove off. Twenty minutes later, her heart was heavy and her thoughts morbid as she parked in front of her house. She sauntered up the steps, and her worries about being alone became very real.

Chapter Fifty

Two months had passed since Stoker had left. Rainey was still not used to being alone, and the highlight of her day was talking to Stoker on the telephone before she went to bed each night.

"Hello?" Rainey breathed into the phone. She glanced at the clock: 3:40 a.m.

The voice gurgled words into her ear.

"Huh?" she said, rolling over and pulling the covers under her chin.

"Kiki and me are coming over in a few minutes. I didn't want to show up unannounced in the middle of the night and scare you."

"Why?" Rainey asked groggily.

"We'll see you in a few minutes."

Rainey got out of bed and dressed. She was freaked out that Boulder had woken her in the middle of the night, and she was convinced that Stoker had been arrested. Thinking about it agitated her because she'd warned him about how bad it was in prison and now here they were.

By the time she pulled the door open, she was wired.

"Come on in," Rainey said, opening the door wider. She walked into the living room as they followed. It wasn't lost on her that neither of them had spoken yet.

"What's going on? It's the middle of the night and you're freaking me out," she said, looking at Boulder.

Boulder rubbed his chin and looked over at Kiki, who looked away, only heightening Rainey's tension.

"I got a call from Andrew," Boulder said, his voice quivering. "There was an incident at the new store." He paused, looking down at his hands to gather his thoughts.

Rainey rubbed her arms, a slow sense of dread creeping up inside her. "What kind of incident?" she asked, both wanting and not wanting to hear the answer.

Boulder pinched the bridge of his nose and gazed at the wall on the other side of the room.

Rainey leaned forward, clutching her midsection. "What kind of incident?" she asked again, louder.

Kiki sat beside her, which in itself was alarming to Rainey.

"There were some robbers," Kiki said, her voice gentler than Rainey had ever known it to be. "Some guys went into the store a couple of hours ago and shot Stoker."

Rainey bounded to her feet, her heart in her throat. "Where is he? Is he okay?" Her mind raced. Stoker had to be okay. He is in the hospital somewhere and they came to take me to him. That's why they woke me in the middle of the night. Stoker needs me, she thought.

Kiki cleared her throat. "He's dead. One of the bullets hit him in the heart."

Rainey pressed her hands onto either side of her head. It was as though she were trying to keep her skull from falling apart. "No, no, no. I'm sure Andrew is wrong. You need to call him again." She pressed her back into the wall. "Call Andrew. Call him right now, Boulder!" she yelled. She frantically searched Boulder's eyes, waiting for him to say it wasn't true. But now she could see he'd been crying, and her heart broke in half. She couldn't believe it was true that she'd lost the only man she ever loved.

"Boulder, please. Say something. Please," she begged.

Boulder looked back at her with a pained expression, then lowered his head.

Rainey dropped to her knees in front of him. "Boulder, you have to make this better. You have to make this right. Stoker can't be dead, okay? Please, you have to say this is a big lie."

"It's not a lie," he said in a hoarse voice. "Stoker is gone."

Boulder fell to his knees and wrapped his arms around Rainey, pulling her into him. Her full body weight collapsed into Boulder then Rainey pressed her face into the crook of his neck, sobbing and begging him to say it was all a mistake.

"Was he alone?" she asked hysterically, trying to picture his final moments, hoping someone was with him when he died.

“He was alone in the store, yes. Andrew was in the parking lot. He’d gone out to his bike to grab something out of his saddlebag when he heard the shots.”

Rainey’s grip on Boulder tightened. The thought of Stoker dying alone was almost too much to bear. “Did Andrew catch them?”

“No, he didn’t. There were three of them, and had Andrew gone after them he probably would’ve been offed too.”

Rainey’s shoulders curled forward and she wept as Boulder kissed the top of her head. She felt small and fragile, as though she were about to shatter into a million fleshy pieces.

Chapter Fifty-One

Kiki sat on the sofa and watched Boulder and Rainey. Losing Stoker was a loss for her too. She'd known him for many years, and he'd convinced Boulder to make her his ol' lady. She owed him a lot, and this was the only reason she tried to be civil to his ol' lady. She peered at Boulder and Rainey, her eyes narrowing. She could see the softer side of her ol' man holding and stroking her back. Faced with tragedy, envy made a home in her belly. Boulder had never comforted her in the way he was now taking care of Stoker's ol' lady, and Kiki would not allow it for much longer.

By lunchtime, everyone from the club came to the house Rainey had lived in with Stoker to show their respects. The women brought cakes, casseroles, and alcohol. They cooked a large meal while Rainey sat slumped against the wall on a kitchen chair. She hadn't showered and was still wearing the oversized T-shirt and gym shorts she'd put on that morning.

When Kiki came into the kitchen Rainey glanced up at her, barely registering who it was, Kiki filled her lungs with air and sat next to her.

"Listen," Kiki said, "Boulder wants you to go in the other room and see him."

Rainey glanced at her with tired eyes. "Why?" she mumbled.

"Because arrangements need to be made and you need to make some decisions," Kiki said tightly, clenching her jaw. "Besides, when Boulder calls, we don't ask why, we go."

Rolling her eyes, Rainey hoisted herself from the chair and walked slowly into the living room, where the men were sitting. She stood in front of Boulder. "Kiki told me you want to talk," she said, feeling lifeless.

Boulder motioned for one of the members to move, and she sat down next to him. "The cops have released Stoker's body to the undertaker, and, he'll be brought back here tomorrow," he said in an even voice. "You'll get

to see him before the club does. You and me will go together—Kiki can come, if that would help."

Rainey shook her head. "I don't need her there. The only person I needed is dead."

Boulder patted her hand. "I know this is hard, but there's some business we have to discuss. Stoker will be cremated and his ashes will be spread the day after tomorrow."

"What?" Rainey said, her head shooting up and looking into his face. "But I need time. You can't do it that quick."

He pinched his lips together. "I'm trying to show you respect because you belonged to Stoker. What I'm telling you is a fact, not a discussion," he said in a firm voice.

His tone penetrated her gloom, and as it did, a small alarm went off inside her, realizing that things with the club would be much different with Stoker gone.

Tense and wired she said, "Okay. Is there anything else you need to tell me?"

"Yeah," Boulder said with a sigh, "we may as well get this all out in the open. You're gonna have to move outta this house by this time next week. One of the members will take over Stoker's position and it's their right to have the house. You'll move into the main house with the other girls."

Her mind raced, thinking about the other girls being passed around from member to member. "I'm not sure I'll be staying," she said. She hadn't actually considered this before, but as she said it aloud, it was clear she needed to get away from the club quickly.

Boulder cocked his head to the side and looked at her intently. "Well, we can talk about that later. For now, eat and get a good night's sleep. Then tomorrow start packing your stuff and I'll take you down to see Stoker in the afternoon."

Rainey nodded and looked around the room at the men. Stoker had been one of them. Her gaze landed on Andrew, who quickly turned away.

Rainey went upstairs, showered, and returned to the kitchen a little while later.

She stood beside Taz, who was making another pot of coffee. "Is Andrew taking Stoker's place in the club?"

Taz's head lowered; her eyes directed at the floor. "I didn't know how to tell you. I mean, you just found out about Stoker and now this. I'm so sorry."

Rainey put her hand on Taz's shoulder and was comforted standing close to her friend, who cared about her loss. "It's not your fault. It's not anybody's fault except for the thugs who killed him." She looked around the kitchen and realized she wouldn't miss leaving the house; it was only Stoker she'd miss. "You're moving in here with Andrew then?"

Taz nodded. "I feel awful. I never wanted this. I mean, of course, every ol' lady hopes that one day her man will be number one or two in charge, but I never wanted it this way."

"I know. Can I ask a favor?"

"Of course, whatever you need."

"I need you to keep me outta the shitter with Kiki. She's hated me since we've met, and now with Stoker gone, I know she's gonna come after me."

Taz gave her a weak smile. "I know all this came crashing down on you, but I don't think Kiki is out to get you. She loved Stoker and I'm sure she's just super sad that he's gone."

***

The next afternoon Rainey got into a van with Boulder, who was taking her to the funeral home. As they drove, she worried about this being the last time she'd see Stoker and saying good-bye to the man she loved.

Rainey was leaning her forehead against the passenger window, thinking about everything that had happened over the past few months. She had tried to get in touch with Winnie since she left with Henry two months ago. The telephone number Henry gave her rang, but no one ever picked up. She had tried to contact Winnie six times since she found out that Stoker died, but still there was no answer. Several times she'd even talked to Leo, who hadn't heard from his sister either, and they convinced each other that Winnie was living the beach life and would eventually call one of them. But now, as she was trying to deal with Stoker's death, not having Winnie to lean on made her life seem much darker and bleak.

At the funeral home, they followed the funeral director on the red and gold carpet and through a set of French doors. When she saw Stoker lying in a coffin on the other side of the room, Rainey's pulse quickened and tears sprang to her eyes. He was wearing a white T-shirt, jeans, and his leather Devils Angels vest. She rushed toward him and looked down into his face.

Stoker's eyes were closed and his hair was combed perfectly in place, just the way he wore it. He looked peaceful, and for a moment she wanted to believe he was sleeping and not dead. When she touched his face, it was cold and her fingers traced his stiff lips, not the lips that soothed her or caressed her; they were gone. Sobbing, she ran her hand over his forehead and paused when she noticed something different about his face.

She turned to Boulder. "Look at that," she said, running her index finger gently under his left eye. "It looks like he has a black eye."

Boulder nodded. "We think he tried to fight off the guy who shot him. Stoker was no easy target. This man, right here," he said, patting his dead brother's chest, "he would fight to save himself or a brother no matter what was happening," he explained, turning to her. "One thing you can be sure about is he died with honor."

Rainey clenched her teeth. There had been no reason for Stoker to die in the first place, and it infuriated her that Boulder and the other club members talked up death like they were about to receive the Purple Heart. But instead of arguing, she stepped aside and sat in a wooden chair near the casket.

The club members filed in a short time later. The line of men seemed never-ending until finally only Boulder and Rainey remained.

The funeral director sat beside Rainey. "You should say your good-byes," he said gently. "I'm going to take him to be cremated."

"No!" Rainey said, suddenly horrified by the thought of leaving him for good. "I'm staying until he's cremated."

"Miss, I know this is difficult—"

Boulder put his hand in the air to silence him. "If she wants to stay then that's what we'll do."

The director responded with a curt nod. "Okay, well, you can follow me and we'll get him ready."

Rainey waited in a dreary room with fluorescent lighting that gave off a yellow tint, which made the brown-tiled walls and floor seem even more depressing. She sat quietly while they prepared Stoker for cremation. Finally, the funeral director came and led her into the cremation chamber. In the center of the space was a simple wooden box, and as she approached, she could see Stoker laying inside still dressed in the same clothes as his viewing.

The funeral director turned to Boulder. "We should give the young lady a minute."

Boulder nodded. He approached the wooden box, leaned over, and kissed Stoker on the lips. "Rest well, brother. I'll see you again," he said, then turned and left the room.

Rainey looked around the cold, sterile environment and down at Stoker. She leaned over the box and rested her head on his chest, trying to feel his heartbeat one last time; giving a final effort to bring him back to life. A sob broke free and she grabbed Stoker's shoulders and held onto him tightly.

"Oh, Stoker. I feel so lost and I'm going to miss you so much. And now . . . now, I'm alone again. I never expected to have to live without you."

Tears streamed from her eyes and snot dripped from her nose. She leaned in and kissed him. She stroked his hair once more. Then she whispered into his ear, "I'll love you forever. Please, watch over me."

After a few minutes, the funeral director came back into the room and offered his arm to her. She grabbed it, and he led her to a room where she would sit for the next three hours and wait for the only man she had ever loved to be turned to ash.

Chapter Fifty-Two

Rainey and Boulder drove back to the house in silence and after he parked in front of her house, he sighed before turning to her. "Look, I'm sorry you have to get outta the house so quick, but that's club rules. Stoker would understand."

"Is that supposed to make me feel better? That Stoker would understand? Because I don't think he would," she spat, sick and tired of hearing about club rules.

Boulder gave her a hard stare, but Rainey was so broken she didn't even flinch. "Now listen, you're gonna stay at the club's common house. I'll let the boys know you're off-limits for a while, but I'm certain they'll be lined up wanting you to be their ol' lady. You can test 'em out, but in the end it'll be the members' choice."

Rainey stared at him, adamant that no one would make that kind of choice for her. "I'm not interested in any of your members. I already told you that I don't think I'm staying. I only came here because of Stoker."

He scratched the side of his face. "That's all fine and good, but it doesn't work that way. Once you become an ol' lady you stay with the club no matter what happens."

Rainey hadn't expected to be forced to stay. Panic ignited every cell in her body. "No," she said, hearing her voice shake ever so slightly. She took a breath and steadied herself. "Stoker never told me that, and anyway, I'm not part of the club. Kiki treats me like shit and I have no interest in any of your members."

"I don't know how to make this clearer for you. You're staying with us." Boulder paused, and she thought she saw a flicker of softness in his eyes, at least she hoped so. "Look, we can talk about you leaving in a couple of

months, but not now. You're vulnerable and there's no telling what you might do. Stoker would want us to protect you."

Rainey opened her mouth to protest, but he put his hand up, silencing her.

"This conversation is over. Now go inside and get some sleep. I'll come by in the morning to check on you. Okay?"

Rainey nodded, unable to think of anything else that might sway him. She opened the car door and stepped out. Before shutting the door behind her, she bent down to look at Boulder. "I don't know where I'm going next, so maybe I will stay at the club for a while. But I'm telling you this, no men will be passing me around. But like you said"—she narrowed her eyes at him —"we can talk about it tomorrow."

Boulder gave her a slow nod.

Satisfied, Rainey slammed the door shut and turned to go inside without looking back. Driving to his house, a smile slowly stretched across his face. That is one defiant broad, she'll fight whoever comes at her, he thought. Rainey's disobedience amused him, which was odd because he knew he wouldn't be amused by any other woman who acted the same way, including Kiki.

Chapter Fifty-Three

The following week, Taz helped Rainey carry a few duffel bags with all of her belongings to the common clubhouse. They dropped the bags just inside the door and walked into the basement to find Boulder. Rainey kept her back straight and her head held high as she approached him. He stopped talking when he noticed her coming his way.

"Hey," she said, looking him up and down. "I brought my stuff. Where should I put it?"

He shrugged. "Look upstairs and find room in one of the closets. That's where all the girls keep their stuff."

She leaned into him, not wanting everyone to hear. "Except I'm not one of the girls, remember? And I'm not the one who insisted that I stay. So where will I be sleeping?"

Boulder opened his arms and swept them over the finished basement. "Anywhere you decide to drop. Unless, of course, you sleep with a member and they let you crash with them," he said, his tone harsh.

Belittled and embarrassed to have lost all of her status as the second's ol' lady, she looked around and back at him. "Whatever, Boulder," she seethed. Her eyes moved to Andrew, who was standing nearby. He shot her a sympathetic look and she hoped he'd do something to help her.

"Hey, um, maybe she could stay in our extra bedroom," Andrew offered, knowing Stoker expected him to take care of her.

Rainey's heart lifted. Oh, yes, please let me stay with Andrew and Taz, she thought.

Boulder shook his head. "Nah, it doesn't work that way. If she stays in your place, then all the other bitches will be complaining that she gets special treatment. We start doing that shit and before we know it, we'll have a bunch of annoyed women on our hands."

Andrew tilted his head. "You have a good point, but the other girls weren't Stoker's ol' lady."

"I don't think so, man," Boulder spat before turning back to Rainey, "Look, go talk to Kiki. She'll figure something out for you."

Rainey was too frustrated and unwilling to give Boulder the benefit of a response. Without a word, she turned on her heel and headed over to where Kiki sat with a few other girls.

"Hey," Rainey said, "Boulder told me you'd figure out where I'm sleeping."

Kiki cackled. "You're looking at it," she said, pointing to the floor.

Rainey put her hands firmly on her hips. "Really?"

Kiki stood and looked her in the eyes. "Really," she said, then slapped her across the face.

Stunned, Rainey froze for a split second, then pulled her arm back ready to punch Kiki, but the other girls jumped on her too quickly and everything went dark a second later.

When Rainey woke, she was lying on a mattress in the heater room in another part of the basement. Disoriented, she tried to take in her surroundings, but it was pitch black.

"What the hell?" she whispered.

Rainey's head was throbbing, and when she touched her forehead, she flinched from the tenderness of the lump that had formed. Confused, she sat up and willed her eyes to adjust in the darkness. It was cold and damp. As the low buzzing noise she'd woken up with in her head subsided, Rainey could hear voices in the distance. A man was yelling. She couldn't tell who it was, but she could tell he was angry. She heard the sound of something smashing. Her adrenaline pumping, she got to her feet, took a moment to steady herself, and walked toward the sound. She kept her hands out in front of her to avoid walking into things. Finally, she touched something solid. She rubbed her palms across the surface until she hit the cold metal of a door handle. She tried to turn the knob, but it was locked.

"Hey! In here! Help! The door is locked!" she screamed, hoping someone would hear her over the man's angry rants.

Rainey paused to listen closer. It was Boulder yelling, and he was threatening someone.

"If you do something like this again, I'll fucking kill you myself," he threatened. "Who the hell do you all think you are? Having a catfight here

and there is one thing, but attacking a second's ol' lady, even if he's dead, crosses the line."

Rainey banged on the door with both fists until finally it flung open. The lights inside the basement blinded her and she squinted trying to make out who stood in front of her.

"Are you okay?" Boulder asked in a much gentler tone from a minute ago.

"Yeah, I think so," Rainey managed, still trying to piece together how she had ended up in the dark room. "What happened?"

"Doesn't matter what happened. Grab your bags, you're going back to your house." Boulder faced the girls across the room at the bar. "I don't wanna hear no shit. She's staying with Andrew and Taz until further notice. I ain't making no exceptions for any of you bitches so don't even ask me."

Rainey barely had time to register what he'd said, when Taz rushed up and took her arm, leading her from the basement.

***

Boulder glowered at Kiki once they were home.

"You'll be sorry if you ever do anything like that again without my permission. You don't give any orders in this club. She could've died, and then what?" he growled. "Then I'm stuck getting rid of a body."

"So what? You have a thing for her or something? Why is Rainey Paxton so near and dear to your cold fucking heart?"

Boulder stomped over to her and grabbed her by the hair. He pulled her into their living room and shoved her onto the sofa. After slapping her twice he put his nose to hers.

"Kiki, you need to stop this shit. You're not the boss here, I am. So here's what I'm gonna tell you. I love you, but if you ever disobey me again, you'll find your ass out on the streets turning tricks for me. Now, do we understand each other?"

Holding the side of her face, she nodded.

"Good. Here's what we're gonna do. Rainey is gonna stay with Andrew and you're going to make sure the other girls bite their tongues. I don't care if they bite their tongues off in the process." He raised his hand in the

air and brought it down on the side of her head. She jolted sideways and put her hands up to shield herself from another blow.

"Okay, I got it."

Later, as Kiki laid in bed after giving Boulder what he wanted, she thought about Rainey. Someday I'll get even with that little bitch.

Chapter Fifty-Four

Feeling awkward in her old home, Rainey sat next to Taz on the sofa, and Andrew was sitting across from them in the recliner. It was painful, remembering that it had once been Stoker's favorite chair, and that he was gone for good.

"I appreciate you speaking up for me and taking me in," she said after a moment.

Andrew nodded. "I made my brother a promise that if anything ever happened to him, I would look out for you. He promised he'd do the same for Taz if anything happened to me."

Rainey put her arm over Taz's shoulder and squeezed it, grateful to both of them.

"I won't stay long, I promise," she offered, already worrying where she would go next. "I told Boulder I didn't want to stay at the club. He explained the club rules, but I won't be with another member, that ain't me. I just need a little time to get my shit together before I can move outta here."

Andrew guzzled from his beer bottle. "There's no rush. And, when the time comes, I'll work things out with Boulder." He looked down at the beer in his hand and back up at her. "Boulder is right, our ol' ladies don't move on when one of us dies. You know, Stoker and me talked about this a lot, he made sure I understood that you came here for him . . . not for the club."

Rainey covered herself with the familiar blanket that was draped over the back of the sofa. "Will you tell me what happened to Stoker?" she asked, wanting to know the details . . . she needed to know if he had said anything, before he died.

He averted his eyes. "There's nothing to tell. One minute I was at my bike, and the next minute I heard shots being fired. I looked up and some guys were running from the store."

"Did Stoker say anything?"

Andrew shook his head. "He was already dead by the time I got to him."

She nodded. "What did the guys look like that killed him?"

Andrew glanced at Taz. Boulder had warned him to be careful with giving her too much information, she was good at getting people to talk by asking a lot of questions.

Without answering Rainey, he got up from the recliner and walked into the kitchen.

"He's not gonna tell me anything, is he?" Rainey asked Taz.

"I don't think there's anything to tell. I think he just said it all." Taz paused and put her hand on Rainey's arm. "Besides, you need to move on with your own life."

Rainey leaned back on the sofa cushion. "It hasn't even been two weeks since Stoker was killed. It's still hard to believe he's gone. How the hell am I supposed to move on?"

Taz reached over and pushed Rainey's hair from her forehead. "Well, first of all, you need to take care of that monster lump on your head."

She blew out a breath. "Yeah, and my bruised ribs and legs too," she said lifting her shirt.

Taz cringed. "Shit, that's gotta hurt."

Rainey nodded, "Hurts like hell. You know, I hate those girls. And I'll tell you one thing, if the day ever comes that I can get even with any of them, I will."

Taz shook her head, not wanting anymore trouble now that she was in a higher position than the other girls. "I think you should let it go. You have more important stuff to think about, like what you want to do next. Do you have any ideas?"

Rainey paused. She had been thinking over the past few days about where she would go and what she wanted to do next. She would continue working at the Drop Inn for a while because it kept money in her pocket. Her transition back into her life without Stoker was bitter-sweet. In an odd way, that filled her with guilt, it was kind of thrilling to think that she could start over and make her own way in the world.

"Well," Rainey said slowly, "I've been thinking a lot about me and Ivy. And if someone would've helped me when I was a kid, after my aunt was

gone, I wouldn't have gone through so much crap. And it's not just me and Ivy. There are lots of kids with screwed-up parents, I see them all over North Philly. I'd love to be the person to help them. I get so excited thinking about that, about making sure other kids don't end up how I did. Then I think, if I can't even help my own sister, how am I gonna help kids I don't know?"

Rainey went quiet and looked at Taz. It was good to tell someone what she'd been thinking and now she was teary-eyed, filled with loss, grief, and hope. She and Taz were friends, but she'd never shared anything so personal with her before. It was nice to share her innermost feelings, and Taz was looking at her with empathy and kindness.

"I think you'd be great at whatever you want to do. But I gotta tell you that thing you said about Ivy, that's not true," Taz said. "You've done so much to help her. You send her money every week and Janis is keeping an eye on her for you, right?"

Rainey nodded, appreciating Taz's encouragement, but she didn't feel better.

"I think you would be great with kids. You're kind, fun, and people like being with you."

Rainey shook her head. "I spent three years in juvie, so I have a record."

Taz smirked. "I'm sure you'll figure something out. You were a kid . . . people can't hold that against you forever."

Rainey wrinkled her nose, pausing to think about it. "Maybe you're right. There might be something I can do," she said with hope.

***

The next week Rainey went to the Drop Inn before her shift, and found Titus in his office.

"I need to talk to you," she said.

Titus eyed her up and down. "Don't even tell me you're quitting too. I had to hire that damn crackhead Noel to fill in for Winnie."

"No, that's not it. But I do need to change my schedule. From now on, I can only work Monday through Thursday."

"Are you kidding me?" he growled.

"No. But I have another person that might be able to fill in for the time I can't work."

"Yeah, who?"

"Just a girl I know. You'll like her."

Titus tapped his pen on the notebook in front of him and looked up at her. She could see he was in a foul mood; it was becoming a common occurrence. Ever since Winnie left there were fewer rooms rented at the motel—he knew she had kept a steady stream of regulars coming in.

"Do you wanna meet her or not?" Rainey pressed.

"Yeah, sure, I'll meet her," he said, then gave her a scathing look. "You know, I've been thinking. Now that your boyfriend is out of the picture maybe you should think about taking over some of Winnie's regulars."

She stepped back. "Excuse me?"

"Yeah, why not? You're a good-looking girl and you need the money, right? I mean, you don't wanna have to live with those biker thugs your whole life."

"You're a jerk, Titus. You know I'm not about to prostitute myself just so you can rent rooms. You knew when you hired me that I wouldn't do that. Nothing has changed just because Stoker is gone."

"Yeah, well, how are you going to take care of yourself then? Or maybe you think you'll find another guy to take care of you," he spat, agitated he wasn't getting his way.

"You're so ignorant. I'll bring the other girl in to meet you. And whatever you do, don't be an asshole or she won't work for you," she warned.

Rainey pursed her lips and left his office slamming the door behind her, vowing to get out of the Drop Inn as soon as she was able. Taz was right, she needed to do something more with her life, and limiting the time she worked for Titus would let her do just that.

Chapter Fifty-Five

On the way home, Rainey got off the bus at Kensington and Allegheny Avenues. Now that she was a guest in what had once been the home she'd shared with Stoker, and given Andrew and Taz were finally in a place of their own, she considered herself an intrusion in their lives.

She stopped in at Jack's, a local dive, for a burger. Inside the faintly lit bar, she took a seat at a booth and allowed herself a moment of peace from her life.

Shortly after her food arrived, a tall, beefy man approached her. "Hey baby," he sang.

She looked up from her food and continued to chew while he stood watching her. "What do you want?" she asked after swallowing.

"Whoa, doll. You ain't gotta be on the defensive. Firefly don't hurt nobody. What's your name, baby?"

Wanting to be left alone to enjoy her food, Rainey glared at him her eyes scanning him from head to toe. He was wearing a black-and-white pinstriped suit, a hot pink shirt, and a yellow tie. Her eyes narrowed, "Did you say Firefly?" she asked. She already didn't like this guy one bit. He was sleazy.

"Yeah, baby, that's right."

"Well, Firefly, you don't have any reason to know my name. What you need to do is to get the hell away from me. I'm not lost or lonely or living on the streets. I don't want to be your baby, your doll, or your whore—so beat it."

"Damn, girl," he cackled, cracking his knuckles. "You gotta mouth on you. Don't get me wrong now, I wouldn't mind the opportunity to tame that wild ass of yours. So I'll tell you what . . . when you change your mind and trust me, you will, you can come crawling back here to Jack's Bar and

I'll be waiting for you with open arms." Firefly turned and swaggered back to his seat at the bar.

Anxious to leave and get away from Firefly, Rainey dropped money on the table and left with most of her burger still uneaten. As she stepped onto the sidewalk, Firefly was right behind her, calling her back. Troubled by his persistence she ignored him, but he snatched her arm.

"One more thing. Ain't nobody talks to Firefly like that. You need to learn to be nicer or maybe somebody like myself will come along and teach you a lesson."

He was making the foul mood he put her in a few minutes ago worse. She moved her face inches from his; she knew the only thing to do was to stand up to him and hope he'd go back inside the bar and leave her alone. "Well, I'm sorry you got your feelings hurt, Ladybug, but you need to leave me alone."

A look of rage passed over the man's face. His bottom jaw jutted out and he lifted his free hand into the air.

"Hey!" a woman screamed from across the street. "Get your hands off of that girl and take your nasty black ass back in the bar."

Firefly whirled around but kept a tight grip on Rainey. "Mind your business, Rosemary. You don't own these streets."

Rosemary, a thin black woman in her mid-forties, trotted over to him. "You see here, Firefly. Tonight, I do own these motherfuckin' streets. We're sick and tired of you latching on to these young girls and turning them out so you can make money. Go get a damn job, you lazy bastard. This community is gonna pull together, you mark my words, and your time in Kensington will be over."

Rainey tried to wrench her arm from Firefly, but he had a death grip on her. She glanced at Rosemary, who was making the sign of the cross. Then Rosemary slapped her palms together loudly, glowered at Firefly, and closed her eyes.

"Dear Lord, give me the strength not to knock this pimp's ass up the block and back down again. Please, just this once, send the devil up from hell to take this prick's sorry soul back with him." She clenched her teeth together. "'Cause I swear, Lord, I'll bust his ass up so bad he'll be knocking on your door, but he ain't going with you, oh no he ain't, Lord, he's heading straight to Satan." She took in a loud breath. "I ask this in Jesus' name. Amen."

Still trying to break free, Rainey kept her eyes on Rosemary, wondering what this kind but strange woman was doing. Rosemary made the sign of the cross again and opened her eyes, leveling Firefly with a stare.

"You heard my prayer," she said evenly. "Don't make the Lord himself come down here and force me to kick the living shit outta ya."

Firefly's nostrils flared. "I don't know who the hell you think you're talking to, Rosemary. There was a time not too long ago you were afraid to look in my direction. You best think about that."

The woman breathed a sigh of relief when she saw a police car cruising toward them. "Oh, look!" Rosemary said curtly. "The Lord done sent the cops to take care of your ass for me." She lifted her hand in the air and the patrol car pulled beside the curb.

The officer in the passenger side, a black man with greenish-brown eyes, put down the window and smiled at her. "Everything okay here, Rosemary?"

Rosemary glanced at Rainey, pinched her lips together, then looked at Firefly, and cocked her head to the side. With that, he let go of Rainey's arm.

She gave the officer a nod and a wink. "It's good now, Officer Davis," she sang in a flirty tone. Then she put her arm over Rainey. "You okay, sugar?"

The girl nodded and let out a sigh of relief. She was happy the woman had showed up when she did. "I'm fine. Thank you."

"All right then. You can come with me now." Rainey raised her eyebrows. Who is this woman?

"Don't worry. You're safe. I ain't like that piece of dog shit," she said, lifting her chin in Firefly's direction.

"Careful, Rosemary. You don't want me on your bad side," Firefly bit back.

"Oh, shut up, Firefly. You don't scare me. You're just a two-bit pimp making money off of other people's misery. Now, if you'll excuse us, we're gonna leave your sorry ass standing here while we walk away."

Rainey held back a smile and followed Rosemary across the street, into a building. Inside, she found herself in a bright room filled with light and colors. A dozen teens were sitting around listening to music, watching television, and reading.

"What's this place?" Rainey asked.

Rosemary smiled. "This is a day shelter for youth and teens."

"A day shelter?" Rainey had never heard of such a thing.

"Ah-huh. It's a place where displaced youth can come during the day. This place keeps them off the streets and out of the hands of people like Firefly."

Rainey looked at the woman closer. "You look familiar. Have we met?"

Rosemary shook her head. "I don't know, sugar. I used to work at the Dollar General so there's a chance we met there. Everyone knows me from that place."

Rainey thought for a moment. Firefly called her Rosemary, and now she connected the dots, remembering the woman pointing to her own name tag many years prior, when Ivy was still a baby. "That's it! Rosemary—yes, I went in to buy food once and you bought me a candy bar. You told me if I ever needed help, I should come back and see you."

Rosemary tilted her head and looked closely at Rainey. "I do remember you," she said. "You came into the store with your baby sister. You looked damn near dead. You was dirty and smelly and starving. Well, I'll be damned, look at you now all clean and pretty." She put her arm over Rainey's shoulder and pulled her in for a hug. At first the girl hesitated, then allowed herself to be vulnerable as a warmth spread through her. Rainey could have stayed wrapped in Rosemary's arms for a long time.

"How've you been?" Rosemary whispered, putting her at arm's length.

"Ah, you know. I'm a Kensington kid."

"You doing drugs?"

Rainey crinkled her nose. "No, never."

"Your parents treating you good?"

"Who?" she asked theatrically.

"Your parents?"

"Wait! I have parents?" she teased.

"Now you listen here, girl," the woman said, wagging her finger. "Don't you play me for a fool."

Rainey's face went blank, thinking she had insulted the woman. "I'd never do that to you."

"Come on, now. Lighten up, I'm just messing with you."

Rosemary studied her for a moment. Then she said, "I told you if you needed help to come back and see me. How come you never did?"

Rainey looked away. "Things happened and well, I . . . I ended up in juvie for three years."

The woman put her hand on the girl's shoulder. "What did you do to get locked up?"

"It's a long story. Bottom line is the police found me sitting with a lapful of heroin and pointing a gun at them. It was all a mistake; the drugs and gun weren't mine, I swear." She looked down at her hands while fighting back angry tears, wishing she could tell her the whole story but she barely knew the woman.

Rosemary nodded. "I believe you."

Her head jerked up. "You do?"

"Sure I do, sugar. I always trust what people tell me until they give me a reason not to. Now, why don't you and me go over there and get some hot tea? We can sit down and get to know each other."

"Sure," Rainey said, feeling heard. "I'd love to."

As she followed the woman across the room, Rainey wondered why it made her feel good that Rosemary kept calling her sugar; but she liked it. Oddly, it gave her comfort. She understood it was a sign of affection.

She watched as Rosemary took two mugs out of a cabinet with THE SANCTUARY written on them in white block letters. Rainey picked up the mug and pointed to the words. "Is that what this place is called?" she asked.

The woman nodded. "That's right. It means a place of safety, a place of protection. There's a lot of our youth in Kensington that need it every day. That's why I quit my job at the Dollar General and came here to work."

As Rainey took the first sip of hot tea there was something deep inside of her that knew her life was about to change. This was everything she'd been looking for and hoped, this would be the path toward a new future.

Chapter Fifty-Six

The next day after work Rainey went to see Rosemary again, excited to know more about what went on at The Sanctuary. The moment she stepped inside the building, Rosemary smiled and rushed to greet her.

"Hello, sugar. Oh, I'm so happy you came back. I wasn't sure which streets you usually sleep on. Do you want something to eat or drink?"

Rainey eyes widened. "Oh, no," she said, waving her off. "I'm not homeless. I was living with my boyfriend, but he died recently and some friends took me in."

"Oh, I'm sorry to hear about your boyfriend. Do you work?"

Rainey mindlessly slid her fingers over the straps of her purse. "I do. I clean rooms at a motel. It's not the greatest job, but it keeps money in my pocket. Anyway, I just told my boss I had to cut back on my days so I have Fridays free to give me time during the day to look for a better job. Then you found me and well, I was wondering if maybe I could work here."

"Now, isn't that a coincidence?" Rosemary said. "I was thinking of you last night, right after I got done saying my prayers. And all of a sudden I realized I don't have no way of contacting you. See, there are lots of kids who come here and I know they wanna talk, but I'm older and I think it makes 'em nervous. It would do them good to have someone closer to their age to share their secrets with. Do you think you could do that?"

Rainey's shoulders hiked up to her ears, not thinking she was qualified to help teenagers without some type of training. "I don't know. I've never done anything like that before," she paused and thought for a moment, "but I can try," she finished, willing to push beyond her fear of failure.

Rosemary chuckled. "I'm sure you'll be great. But if you are really interested, know that it would be volunteer work. We can't pay you any money right now. The guy who owns this building lets us use this space

for free. Donations pay the electric and water bills and we use whatever we can get from the local stores and restaurants to keep food and things on hand. We also take donations of clothes and the sort so we can offer these kids something clean to wear."

"That's fine. I still have my job. I can be here on Fridays, Saturdays, or Sundays. They're the days when I don't work at the motel."

"That's great, sugar," the woman said, patting her on the back. "I'm happy to have you here. I can already tell you're gonna be real good for these kids. You're at least eighteen, right?"

"Yeah, I'm twenty. So, what do I do? How do I get started?"

Rosemary pointed to several teens out in the main area. "You just go out there and make yourself available. Talk to them. Be curious about them. You see, no one is ever curious about how someone got down on their luck, they are only ever curious about the people who rise to the top. We forget how important it is to listen to people who've never been heard before. Did you ever notice that?"

Rainey nodded, recalling the burden of not being heard. "I know what that's like."

"Of course you do. That's why you're going to be perfect here. Now, I know you told me you spent time in juvie. Normally you'd have to fill out a bunch of paperwork and you'd need to pass a background check, but I'm gonna skip those for now because I trust you, like the owner of this building trusted me when he let me work here. I could get in a lot of trouble now, so don't disappoint me. Hear?"

Overcome with a sense of belonging, Rainey put her arms around the woman's waist. "I won't let you down, I promise."

"Okay, good." Rosemary patted her on the back and pulled away. "Let me ask ya," she said, looking into Rainey's eyes, "whatever happened to your little sister?"

Rainey faltered. She wanted to dodge the question, wishing Rosemary hadn't asked so soon. She looked into the woman's face, and there was genuine interest. "When I went off to juvie, Ivy stayed with my parents. The last time I saw her she was drunk, and I took her home with me for a couple of days . . . she's just a kid." Rainey paused, uncertain she wanted to go on.

Rosemary searched her eyes and shook her head. "Nah, that's not all, there's something else in there."

Rainey nodded and sighed. "Well I . . . um, I saw her about three months ago, selling drugs for one of the big dealers." She held back the tears that pricked her eyes. "I haven't seen her in a while." With shame bearing down, her breath hitched. "My little sister hates me," she whispered. "She thinks I left her on purpose. That's what my stupid parents told her."

Rosemary tapped her index finger to her forehead. "Is she the short, dark-haired kid selling drugs down the road a bit?"

Rainey shrugged. "I mean, yeah, she has black hair, but that could be anybody. I saw her selling about two blocks from here."

"Yeah," Rosemary said, pressing her lips together. "I think I've seen her on the streets pushing dope for that lousy bastard Jiggy."

Rainey's heart boomed in her chest. "Wait. Then that's Ivy. I can't believe this. You know who Jiggy is?"

"'Course I do. I've been on these streets a long, long time."

"When was the last time you saw Ivy?" Rainey asked, hoping to get any kind of update on her sister.

"Just a couple of weeks ago."

"How did she look?"

"I can't say for sure; I've only seen her from a distance. I'll tell you this, though, that lifestyle grows you up real fast."

Rainey nodded. "How do you know Jiggy?" she asked hesitantly.

Rosemary chuckled. "Sugar, I started hooking on these streets when I was sixteen. Jiggy wasn't even done shittin' yellow yet." She laughed. "By the time he came on the scene I was old, and ain't nobody wants to pay an old broad for sex. That's when I started working in different stores. I had more jobs over the past ten years than I got fingers and toes combined."

"Really? You were a hooker?" Rainey asked.

Rosemary nodded. "See that, things we learn from people are surprising. I was a prostitute on these streets for years, I ain't ashamed of it neither just like you shouldn't be ashamed of being in juvie. I could tell you was embarrassed about being locked up when you told me your story. The way I see it is, all my experiences make me the person I am today. See now, my past matters, and so does yours. That's why I wanna help these kids. Believe it or not, I was one of the lucky ones. I had lots of hooker friends back then who didn't make it outta the business alive."

Rainey was relieved to know that Rosemary had a sketchy past too. The woman was so kind and spent her time serving the teens in the community, making an effort to change lives for the better. She was truly a role model of

someone who lifted themselves out of their circumstances, and she wanted to be just like her. She'd been carrying an enormous amount of disgrace because of her time spent in juvie, and now it didn't seem so bad. She realized it was possible to make something good out of her life too.

"I take it you're worried about your sister hanging around with that loser Jiggy?"

Rainey nodded. "He's a lot of the reason I went to juvie," she said.

"He try to turn you out?"

Rainey shook her head and took a deep breath. She hadn't spoken of it in a long time, but something about Rosemary made her want to confide in her.

"He was about to rape me when the cops raided my house that night—the night I was arrested," she said. "My parents were . . . they were letting him have sex with me to pay off a drug debt they owed him. I'd only just turned fourteen. The drugs and the gun the cops found me with belonged to him."

Rosemary put her hand over her mouth. "And here I thought I've heard it all."

"I'm worried he's having sex with my little sister." Consumed by sorrow, she held back her tears, overwhelmed that she wasn't able to make a difference in Ivy's life.

Rosemary let her cry it out, allowing her to work through the sorrow. Then she asked, "How old is Ivy now?"

"She's eleven."

Rosemary shook her head. "Mm, mm, mm . . . Lord, have mercy on that child."

"I know, it eats me up," Rainey said, the full realization of what might be happening to Ivy hitting her all at once. "I used to know a woman named Mona. Ivy and I met her on Kensington Avenue. She gave us a couple of dollars to buy food. Anyway, she warned me about Jiggy . . . that he wasn't nice and he hurt people during sex."

"Yep, that's true. He's a real piece of shit. I've had some girls in here over the years who got caught up with him. I know all about how nasty he is. But you listen here, Ivy is a little white girl, and to him that means she's worth her weight in gold. The cops will never suspect she's selling for him. Let that give you a little comfort."

Rainey knew that what Rosemary was saying was true, as much as she hated to think about it. Drug dealers and pimps are the same, they hang

onto what makes them the most money. In a sick, cruel way Rosemary was right. Ivy was worth more to Jiggy alive than dead.

Chapter Fifty-Seven

Rainey had been volunteering at The Sanctuary for almost three months, and in that time, she had become a happier person and thrived on having a purpose. Rainey loved her work at the shelter, spending time with the troubled teens, lending a listening ear, or sharing a warm hug. To make things even better, Rainey and Rosemary had grown attached and they had come to rely on each other.

One morning, in late August, Rainey headed to the shelter to work, but also to ask Rosemary for advice.

Rosemary looked up when Rainey walked in. "Oh, good morning, sugar. Did you sleep well?"

"I did," she said. "Um, I was hoping to talk to you about something. I need to get your opinion."

"Sure. Whatcha got?"

Rainey pulled a chair out and sat at a nearby table, and the woman sat next to her.

"I've been living with my friends since my boyfriend died four months ago, and I need to move out."

"Oh, baby girl, did they throw you out?"

She wrung her hands together, nervous but excited about being on her own. "No. They'd never do that. It was my idea."

"Can you afford your own place?" Rosemary asked.

Rainey nodded. "I think so. I have some money saved and I saw a couple of ads for rooms to rent. I can probably afford that."

"Okay, then what's the problem?"

Rainey twirled the ends of her hair. "Well, I live with the Devils Angels," she said. "When my boyfriend died, I wasn't allowed to leave."

Rosemary's eyes bulged. "Well, this is new. You never told me about the club. I suspect the Devils Angels want you to stay with them?"

She blew out a loud breath. "I haven't brought up leaving since my boyfriend died and I moved in with my friends. I mean, I've really separated myself from the club and I hardly ever see anyone except for the friends I live with. I'm thinking maybe it won't be a big deal now since so much time has passed."

Rosemary grew quiet, pulling on her ear, thinking about how to best handle the situation. "I know the guy who runs that club."

"Boulder?" Rainey asked.

"Ah-huh." Rosemary's jaw was clenched tight and she averted her gaze.

"Of course you know Boulder; everyone knows him. Well, what do you think I should do?" Rainey asked nervously. Rosemary's stiff body language told her the woman had a strong opinion and hoped it wasn't a sign that she thought they wouldn't let her leave.

She ran her hands up her neck and over her cheeks. "Well, Boulder can be a real sonofabitch. However, he does love to help the kids. See, that's the good thing about the bike club, they support abused kids. You know, donate money and stuff."

"I've never seen any of them in here," Rainey said, biting her bottom lip.

"And you won't, either. They give money through charities that help us out." Rosemary narrowed her eyes and looked into her face. "What are you needing me to do?"

"Just tell me how you think I should handle it with Boulder."

"Okay, let's see. First, you need to sit him down privately where there ain't no distractions. Tell him about the work you're doing here. You should tell him that you'd never discuss the club with anyone. I don't know how much you know, but he'll need reassurance. Loyalty is everything to the club."

"What if Boulder says no?" Rainey asked, wanting to be prepared for the worst.

"Sugar," she said, taking her hand, "there ain't nobody in the world that can tell you what to do unless you let them. If he says no, tell him you're doing it anyway. Oh," she said with a bold smile, "and be sure to tell Boulder you're working with me now."

"How do you know so much about Boulder and the club?"

"'Cause when I was your age, I had regular customers from the Devils Angels. They always treated me good. Never mean or nasty. All they

wanted was to have a few drinks, a few laughs, and get laid . . . that was about it. There ain't no blacks in their club, but that don't mean they didn't like me. In fact, most of them came to me because I was black. One of them told me I was different, better than the white girls that hung around them all the time. I liked that they saw me as special, it made me feel important. Besides, they paid me good too," she added.

"Thanks for telling me all of that, it makes me feel better about talking to Boulder," she said.

The girl walked over to several teens watching television and they immediately made space for her to sit down. Rosemary watched from a distance and admired Rainey. She knew the girl was strong and would navigate through anything life threw her way.

***

"How have you been?" Boulder asked when he opened his front door the next morning.

"I'm fine," Rainey said anxiously. She hadn't seen much of Boulder in the past few months and she wanted to get past this conversation.

"Good. Come on in. I sent Kiki to the clubhouse to do some work for me. You sounded serious on the phone yesterday and I wanted to make sure we weren't distracted."

Rainey gave him a stiff smile. She was more on edge than she thought she'd be, but she knew she had to go through with this to move on with her life. "I want to talk to you about something I'm doing," she said, getting right to the point. "First, I want you to know that Stoker never shared with me what the club actually does, but even if he did, I would never tell anyone. That's not who I am."

Boulder pulled two beers from the refrigerator and offered her one. She shook her head and took a seat at his kitchen table, and he sat across from her. "Okay, so why are you bringing this up now?" he asked.

Rainey twisted the ring on her finger. She looked off into the distance and pushed her hair behind her ear, gathering her courage. "So, I've been working at a place called The Sanctuary, it's a day shelter for kids and teens."

Boulder nodded and guzzled his beer. "I know of the place."

"Right," Rainey said, nodding. "Anyway, I volunteer there, and I really love it. I want to be able to be around more, so I'm going to move out of Andrew's house and rent a room closer to the shelter."

Boulder gave her a close look. "Are you asking me or telling me? Because there's a big difference."

She looked at him straight on, wanting this more than anything. "Both." She sat up straighter. "Look, I know that loyalty is everything with the club. Once Stoker died my whole life changed. He's gone and my little sister is still living in that hellhole. I need something meaningful in my life, and the shelter gives me that. I need to be on my own, to find my future. I can't stay with the Devils Angels forever just because I loved a man who was a member."

Boulder got up, walked over to the kitchen window, and paused a moment before speaking. "It's not a usual request from an ol' lady," he said, then turned around and gave her a small smile. "Now, I know you're not the usual ol' lady either. Still, I think you'd be better here with another one of our members."

Rainey got up and walked over to him. She took his hand in hers and looked into his eyes. "I don't want another member. The member I loved died, and when he did, he took a part of me with him. So please, I'm asking you to help me move forward."

Boulder turned back to the window. "If I agree, I need to know you'll never talk to anyone about the club. Not about the job you could've had or anything else you know."

Rainey smiled, thinking she'd convinced him. "I swear, I'll never tell anyone. By the way," she said with a mischievous smile, "Rosemary said to tell you I'll be working with her."

"Ah," he said, nodding. "Rosemary is like a classic car, just gets better with time. Now, that's a woman who can be trusted."

Boulder looked into her eyes for a long moment as she looked back. Looking away, he moved toward the doorway to the living room. "Okay," he said, stopping suddenly, "make your plans. But I want you to understand that once you leave you can never come back."

Rainey was thrilled and her heart was pounding so hard, she worried Boulder might hear it beating in her chest. "Thank you," she said, rushing to him. "Can I ask one more favor though?"

"What's that?" he asked dryly.

"Can you still have Janis watch out for Ivy?"

Boulder paused. "I'll see what I can do, but I can't make any promises now that you're leaving."

"Just for a while," she pleaded, "until I get on my feet and can get her out of that house."

Boulder nodded.

"I appreciate it," she said and walked to the front door.

"When are you leaving?" he called after her.

"Tomorrow."

She didn't know where she'd stay and didn't care. Boulder had agreed and she understood the best thing for her to do was to get out of there quickly. She'd learned from Stoker to never give someone time to change their mind once they have agreed to give you what you want.

Chapter Fifty-Eight

"You're leaving tomorrow?" Taz shrieked, shocked by Rainey's news.

Rainey nodded. "Yeah, I talked to Boulder and it's all good. All I have to do is pack my stuff, so there's no reason to wait."

Taz looked at Andrew with her mouth hanging open. He gave her a nod.

"Where will you live?" Taz asked, still reeling.

"I'm going to rent a room from a lady that has a house close to the day shelter," Rainey said, which was almost true. She'd found an ad in the paper for a room that seemed good but just hadn't called yet.

"And you're still gonna work at the motel?"

"Yeah, for now. Until I can find something better. The shelter is volunteer work so I don't make any money there."

Taz spent the rest of the evening whining and moaning about her leaving, but in the end, she wished her well. The next morning, Rainey put all of her belongings into two duffel bags and took a taxi to The Sanctuary.

Rosemary smiled when she saw her walking in. "Well, looks like you had a good discussion with Boulder."

"I sure did. I took all of your advice, including dropping your name."

Rosemary looked at her duffel bags. "That all your stuff?"

Rainey nodded.

"I'm assuming you have somewhere to go?"

In a quiet voice she said, "Not yet."

"Oh, I see. Then I think you best start looking for something. I'd offer you to stay with me, but I live in a one-bedroom, one-bath apartment. It's tiny, but it works for one person."

"It's okay. I found a lady that rents rooms and I'm gonna call her," Rainey said hopefully.

"Rooms by the hour?" Rosemary joked, raising her eyebrows.

"Very funny," she replied, letting out a short giggle. "No, not by the hour. And it's not too far from here, so I can walk."

"All right. Well, you better get on the phone and call that person up right quick. Get your little ass over there and see if you like it."

Excited, Rainey pulled the ad from her pocket and dialed the number.

"Hello," a woman grunted.

"Hi, I'm calling about the room for rent."

"Yeah, and?"

Rainey hesitated. "Oh. And, I want to come over now and see it. I'm only about ten minutes away. Would that be okay?"

"First off, what's your name?"

"Rainey. Rainey Paxton."

"You looking to share your room with someone?"

"No, it's just me."

"You got a real job, Rainey Paxton?"

"Yes, I clean motel rooms."

"Sounds like you're well on your way to the top," she cackled sarcastically. "Okay, come over and we can talk more." Then she hung up abruptly.

With the conversation leaving Rainey on edge, she groaned. All I need now is the landlady from hell.

Ten minutes later, Rainey plastered on a smile as the woman opened the door. She looked to be about fifty years old. She was tall and slender. She wore skin-tight jeans and a low-neck sweater that revealed her wrinkly cleavage.

"I'm Rainey," she announced.

"No kidding. Come on in. I'm Gladys."

Inside, Rainey's eyes scanned the house. There was a long table in the hall with at least fifteen candles sitting on top. The living room had hardwood floors with a red velvet sofa and a matching loveseat.

"This is my living room," Gladys said, pointing. "You don't have access to it so don't let me catch you in there. You can keep a TV in your room upstairs."

Rainey nodded and followed her farther into the house.

"This is the kitchen. You can use the bottom shelf of the refrigerator; that's it. Don't ever touch my food or booze. You can use the stove and sink, but you need your own dishes and shit. Clean up when you're done;

if I find dishes in the sink, I'll throw them away and kick your ass outta here."

Gladys's directness reminded her of Tootsie, and Rainey had to hold back a smile. She looked around the sparse kitchen. "I don't do much cooking. Usually simple stuff that I heat up, and I eat a lot of cereal."

The woman scoffed. "Yeah, okay. Come on, let's keep moving, I got shit to do." Upstairs, Gladys opened the door to the first room on the right. "This would be your room."

Rainey walked in and looked around. It was old and there was a musty smell like wet cardboard. A single bed was pushed against one wall, with a window on the other. A wood dresser and chair were on the third wall.

"You need to have your own sheets and stuff."

Rainey eyed the bare mattress. "That's no problem."

Gladys huffed. "I'm happy to hear that's no problem. Listen, honey," she said sharply, "I'm renting the room because I need the money. I like my privacy and I'm not looking for a friend."

Turned off by the woman's abrasive words, Rainey turned to meet her eyes. "Okay, that's fine. I'm just looking for a place to sleep."

"Good. I'm glad we got that straight. As long as you stay outta my business, we'll be fine. You can use the bathroom down the hall. It's three hundred a month." She jutted out her hip and watched Rainey.

"I'll take it."

The woman held her hand out with her palm up. She looked at Rainey and down at her hand. "Well?"

"You want the money now?"

"Yeah, what the hell did you think? You were gonna come here and schmooze it out of me for nothing? This room is a hot commodity in this part of town."

This old woman is full of shit, Rainey thought. "Um, sure, that's not a problem."

"Good," she sneered holding her palm out again.

"I don't have the money on me. I have to go grab my bags and I'll come right back. I'll give you the three-hundred bucks and you can give me a key to the front door."

Gladys looked her up and down. "Why the hell are you still standing here? Get moving. I'm expecting company in an hour, so you better make it snappy."

***

Rainey pulled the door open and sluggishly walked into The Sanctuary.

"Well, how was it?" Rosemary asked.

"The house is fine, kinda beat. My bedroom smells bad, but whatever. The woman Gladys is a grump, but I'm sure it'll be fine."

Rosemary patted her back. "It's okay to be nervous. It's the first time you'll be on your own. It's to be expected."

Rainey blew out a nervous breath. "You always know what to say to make me feel better."

***

An hour later, Rainey handed Gladys the three hundred dollars. After putting her clothes into the dresser she headed downstairs, passing the table where the candles were now all lit.

Gladys was in the kitchen and turned as Rainey approached. "Here's your key."

Rainey slid the key into her pocket. "I'll be back later."

The woman poured two glasses of wine. "I really don't care when you come back, just make sure you don't disturb me. I'm having a guest over, something you will not be able to do in my house."

"Got it," Rainey mumbled.

As she walked back to The Sanctuary, Rosemary's words sunk in. She was finally on her own, renting a place, and living her life. With this in mind, her chin lifted and her step grew stronger as she marched back to the shelter. She turned the corner and stopped dead. Her newfound confidence drained away instantly. In the shadowy light of dusk was Ivy. With the cooler fall weather upon them, Ivy's hands were in her coat pockets and she was bouncing up and down on her toes, as if she were freezing.

She approached her slowly and stopped a few feet away. "Ivy? It's me."

Her sister just looked at her. "How many bags you want?"

Rainey stepped out of the shadows to let Ivy see her better. "No, it's me, Rainey."

Ivy's eyes bounced around, checking the streets. "Get outta here. You're gonna get me in trouble."

"What do you mean?" Rainey asked, concerned.

"I mean Jiggy will be back to get me and if he catches you here, I'll pay for it. He hates you, and if he sees me talking to you, he'll be really mad. Just get away and don't talk to me again."

Ivy backed away, then turned and ran. Rainey stood speechless, as if someone had smashed her in the head with a baseball bat—nothing registered, nothing made sense. Then hot fingers of anger clawed at her insides.

As she stood on the sidewalk, gazing into the night, all that was left in her was hate for a soulless man.

Chapter Fifty-Nine

Coming to her senses, Rainey ran after Ivy. Luckily, she caught up to her quickly. Lunging forward, she grabbed her by the arm and brought her to a sudden stop. Ivy yanked her arm away but didn't run again. Rainey kept a close eye on her as they both took a moment to catch their breaths.

"I never set out to hurt you," Rainey said once Ivy had calmed down. "Never. And now I see you with Jiggy. I know him too, you know. He was hanging around our house before I was sent to juvie. He's a bad man. I'll do whatever I can to help you get away from him."

Ivy's eyes filled with tears, and for a moment Rainey thought she had gotten through to her. But then those same eyes hardened. "You can't help me," Ivy said, giving her a look of disgust that cut Rainey to her core. "Don't you get it? Mom and Dad gave me to him. Why can't you get it through your dumb head that it's too late? He does things to me, and if he sees me with you, he'll hurt me more."

"What things?" Rainey asked, her heart in her mouth.

"I don't want to talk about it. Okay?" she screamed.

"Come with me for a few minutes then. Seriously, real quick," Rainey pleaded. "I wanna show you something."

Ivy crossed her arms over her chest. The quiet night air hung between them. She looked up and down the block. "Okay, but hurry up."

Not wasting a moment, Rainey walked swiftly to The Sanctuary with Ivy beside her.

When they stepped inside, Ivy turned to her with a scowl. "What's this place? Why are we here?"

"This is where I volunteer my time and kids come here during the day to be safe. You can come here anytime you want. You'll never be turned away."

Rainey held back, watching Ivy step deeper into the shelter. She wanted to let her take it in on her own, without any pressure. Rainey took her there hoping the warmth that permeated among the people who sought refuge would entice her.

Ivy walked around the shelter. There were kids of all ages, and for a moment she thought how nice it would be to be protected from her home life. She was forced to sell drugs, and as for Jiggy, she was his 'girlfriend at heroin house,' he told Ivy constantly.

From across the room, Rosemary caught Rainey's eyes and approached. "Who do we have here?" she asked, turning to Ivy.

Ivy glared back at her with wild eyes. "None of your fucking business. Why are you asking me who I am? You gonna run off and tell somebody that I came in here? You ain't no different than any of the other assholes that hang around my house, and they always tell on me."

Rainey wasn't surprised by Ivy's outburst. After all, she'd been on the receiving end enough to know her sister was brutal with her words. But Rainey didn't intervene, knowing that Rosemary could handle herself and maybe even get through to Ivy better than she could. She watched as Rosemary's expression turned into a cold, hard glare. Here it comes, she thought, bracing herself.

"Listen, honey," Rosemary said sharply, "I can see you've had a hard time of it, but talk to me like that again and you might meet the backside of my hand." She took in a long breath and her tone deepened. "You ain't the only soul on earth that's been dealt a shitty hand, so you best check yourself quick. I run this place, and the one thing I'm not is a goddamn snitch. You're barking up the wrong bitch tree, honey."

Ivy's mouth dropped open and the creases on her face eased. She moved a step closer to Rainey as if seeking her protection, and muttered a quiet "Sorry."

"That's right, you better be sorry. I spent some twenty years on the street, so I know all about being a hardass. But in here," Rosemary said, waving her hand around the room, "we show each other respect. Now, I don't know what happens in your house, but I can tell you there ain't no assholes working here and ain't nobody gonna tell anybody about you being here."

Ivy shimmied even closer to her sister, which Rainey liked. Then Rosemary looked back and forth between Rainey and Ivy. Rosemary's hand slowly came to her mouth.

"Is this—" she said, her eyes pivoting to Rainey.

"Yes, this is Ivy. I was just telling her she could come here whenever she wants. That she's always welcome."

Rainey turned to her sister and grinned. "Ivy, this is our welcoming committee," she chuckled, pointing to Rosemary.

"Oh, mercy me. Let me take a look at you, child." Rosemary pushed Rainey to the side to get to Ivy and placed her hands on her small shoulders. "The last time I laid eyes on you, your sister was carrying you in her arms. My, oh, my, you sure as hell look alike. You ain't got the same hair or eye color, but your features are the same."

Rainey looked down at Ivy and noted Rosemary was right. Rainey studied her sister for a moment. They shared the same plump lips. Their eyes were different colors but were the same shape, and their noses were identical. She met Ivy's eyes and smiled. Ivy reacted by pulling the hood of her sweatshirt up to cover her head.

"I don't think we look anything like each other," Ivy said, looking away.

Rainey jumped into the conversation. "You know, it's funny, when you were a baby you looked exactly like Mom, but now that you're older, you look more like me and Aunt Sophie."

Ivy shrugged. "Okay, whatever."

Rainey took a few steps forward and asked, "Would you like to sit down and have a snack? Maybe a cup of hot chocolate?"

Ivy shook her head. "No, I have to get outta here before—"

Her sister touched her arm, desperate for her to stay, even just a little longer. "It's okay. Maybe you can hang out for a few minutes."

"No, I gotta go," the young girl said, strutting toward the door.

"Ivy!" Rainey yelled after her. "Remember, you can come back here whenever you want to. I'll help you. I swear."

Ivy turned back for a moment; her eyebrows knitting together. "I don't think so," she stammered. "It wouldn't be good for me if I got caught here. Don't come looking for me anymore."

The door closed behind her, and Rainey turned to look at Rosemary, feeling the full depth of her sadness. "I've lost her," she said. "She told me things are bad and that Jiggy hurts her. She's afraid of him; not that I can blame her, he used to scare the crap outta me. I don't want to imagine what it's like for her; it tears me up."

She held her stomach and her bottom lip quivered as she leaned into Rosemary, who put her arms around her. "You listen to me real good. You did the best you could do for that child. You were a baby yourself. Besides,

you couldn't help it that you was sent away. I knows you raised that child. I saw you all those years ago, holding that baby in your arms like you was her mama."

"She was the only light I had in my life," Rainey said, pain shooting through her heart at the memory. "I spent every day trying to figure out how to keep us safe and fed. It . . . it . . . oh, never mind."

"No, now come on, spit it out."

"This is going to sound dumb, but when I think back to those days. as bad as they were, sometimes it feels like life was easier . . . less complicated. We had nothing, not even food to eat, but I had my sister close to me—I could hold her and give her the love she needed, that we both needed. Now I work and I'm living on my own for the first time. But Ivy's life is horrible."

Rosemary sighed and pulled her a little closer. "Child, it was simpler because even though you only had a little control over Ivy, at least you had something. You haven't been able to take care of that girl for a lot of years and it's gotta be hard to see her now. She's moving drugs and she's got the mouth of a hooker." Rosemary chuckled. "But you gotta see that it's your momma and daddy who let you girls down. They're to blame for what happened to you and what's happening to your sister right now, only them."

Rainey's chest heaved and a loud sob broke free. "Then why do I blame myself? Huh? I have so much guilt that I'm finally living my own life." She took quick breaths. "We both know that Jiggy is forcing her to have sex with him. She's eleven, Rosemary, she's a little kid!" she cried. "That shit keeps me up at night."

Rosemary guided her into the back, away from the teens who had started noticing what was happening. She sat her down on a folding chair and kneeled in front of her.

"You need to pull yourself together," she said in a stern tone. "That little girl is gonna need you someday and you need to figure out how you're gonna take care of her. Instead, you're sitting here feeling sorry for yourself, crying over something that was never your responsibility in the first place. You need to get your head straight, you hear me? You ain't no good to any of these other young people when you're acting a fool. Now, go wash your face and get out there and do the work that you came here to do."

Humbled, Rainey sat up straight and swiped at the tears on her cheeks. "You're right. I'm sorry."

"I know I'm right, sugar. I don't need you to tell me that. See, the difference between you and me is that I believe I did my best with what I was given. I survived all those johns and my pimp because I did what I had to do. You, on the other hand, you just wanna boo-hoo-hoo about all the shit you didn't do instead of seeing what you did do to keep yourself alive."

Rainey rested her elbows on her thighs and thought about how far she'd come. After taking care of a newborn baby, she'd survived her home, juvie, and was able to talk her way out of the Devils Angels. But that didn't alleviate the burden that rested heavily on her heart. Yes, she told herself with a sense of accomplishment and pride, I have made the best out of everything that's been handed to me so far, but there's still more work to do.

Rainey stood with a sense of purpose and went to the bathroom. After splashing her face with water, she walked back out into the main area and sat on the sofa next to one girl that came to the shelter often.

"Hey, Kennedy. How are you doing?" Rainey asked, more determined than ever to make a difference in the lives of others.

"I doin' real good, Miss Rainey. I got me a job today. I'm gonna be taking food orders at the fast-food restaurant right down the street."

Rainey gave Kennedy a high five. "Way to slay that shit in. I'm so proud of you."

The teenager smiled. It wasn't often, if ever, that she received praise from anyone. The two sat and talked for a few hours before Rainey's stomach growled like a monster on the prowl. Blushing, she stood, said her good-byes, and set off to eat.

On the way home, she stopped at a store on Kensington Avenue and bought herself a cheap blanket and pillow. Later, she lay on the bed of her rented room, thinking of Stoker. She still missed him but was happy to be away from the rules and restrictions of the club. Soon her thoughts drifted to Ivy, remembering her as a baby. Rainey hugged her pillow tighter, remembering how they held onto each other as they slept. She was barely able to sleep that night, and shortly before morning and still restless, Rosemary's words sunk in. This was Rainey's first night on her own, in a place she had found and paid for. A sense of independence washed over her. She had conquered her past challenges and had clung onto the piece of herself that could still love, the piece of her heart that her Aunt Sophie had nurtured when she was a child.

As she drifted off to sleep, Rainey's heart was set on helping not only Ivy, but also others living in a toxic home. Rosemary was right. She knew that to move forward, no matter how bad things got, she had to remember that the light of today was far more fierce and powerful than the darkness of her past.

Chapter Sixty

Kennedy was back at the shelter the next day. A sixteen-year-old loner, she'd grown up secluded from her peers since she was a toddler until just recently. She'd talked to Rainey about how her single mother spent her time trying to get men to take care of her, and so had gone through many boyfriends instead of taking an interest in her daughter. She was an only child and from the time she was seven, she'd spent most nights alone in their apartment while her mother went to bars, prowling for men. Kennedy had been raised on welfare, food stamps, and living in public housing. Kennedy only knew poverty and despair, and she loved that The Sanctuary gave her an escape from that life.

When Rainey arrived with a cup of coffee in hand, Kennedy called out to her right away.

"Miss Rainey?" Kennedy shouted, waving her over.

"What's going on, Kennedy?" she asked when she approached, but the teen just frowned and shook her head. "Did something happen?" Rainey pressed, setting her coffee down.

Kennedy nodded.

"Do you want to talk about it?"

She nodded again and looked around at the others in the room with them.

"Do you want to go into Rosemary's office and talk?"

Tears dribbling down her cheeks. Kennedy let out a soft moan and curled her arms over her head before she followed Rainey into the office.

They sat facing each other. Rainey's instincts told her that the deep lines on Kennedy's face were signs of fear. Rainey immediately spotted yellowish-purple bruises on her dark chocolate forearms. She reached

across the table and placed her hand over Kennedy's, but the teen slowly pulled it away.

"Sorry," Rainey said. "I didn't mean to make you uncomfortable."

In a voice that was barely a whisper, Kennedy said, "It don't make me uncomfortable, Miss Rainey, I don't like being touched."

"I understand."

Kennedy continued in a shaky voice, "People been touching me since I was little. People that I didn't want to touch me like all my mama's boyfriends. You ever get touched by people that you don't like?"

Rainey nodded slowly, her own demons surfacing, and she pushed them from her thoughts and focused. "Yes, I was young. It confused me and it made me feel dirty and damaged."

Kennedy nodded. "Well, after we talked all that time yesterday, I started thinking that I can trust you. Can I? Can I trust you?"

Rainey leaned forward and looked into her eyes. "You can."

"Well, I'm real worried because I think I'm pregnant."

Rainey held back the gasp her gut was pushing out and then collected herself. She didn't want Kennedy to think she was shocked. "What do you mean you think you're pregnant? Have you taken a test?"

"No, but my gut is sick every morning and my boobs hurt. I ain't had my period in almost two months." Kennedy looked at her with pleading eyes. "I don't know what I'd do if I ended up having a kid."

Rainey took a deep breath, trying to maintain a calm impression. "Okay, the first thing you have to do is take a pregnancy test. We can go to the free clinic and they'll give you one right away. I can go with you."

"Yeah, I'd like that—if you'd come too," Kennedy said, looking relieved. A moment later, her face clouded again. "But what if I am?"

"Let's find out for sure first," Rainey said, giving herself time to come up with a plan.

***

Three hours later, while sitting in a dreary examination room, a nurse confirmed that Kennedy was pregnant. Rainey looked at the confused teen as she lowered her head and wept openly.

Rainey's instinct was to rush over to her, but she wanted to give Kennedy a moment to absorb her reality. Her only thought was to get the girl out of there and back to the shelter where they could talk privately.

When Kennedy looked up, Rainey moved over to her. "It's going to be okay," she whispered. "Let's get out of here."

The two girls left the clinic in stunned silence. By the time they were sitting in Rosemary's office back at the shelter, Kennedy had gathered her thoughts.

"Tell me how I can help you," Rainey said.

"I need you to decide if I'm keeping it or not," she said, sounding determined.

"Well, I can't do that for you. That's something you need to decide on your own, Kennedy. Do you know who the father is?"

The teen looked down at her lap and nodded. "Yeah," she said, her fingers playing with the pendant on her necklace. "He tells me I'm his girl, but I ain't. I never wanted to be with him, and he never gave me no choice. He just started riding me one night when I was sleeping. When I woke up, I tried to fight him off, but he was too strong for me."

Rainey looked at Kennedy's forearms. "Did he put those bruises on your arms?"

"Yeah, he's a mean bastard. I hate him more than I hated any of the others. See, most all of my Mama's boyfriends had me, but this one hit me all the time and now he gots me pregnant."

"Does he live at your house?" Rainey asked, thinking of how awful it would be for Kennedy to have to go home to him now.

She shrugged. "Mmmm, sorta. He lives there whenever he wants to and my mama doesn't tell him no because she knows he'll beat her black and blue. The nights he's gone are my best nights to sleep. I'd say he sleeps there maybe five nights a week, the other nights he stays out with his friends and don't come home until morning."

"Does your mama know what he does to you?" Rainey asked gently.

Kennedy pressed her palm over her lips to hold back the cry pressing its way out of her and just shook her head. "I don't know how I could've let this happen," she murmured.

"You didn't let it happen, Kennedy," Rainey said firmly, looking her in the eyes. "You just told me he forces himself on you. Who is this asshole?"

She averted Rainey's gaze. "He calls himself Smarts. I hate him and he ain't smart at all. Dumbest pig I ever met. The only thing he knows how to do is hurt women."

"Can you tell your mom about Smarts?" Rainey pressed, though she wasn't hopeful. If all of this woman's boyfriends had raped her daughter, she had to know this was happening.

"No, I would never do that 'cause she'd whoop my ass." She grabbed a napkin from the table, dabbed at her eyes, then folded the napkin into a small square. "Mama will think I asked for it. She tells me all the time that a girl only gets what she's askin' for." She paused and a slow smile spread across her face. "I guess that's why Smarts is always smacking my mama around, 'cause she asks for it." Smiling, Kennedy put her hand over her mouth to cover her crooked teeth.

Rainey shook her head softly. "Well, I think your mama is confused. She sounds like a fucking idiot." She caught herself. "Sorry, I shouldn't have said that, I get angry sometimes. I hate it when parents don't protect their kids."

"It's okay. My mama ain't nice to me, so I kinda like it that you got mad at her."

I'd like to bash your mother's face in, Rainey thought.

Kennedy rocked forward to the edge of the chair. "There was this one time, I told him to stop touching me and he beat me real bad and told me not to ever try to boss him again. So I never said nothing to him after that." She paused, then a look of alarm crossed her face. "Do you think it's my fault I got pregnant 'cause I ain't stronger?"

"No, this isn't your fault. Don't ever say that again. Don't think that either." Rainey rubbed her sweaty palms on her jeans, feeling ill-equipped for this kind of conversation. Buying herself time, she got up and walked over to the small refrigerator that Rosemary kept in her office. She pulled out two cans of soda and brought them back to the table.

"I know you can't talk to your mom about Smarts, but can you tell her that you're pregnant?"

The teen looked up at her. "I guess I could. She might beat me for it, but if she finds out the baby belongs to Smarts, she'll blame it on me. Then I'm sure she'd kick me outta our apartment. Mama always sticks up for him. I'd rather not say nothing to her if I don't have to." She lifted the soda and held the cold can against her forehead. "So what do you think? Should I tell mama I'm pregnant?"

"Well, eventually your mom is going to notice you're pregnant. Now, if you wanna keep it then we need to talk to Rosemary to see if she knows of any resources for you, where you could go. I don't know if the government will help you with money and a place to live if you're only sixteen. If you don't want to keep it, then you have other options."

"What kind of options?" Kennedy asked.

"You could have an abortion or you could have the baby and give it up for adoption."

"I think I like the second one better."

"Okay. I'll tell you what. Let's talk to Rosemary when she comes in. Then you and me can go back to the clinic. We can talk to one of the doctors or counselors there; I'm sure between all of us we'll figure out a plan."

"Yeah, okay," Kennedy said, taking a deep breath. "I like that. Can we go tomorrow?"

"Tomorrow? Why not today?"

Kennedy stood, fixing her shirt and flattening her hair. "Because today I wanna hang here since Brittney said she was coming in. I miss her and I want to see her."

Rainey noticed the change in her demeanor immediately. Suddenly, Kennedy was smiling and bouncing on the balls of her feet. Most people knew Brittney, a happy girl who was nice to everyone. She'd been kicked out of her home when she was thirteen and had been living on the streets for two years. She was also openly gay, and seeing the way Kennedy's eyes were lit up, Rainey suspected she had a crush on Brittney.

"Okay, tomorrow then," Rainey agreed.

"Thank you, Miss Rainey."

"Can you just call me Rainey?"

Kennedy smiled and shook her head. "Sorry, no. I was brought up to put a handle on it. I gots to be respectful to my elders. Now, if someday I call you Rainey, that's when you better watch out for me," she said, grinning.

Rainey chuckled. "Okay, but I'm not that much older than you."

"Older is older," the girl quipped.

"Whatever," Rainey said with a burst of laughter.

After Kennedy left the office Rainey sat alone for a few minutes thinking over what the girl had shared with her. How her struggles could have been Rainey's if things had gone a different way. Her mind wandered to the first

time Freddy had assaulted her, then to Jiggy and the misery that Ivy must be living.

Later that afternoon, after speaking with Rosemary, they had a plan for Kennedy. The girl decided not to abort the baby, and Rosemary reached out to an adoption agency. They would take care of Kennedy's medical expenses, and with her mother's approval, they would give her ten thousand dollars to cover living expenses. Knowing that her mother would never turn down the money, Kennedy seemed relieved by the solution. She was confident that the money would outweigh her mother's anger that she let herself get pregnant.

Chapter Sixty-One

Over the next few weeks at The Sanctuary, Rainey sat in the common area, hoping each time the bell rang over the door, that Ivy might walk in. She'd gone to her parents' house several times, hiding in the dark of night and watching the front door to get a glimpse of her, but hadn't had any luck. Enough time had passed that Rainey was getting worried that something had happened to her.

One afternoon after working a shift at the motel, Rainey arrived at The Sanctuary, and Rosemary called her into her office.

"Hi, Rosemary. How's everything going today?" she asked, putting her purse down.

"Well," she said, resting her hand on the desk. "Things could be better."

"Why? What happened?" Rainey asked.

"Kennedy stopped in this morning and she was pretty beat up. After waiting almost three weeks, she finally got the nerve to tell her mom she was pregnant and keeping the baby. Problem is, the mother didn't care as much about the money as she did who got her pregnant." Rosemary glanced in Rainey's direction, "I have to assume she knew it was her boyfriend and wanted to hear Kennedy say it, which she eventually did. But just as Kennedy suspected, her mom thought she had seduced her boyfriend. What's that asshole's name? Smarts?"

Rainey nodded, nervous about what Rosemary would say next.

"Yeah, so Kennedy's mother told Smarts, and he went on and beat the girl's ass after her mother was done beating her. I swear, child, her top lip is the size of a lemon."

"Where's she now?" Rainey asked as bile pressed its way up her throat.

"She's in the hospital. Her mother and that idiot man of hers kicked her out, literally. Shortly after she got here, the girl had blood seeping down her

jeans. We rushed her down to the clinic and she was having a miscarriage, so they called an ambulance. It's a right damn shame for that girl. She's a good kid, you know?"

Rainey nodded, her heart hurting for Kennedy. "Yeah. Kennedy told me her mother would take Smarts' side and that if her mother kicked her out, she'd stay with Brittney for a while."

Rosemary shook her head. "Don't Brittney live in a tent encampment off of Kensington Avenue, near McPherson Square?"

"Yeah, she's been living there for a while."

Rosemary's head flinched back and her eyes narrowed. "What the fuck does Kennedy think she's gonna do living there? She can't even take a shit like a normal bitch."

Rainey flopped into the chair on the other side of the desk. "Really? You of all people gotta ask that? She was being raped and beaten at home. We both know it's better to shit in a bucket than to live in fear."

The older woman put her hand over her forehead. "Yeah, yeah. I know. It's just that I like that kid. She's bright and ambitious, you know? I'm afraid she's gonna end up with a pimp and her black ass will be hanging out of a short skirt soon."

"Nah," Rainey said, shaking her head. "Kennedy knows about pimps and I think she'll be careful. Besides, she has a crush on Brittney, and after watching the two of them together, I'm pretty sure it's mutual. Brittney has learned how to hustle and that's kept her from prostitution."

"And by hustle, you mean selling dope?" Rosemary asked, arching an eyebrow.

"No. By hustle I mean she waitresses, cleans houses, hands out flyers for stores . . . she does whatever it takes to keep herself fed."

"Oh, I see." Rosemary opened a desk drawer and pulled out her purse. "Well, I'm gonna drive over to the hospital and check in on Kennedy. I'd ask you to tag along, but somebody gotta stay here and keep an eye on things."

"Yep, that's fine." Rainey looked down at her lap and back up at Rosemary. "I was hoping that Ivy would come back. I haven't had eyes on her in weeks. I'm worried."

"I'm sorry about all that. I haven't seen her neither. I'll keep an eye out, though." Rosemary pulled her keys from her purse and began to leave. She stopped at the office door, "Oh, shit. I forgot," she said returning to her

desk. “The owner of the building is stopping by to pick this up,” she lifted an envelope from the desk and handed it to Rainey.

“What is it?”

“The permit renewals. He’s a good man that one is. He takes care of everything. Anyway, you be nice to him ’cause you remember, he lets us be here for free.”

“Oh, please, I’m nice to everyone.”

Rosemary put her hands on her hips and shot Rainey a glare. “Nice?” she said, grinning. “Like you were nice to that drunk who stumbled in here last week. You grabbed him up by the scruff of his neck and threw him out the door. That’s exactly what you did, Miss Nice.”

Rainey smirked at the memory. “That’s different. He could’ve harmed the kids. If you remember, he was shouting about how pretty the girls were and he smelled like the inside of a cheap whiskey bottle.”

“Oh, I remember correctly enough. You done real good that day,” Rosemary said. “And I was proud of you for standing tall for the kids in here. I’m just sayin’ this man, the owner, he ain’t gonna harm no one.”

“Yeah, yeah, I got this,” Rainey said, nudging Rosemary through the door. “Tell Kennedy I was asking about her and that I’ll see her when she gets back here.”

Once Rosemary left, Rainey went into the main room and settled onto the sofa next to Annie, who was a regular. They were watching television when the bell over the door dinged. Rainey looked over her shoulder and froze when she saw who was standing inside the entryway. It was a man. A man she recognized. A man she hadn’t seen in a long time. She stood and walked toward him slowly as he watched her intently. At first his face was relaxed, but when it registered who he was looking at, the sides of his lips rose into a smile.

“What the hell are you doing here?” she cried.

Chapter Sixty-Two

Rainey stood gawking at Agent Lindquist; undeniably happy he was there. The last she'd seen of him was at her sentencing hearing and she tried to calculate the time in her head. It had to be six years ago, maybe? His hair was short now, but other than that he looked the same.

With a smile plastered on his face, he said, "Rainey, it's . . . it's so good to see you. You look fantastic. What are you doing here?"

"I'm a volunteer here now," she said proudly. Then Rainey's eyes narrowed. "Wait. Are you here because you think someone is selling drugs? Because they're not. We're on top of these kids. So if one of them did something all I'd ask is that you give them a second chance, let us work with them," she rambled.

Lindquist cracked another smile and shook his head. "Rainey Paxton, you haven't changed a bit. Always saying what's on your mind. I'm not here on police business."

"Whew," she said, blowing out a breath. "Anyway, I can't believe you're standing here. How have you been? What have you been up to? Catching the bad guys, I hope."

"I'm trying. As you probably know, catching the bad guys can be difficult," he said.

She had forgotten how much she liked Lindquist. He'd always been a decent guy and had treated her with respect. "Oh, I know. Those bad guys are very tricky. I guess that means you haven't found a way to put these Kensington drug dealers in jail for the rest of their pathetic lives."

"Oh, okay. So, we're getting right to it," he chided. Then he got serious. "We do the best we can to keep our streets clean of drug dealers. It's somewhat of an uphill battle," reciting the official DEA answer. He looked

behind her into the office. "But so you know, I came here to see Rosemary; she's expecting me."

The girl shoved her hands into her jean pockets. "Oh, she had to run out."

Lindquist crossed his arms over his chest.

"Hold on," Rainey said, eyeing Lindquist. "Are you the mystery guy who owns this place?"

Lindquist shrugged. "Guilty."

"Wow. Look at you, you're not just a cop but also a cop with a heart," she said with a snicker. "Rosemary left an envelope for you in the office," she said.

Inside the office he stood awkwardly, watching her. Rainey felt a little self-conscious as she sat at the desk. "Why do you look nervous?" she asked, trying to deflect her uneasiness.

"I'm not nervous. I was just wondering—you look amazing—the last time we saw each other you were just a kid. How old are you now?"

Rainey blushed. "Twenty and a half," she said proudly.

"Oh yeah, that half a year counts now. Wait until you're forty and a half; you'll tell people you're barely forty," he laughed.

"I have a really long time until I get to be that old," she teased.

Lindquist took in the smooth contour of Rainey's face. Her blond hair fell over her shoulders like long, thin trickles of fresh honey. Something stirred inside his stomach that he tried to ignore, but he couldn't take his eyes off of her.

"What are you staring at?" she asked nervously. "You're making me self-conscious."

He shook his head and held up a hand. "Sorry. It's just that you've grown up. How have you been? What have you been doing?" he asked, sitting across the desk from her.

"Well, the short version is after I left juvie, my parents wouldn't let me go back home. I got a job cleaning rooms at the Drop Inn Motel, met a guy, and moved in with him, but then he died. Now I'm renting a room from a grouchy woman a few blocks away. I still work at the motel to pay my rent, but I spend the rest of my time volunteering here," she rattled.

"The Drop Inn Motel, huh?" he grimaced.

"I clean rooms there, that's all. I never got into anything else," she said.

"Oh, I'm sorry, I didn't mean to insinuate anything bad."

"I guess it was the way your nose wrinkled," Rainey said, feeling drawn to him remembering how he would sit and talk with her in juvie. Or when he checked on or brought her a new dress to wear to court.

"Rosemary told me you own this building and don't charge us any rent, so we can afford to run this shelter. I guess being a drug agent pays a lot of money," Rainey said.

He chuckled. "No, actually when my uncle died several years ago, he left this building to me. He didn't have any kids and never got married so I was the closest thing to a son. I inherited this place and wanted to do something for others." He paused, but decided to tell her. "Actually, it was partly because of you, Rainey. You made a lasting impression on me."

"Me?" Rainey asked, feeling both confused and flattered at the same time.

Lindquist nodded. "I was sorry about how things turned out for you, and wished I could've done more to help. I knew your parents weren't supportive, and well, it seemed you were all alone," he admitted. "That stuck with me."

"I was all alone," she said, thinking back to her first days in juvie.

"How's your little sister doing? I remember how much she meant to you. Have you seen her?"

Rainey shifted in her chair. "I saw her a couple of times. She's . . . she's just gimping along, like I did. My parents won't let me see her."

"How old is she now?"

"Eleven," Rainey said. "She came here once. Well, I practically dragged her here, but that was a while ago. I haven't seen or heard from her since. I go to the house every week and watch, waiting to see her. But that's been pretty useless."

"I'm sorry I couldn't do more for her. I really did try. I kept my eyes on the house whenever I could." He looked into her eyes. "If she's anything like her older sister I know she'll make it out of there just fine."

Rainey looked at Lindquist, probably for the first time. His eyes were so green they almost shimmered. His hair had been cut short and was a deep, chocolatey brown. Her gaze roved to his broad shoulders and roamed over the muscles poking out from below the short sleeves of his T-shirt. Realizing she was staring, she quickly walked over to the refrigerator and offered him a soda. As he grabbed for the can, her fingers brushed the top of his hand. A rush of warmth spread through her. Instead of backing away, he stepped closer.

"You know, it's weird how one day I'm a kid and you're an adult and the next day we're both adults." Her heart was pounding in her chest. She couldn't believe she'd spoke those words out loud.

"I'm sorry? I don't follow," he said as his eyes shifted away and back.

Rainey blushed, but she didn't want to lose this opportunity to reconnect with him. "Oh, I don't know. I guess what I'm saying is I'd like to catch up on things and get to know you better. Do you think we could grab lunch sometime?"

He fidgeted in the chair and took a sip of soda. "Things?" he murmured.

"Yeah," she said. "You know, things regular people talk about."

"Sure. Sure, that would be nice."

"Great. When?"

"Just as pushy as ever," he joked, shaking his head.

"Yeah, yeah, yeah," she said, giddy that he'd actually said yes and eager to make it happen as quickly as possible. "How about tomorrow afternoon? Would that work?"

"Um, tomorrow works. I'll stop by here and pick you up on the way. I can take us to a place I like in South Philly."

"Perfect. Tomorrow is my day off from the motel. Does noon work?"

"Yeah, that works," he said, giving her a broad grin. He stood and made his way to the door. "See you tomorrow."

"Yes, you will. Bye."

Alone in the office, Rainey thought about Lindquist. She couldn't believe how differently she saw him now. Her attraction was confusing. He was handsome, something she hadn't noticed before, and his kindness to her when she had been at her most vulnerable couldn't be forgotten. She walked out into the main area, and thinking of her lunch with him the next day, butterflies fluttered in her belly.

Chapter Sixty-Three

Agent Lindquist walked into the shelter a few minutes before noon. He stood just inside the door, and as Rosemary rushed to him, his eyes searched the space behind her. His sight landed on Rainey, and a small smile pulled at his lips.

"Oh, Agent Lindquist. I understand you're taking my girl to lunch today. Is there a problem you're sniffing out that I oughta know about? You suspecting she done something bad? 'Cause she's a good girl, mouthy, but good."

Lindquist laughed quietly. "No, Rosemary, everything is fine. I have to say the two of you are just alike. I met Rainey about six years ago. We have some history together."

"What kinda history?" she asked, getting up on her tiptoes to look into his eyes. "She already told me about her time in juvie and why she was arrested, so I hope you ain't here about that 'cause she served her time. Besides, the girl said it wasn't her stuff and I believe her too."

He shook his head softly. "I'm not here because Rainey has done anything wrong," he assured her, patting her shoulder.

Rosemary placed her palm on his cheek. "That's what I was looking to hear." She turned and waved Rainey over.

"Hi," Rainey said, smiling as though she'd just won the lottery. "I'm ready to go."

Rosemary put her hand on her hip. "Is you now?"

Rainey's eyes met hers. "Yes I is, Miss Rosemary," she teased. "I'll be back. It's only lunch."

The older woman chuckled. "Okay, be careful. Although I'm not sure how you can't be safe when you're in the company of a cop," she bantered.

Outside, the wind whipped and Rainey pulled the top of her jacket tighter. "So, Agent Lindquist, where's your car?"

"I parked a couple of blocks down," he said, pointing to the right. "Hey, how about if you just called me by my first name, Sam?"

Rainey lit up, liking the sound of it. "Okay, Sam. Where are we going to eat?"

"La Famiglia."

She cocked her head and rolled her open hand at the wrist.

"Oh, it's an Italian restaurant. I've been eating there for a long time. Best food in town."

Rainey nodded. "Okay, good. I like Italian food."

Inside Sam's car, his scent hit her nose. "Smells good in here," she said side-eyeing him to get a glimpse at his face again. "So, are you Italian?"

"I'm half," he said, smiling. "My mother comes from a big Italian family. I was born and raised in South Philly. My father is Swedish. His parents came from Sweden and raised my father in a mostly Italian community not far from where my mom grew up. They met at a movie theater one night and started dating. My Italian grandparents weren't happy at first, but eventually he won them over. So the long answer is yeah, I've been raised Italian for the most part."

Rainey listened intently as he described his background, absorbing everything he shared about himself.

"How about you?" he asked, glancing over at her.

"Oh, um, no one has ever asked me that," she mumbled, suddenly nervous about how to answer. "My mom is Greek and my dad is Scottish and English. I grew up in a shithole, but you already know that, and I was raised as white trash for the most part. We didn't have any family traditions. We didn't even celebrate Christmas. Everything was always centered on drugs. One day bled into another."

Sam cringed. "Oh, sorry."

"For what? It wasn't your fault."

"Sorry I asked."

Rainey turned sideways in her seat. "Look, I like that you asked. I don't want to be treated differently than other people. I'm just a regular person who grew up the hard way. I like that you told me about your parents."

They were quiet for a moment. Then Rainey, her mind racing with thoughts of how he helped her when she was young, reached her hand over

the console and placed it over his. "You know, I really appreciate all that you did for me back in my days at juvie. It meant a lot to me."

At the touch of her hand on his, Sam's heart sped up. He slowly pulled away and put his hand back on the steering wheel.

Rainey adjusted her body forward, and smiling, she looked out the front window.

"Where did you go when you got out of juvie?"

"I stayed with a friend of Tootsie's. Her name is Winnie and we became good friends, but she lives in Florida now."

"Oh, there's a name I haven't heard in a while, I forgot about Tootsie," Lindquist said, shaking his head. "A lot of cops had a problem with her when she was on the streets."

"That's because they don't know her," Rainey said, feeling defensive about her friend. "Tootsie is a good person and has deep feelings. Just like me, her upbringing ruined her. But she saved my ass in juvie. You have no idea."

Sam shrugged. "Okay, so tell me how you lost that pinky finger. Did Tootsie have something to do with that?"

Rainey looked at the stub and cringed. She'd gotten so used to it over the years it didn't even bother her anymore, but she knew what he was getting at. "Oh, that? It was an accident. Got caught in a bathroom door," she lied. She held her hand up, "I think it gives me character."

"I see. That's how you want to play it," he said, teasing.

"Hey, what happens on the inside isn't shared with cops. That's just outright wrong. But here's what I'll tell you . . . losing my pinky saved my life."

"Well, you might not tell a cop, but you can tell me. I'm your friend now," he said.

Rainey leaned her head on the passenger window and smiled. "I never said we were friends. Jeez, it's only lunch. Getting a little bit ahead of yourself, don't you think?"

When Sam didn't respond, she whipped her head toward him. "I'm joking! See, that's the problem with cops, you're all tight-assed. Probably because you see too much bad stuff."

"I'm the least tight-assed cop you'll ever meet," he bantered.

"Oh, yeah?" Rainey said, grinning. "I don't know about that."

"Trust me, it's true," Sam said, glancing at her.

Rainey blushed. "If you say so."

"Anyway," he said, "it looks like you're doing good things with your life, I'm proud of you." He pulled over to the side of the road, parked the car, and looked up through the front window. "Here we are. I hope you're hungry."

Rainey was flattered that Sam had noticed that she was no longer the scared girl locked up in juvie and had worked hard to make her life better. This is going to be a very interesting lunch, she thought.

Chapter Sixty-Four

Rainey sat next to Sam and pretended to scan the menu, but her stomach was flittering so much she couldn't pay attention to what she was reading. There was a tension between them, an energy that buzzed like a shiny, bright light. She was attracted to him, and that confused her. This was the same man who had busted her when she was fourteen. He was also the same man who had consoled her in her youth while she cried and sought mercy. He knew who her family was and how she was raised. Yet here he was anyway, seemingly without judgment, sitting with her at a nice Italian restaurant.

"Whew," she said aloud, trying to cut the unspoken tension. "This is weird, huh?"

"What's weird?"

"Well, six years ago you were the only adult in my life who gave a shit about me and now here we are having lunch together."

Sam draped his arm over the back of her chair. "Yep, life is funny sometimes. Do you know what you're ordering?"

Rainey glanced down at the menu, but her stomach wasn't in sync. There was rarely a time when she couldn't eat, but her senses were so heightened and she was so distracted that food wasn't appealing.

"Um, I don't know," she said. "What are you having?"

"I'm going to have the salmon. It's always a winner here."

"I guess I'll have that too."

"Have you ever eaten salmon?" he asked, eyeing her.

She shook her head. "No, but I haven't found anything I don't like yet." Her face grew dark. "That's what happens when you're raised on hunger."

"Yeah, that reminds me," he said, having waited for the right time to tell her, "I wanted to talk to you about Ivy. I did get some money and food to

her when you were in juvie. It wasn't often, but I had someone who helped me out."

"Buddy?"

"No, it was a friend of hers. I knew her from a self-defense class I'd taught and I asked her to go in and see Ivy as a favor to me. But it wasn't long before she didn't feel safe. She didn't use drugs or alcohol and that whole scene freaked her out."

"I'm glad you tried to help my sister. Thank you."

"I didn't tell you so you could thank me. I told you so that you know I tried. You asked me to help, and as little as it was, I did what I could."

She gave him a smile and he looked across the restaurant, wondering how to tackle his next question. Leaning into her, he said, "I'm curious about something. When you lived with your parents, did you ever remember seeing a guy called Jiggy?"

Rainey's whole body stiffened, but trying to act casual, she grabbed a roll from the basket on the table with a shaky hand. "Yeah, sure, I met him."

He glanced at her. "Is there something about Jiggy you want to tell me? Something you wouldn't tell me when you were a kid?"

She gazed into his eyes, wondering if he already knew and cautious about what she should tell him. She had to consider Ivy, who was still living under Jiggy's control. "Jiggy was going to rape me right before you walked into my bedroom that night."

Sam paused and looked at her intently. "Did he ever rape you?"

"Nope, as it turned out I got arrested and he never had the chance," she said, eyeing him.

"You could've confided in me."

"Come on, Sam, you were the arresting agent. I was trained from birth not to tell anyone the things that went on in my house. Not a teacher, a police officer, no one." She paused and looked up at him. "Not even if it meant I had to spend three years in juvie."

Sam sighed, not surprised to hear her say this. "That's really shitty."

"Yeah, I know."

He patted her shoulder and purposely changed the subject. He wanted to know about her. All about her life after she left juvie. "Tell me about where you're staying now."

"Well, like I said, I rent a room in a house about three blocks from The Sanctuary. My landlady, Gladys, is kind of bitchy. She won't let me have

anyone over and I can only use my bedroom, one of the bathrooms, and the kitchen. I think she might be a prostitute," she said with a short giggle.

"Most of the prostitutes work Kensington Avenue and, some motels," he remarked.

"Gladys is old, though."

"How old?"

Rainey took a sip of water and shrugged. "I don't know. I guess she's around fifty."

"Fifty?" Sam said, chuckling. "That's a little senior in the prostitute world."

"What can I say? I guess she does what she needs to do to make ends meet. She looks great and when her gentlemen 'friends' are there I'm not supposed to walk downstairs." She laughed. "I can hear her going at it from my bedroom. It's so weird."

"I can only imagine how uncomfortable that would be for you." Sam paused for a moment. "I hope you don't mind me asking, but yesterday you mentioned that you moved in with a guy, but he died. What happened?"

"He was murdered," she said in a pained voice.

Sam pressed out a loud breath. "Oh, I'm very sorry to hear that."

"Thanks. It was a shock when it happened, but I've been able to put my life back together and start over," Rainey said quietly.

"What was he like?" Lindquist asked, curious about the kind of guy she'd been attracted to.

She hadn't talked about Stoker in a long time. Now she wanted to share the story of their relationship in her own way. "His name was Stoker. He was a member of the Devils Angels. We were close and, like all couples we had been through a lot together. He was my first boyfriend, and while I wasn't crazy about his club, I enjoyed the time we shared." She glanced at him and he was watching her intently. "He was out of town setting up some businesses for the club when some guys went into the shop and killed him," she explained. Tears stung her eyes, "I swear, I attract tragedy. You better run while you can. Being friends with me can bring a heaping load of shit down on you," she said, half joking.

As the lunch went on, each shared pieces of their lives. By the end, Rainey realized how much she had enjoyed being with Sam, and he had been thinking the same about her. They were having such a good time that neither of them wanted to leave when it was time to go.

On the drive back to Kensington, Rainey rested her head against the car window. "You know, when I was in juvie, I thought I'd never have a normal life. I'm not saying that I have it all, but I have what I need now. Everything except Ivy. I know that someday I'm going to get her and take care of her." She turned and looked at Sam. "The night I was arrested I promised her I would go back for her. I haven't made good on that promise, but I will."

Sam nodded. "I think you can do anything you set your mind to."

***

As Rainey laid in her bed that night, all she could think about was Sam Lindquist. She replayed their conversation, remembering how good it felt to be sitting next to him, spending time with him. Her body tingled as she imagined his face, his lips, and those dreamy green eyes.

Chapter Sixty-Five

A week later, when Rainey finished her shift at the Drop Inn, she found Sam waiting outside in his car. It alarmed her at first, but then she relaxed, reminded of the way Stoker used to wait for her.

"What are you doing here?" she asked, walking closer to him.

"I have something I want to discuss with you," he said, no trace of the light-hearted man from the week before.

"What is it?" she asked, her nerves fraying.

"Come on," he said, opening the passenger door. "Get in."

When Sam was sitting next to her, she looked at him, "What's going on?"

"Ivy was picked up this morning. She's being held at the station," Sam said, not making eye contact.

"Fuck!" Rainey yelled. "What was she arrested for?"

"Public intoxication. She was staggering around Kensington Avenue and stumbled from the sidewalk in front of a car . . . a police car. They took her in and called your parents."

Rainey's muscles relaxed. She'd been afraid it was for selling drugs, which would have been a much more serious offense. "Okay, and are they going to get her out?" she asked, considering Ivy was her parents' golden goose.

"I'm not sure. But I thought I should come and tell you about this."

"Take me to the station," Rainey said. "I'll bail her out."

"You can't. She can only be released to a parent or a legal guardian. I'm sorry."

"Drive me to my parents' house." Rainey was only focused on Ivy, and getting her released from jail.

"I don't think that's such a good idea."

Anger flared up inside of her. "Not to be rude, but I have to go there right now. She's my little sister. I have to try to talk to those two idiots."

Without a word, Sam put his car in drive and headed toward Kensington.

***

Sam parked across from her parents' house and turned off the engine.

"I'm coming with you," he said.

She shook her head, still watching the house. "No. You can't come. If they recognize you, they'll think I brought the cops."

Sam considered for a moment. "Okay, but please be careful. I'll be waiting right here."

Nodding, Rainey rushed from the car, then ran across the street and up the battered porch steps. She grabbed the knob on the front door and turned it slowly. Poking her head around the door, she spotted her mother smoking a joint on the sofa and her father rocking, strung out on the floor in front of her. Adrenaline coursing through her, Rainey took long strides over to them. As she approached, Miranda pulled a long hit from the joint and looked up at her daughter. She let out the smoke in hacking coughs.

"What the fuck are you doin' here?" Miranda barked.

Peter looked up and hoisted himself to the sofa next to Miranda.

Rainey looked from one to the other with disgust running through her veins. "I'm here because Ivy is at the police station and she needs you to go get her out."

"Oh, that?" Miranda said, taking another hit from her joint. "Let her stay there for a while. Maybe she'll learn not to stumble around town when she's blitzed."

"She's a kid. She should never be blitzed. The only reason she's blitzed is that she learned it from the two of you." She looked at her father. "Dad, she can't stay in there. She's scared and alone. You have to help her."

"Hey," he said. "I'd like to, but we ain't got the money to throw away on her stupidity."

Rainey placed her hands firmly on her hips. "I'll pay the bail."

Miranda scoffed. "Oh, yeah? What? You rich now or something?"

Rainey bent at the waist and looked her mother in the eyes. "No, I'm not rich. I clean motel rooms to make money. But I'm willing to give up my only savings if it helps Ivy."

"Well, ain't you Mother Teresa?" Miranda mocked. "I'll tell you what, give us the money and we'll go down today and get her out."

"Do you think I'm stupid?" Rainey spat. "I'll meet you down there and I'll give the money to the cops to pay her bail."

Miranda looked her daughter up and down. She's turned out just like my sister, Sophie, she thought with jealousy and resentment.

"What's in it for us?" her mother asked, looking at Peter, who nodded.

"You get your kid out of jail without having to pay for it," Rainey said through clenched teeth.

"Mmmmm. I don't know. It's gonna take us a lot of time to do all that shit," Peter grumbled. "You give us an extra two hundred bucks for our time and we'll be there."

Rainey pointed in his face. "I hate you!" Then she pointed at her mother. "And I hate you too! I'll give you two hundred dollars, but you need to be at the police station in two hours. That gives you time to take a shower. You both smell like the devil's ass." She turned and stomped out of the house, not waiting for either of them to answer her and hoping that the promise of money would make them show up. She got into Sam's car and said, "Get me out of here, please."

As they were moving down the block Sam asked, "What happened?"

"They're going to meet me at the police station in two hours. I'm going to pay Ivy's bail and give them two hundred bucks for their time."

"Are you kidding me?"

Rainey pinched her lips together. "I wish I was," she said, letting out a soft moan. "The extra money is the only way they'll do it."

"They're assholes," he remarked.

"I told you that about a hundred years ago," she snapped. Rainey stared out the front window for a while, then turned to Sam. "I'm sorry. I didn't mean to get angry at you. I appreciate your help. I'm stressed about Ivy, that's all."

"I know," he said, smiling. "Who cares if you get angry? These are tough issues. I think you're a person who has always been outspoken and carried dreams of having a much better life than the one your parents gave you. A life that you're willing to fight for."

She nodded. "And love. I've always believed that I would find true love."

"Like with Stoker?"

She shook her head. "No, not like that. A love where I come first, never second."

Chapter Sixty-Six

Rainey stood outside the police station, waiting for her parents to arrive. They were already thirty minutes late and she was about to go inside to get Sam when she heard their car sputtering toward her. She watched; eyebrows arched as Peter took two parking spaces. As the car doors flung open, the lot was filled with the sound of squealing, rusty car door hinges.

Rainey crossed her arms over her chest as they approached. "You're late. I was just going to leave."

"You got our money?" Peter asked.

She pulled a wad of bills from her pocket and jerked her arm back when he moved to take it from her. "I don't think so. You'll get your two hundred bucks after we get Ivy out."

Peter put his face close to hers, and when his rancid breath filled her sinuses, Rainey jerked her head back. His face inched closer, "If you fuck us over and don't give us the money you promised, Ivy will pay for it when we get her home."

Rainey put her hands on his shoulders and moved him away from her. "You'll get your money, don't worry. Because after all, getting high is the most important thing in your lives." She turned to her mother. "More important than your kids."

Miranda shrugged. "If you're trying to make me feel bad, it ain't working."

"I know it's hard to feel anything, since neither of you has a heart," Rainey spat at them, walking away. She pulled the door open and stepped inside. She walked up to a window where a man in a police uniform was sitting. "We're here for my sister, Ivy Paxton."

"Are you her guardian?"

"No, but they're her mom and dad," she said, pointing to Miranda and Peter, who had trailed in behind her.

"All right. You can have a seat and we will call you when we're ready."

Rainey nodded and was comforted when she noticed Sam standing several feet behind the officer. Sam gave her a reassuring nod and she guided her parents over to a wooden bench.

"What the hell are we sitting here for?" Miranda barked.

Rainey rolled her eyes. "They need to process her out." It was hard to remain patient when her parents showed their true characters. "We have to wait until they call us. Did you bring your driver's licenses?"

"Now look," Miranda spat, "you never told me about no license."

Rainey's temper flashed. "Are you serious right now? You don't know you need to bring identification to the police station to get your kid out?"

"Hey, don't you dare question me," Miranda snapped.

"Both of you shut the fuck up. I have my license," Peter said.

"You know, I don't understand why you two ever had kids. You don't love us. You never took care of us. You abused us and let other people do horrible things to us. I wish I was never born to either of you," she said.

"We had kids because we got pregnant," Miranda said casually.

"You never heard of birth control?"

"I would never take something that the government told me was safe," her mother rebutted.

"I see, you just buy bags of dope with no idea what's in them, melt them down into liquid, and then push it into your arm through a needle that other people have used and you're worried about taking birth control pills because the government approved them? You're truly out of your mind."

Infuriated, Rainey looked across the room and met Sam's eyes. He knew even with the distance between them that they were arguing. Sam nodded and disappeared for a moment before reappearing in the main room.

"I'm Agent Lindquist," he said as he approached. "I'll take you back and we'll bring your daughter in."

Peter stood, wagging his finger. "I know who you are. You're that asshole who came to my house that time. You're that drug cop." He turned and grabbed Rainey's wrist, pulling her forward. "You probably remember my daughter. You sent her to juvie for a while—drug charges. You should've kept her locked up."

Rainey grimaced and yanked her wrist from his grip. A flush crept across her cheeks. She had a compulsion to flee. She racked her brain for a clever

response, but nothing surfaced. In a meek voice she managed, "That would be great if you could take us to see Ivy."

Lindquist glared at Peter, then at Miranda. "Model parents," he muttered under his breath.

Inside the room, Rainey waited for more than an hour, with her parents continually whining. Finally the door opened and Rainey leaped up and went toward Ivy with her arms open.

"Ew," Ivy squeaked, jerking back from her. "Don't touch me."

The policewoman standing behind her gave Rainey a solemn look. "Well, that was rude," she directed at the young girl. "Seems like you have an attitude problem."

Ivy turned to her. "Seems like you need to mind your own business."

"Excuse me?" the officer said.

Trying to prevent another fight, Rainey stepped between them. "I'm sorry, officer. My sister has been through a lot. She's just tired and wants to get out of here. She didn't mean anything by it."

"Whatever you say, but I'll tell you if she were my sister, I'd leave her here until she learned how to show respect."

The hairs on Rainey's arms prickled her skin as she gave the officer a tight smile. "My sister has been through very hard things in her life. Being polite was never a priority. We'll be fine now. Thank you."

Rainey glanced at Ivy, who was pressing her fingers against the smile on her lips. When the officer left the room, Rainey moved closer to her sister. "Don't be so rude. These cops won't put up with it."

Ivy rolled her eyes. "Oh, you're the expert 'cause you spent time in juvie?" she asked sarcastically.

Rainey pulled out a chair and sat. "Well, let's just say I know a lot more about prison than anyone else in this room."

A short while later, Lindquist joined them with another officer, who went over the paperwork with Peter and Miranda. Then Rainey pulled five hundred hard-earned dollars from her pocket and handed it to the officer. Fifteen minutes later, the damaged family of four walked out of the police station.

Outside, Peter put his hand out and Rainey placed the two hundred dollars in it as her stomach clamped down, thinking of all the things she had sacrificed to save her money.

Ivy watched the exchange. Her eyes narrowed as her gaze bounced from her sister to her father. "What is this? Did you make her pay you to come and get me outta here?" she yelled.

Peter smirked. "Don't get all worked up. You're lucky we came at all. Next time you get wasted keep your scrawny ass in that house, where it belongs. We won't come to get you again."

Ivy rolled her hands into tight balls, stomped her feet, and walked to the car.

Rainey turned to her parents, hoping this was her chance. "Look," she said, trying to keep her voice light, "I know it's hard to have a kid her age. Maybe I can help you. You know, she could spend some time with me."

"You're outta your mind," Miranda grumbled. "We don't want her turning out like you. You're just like your Aunt Sophie, always have been. A nosy know-it-all. I knew that her spending so much time with you would be a problem."

The mention of Sophie sobered Rainey.

"Have you been to see her?" she asked timidly.

"See who?" her mother asked, lighting a cigarette.

"Aunt Sophie."

"Yeah, sometimes I go there." Then she shivered, "I hate those places. They give me the heebie-jeebies."

Rainey thought about asking more questions, but knew her efforts were futile. Besides, who was she to judge? She hadn't done a good job of finding time to visit her aunt either.

Rainey was lost in her own guilt when Peter took Miranda's hand and they headed toward their car.

"Don't come to our house again!" Peter yelled over his shoulder.

Rainey stood watching them. She wondered why fate or God or nature or whatever there was out there had been so cruel to have given her to them.

As they drove by her, Miranda flicked her cigarette out the car window and it landed at her daughter's feet.

She watched until their car was out of sight. Sighing, Rainey turned to go back into the police station when she saw Sam coming out the door. His eyebrows were drawn together and he wore a pained gaze.

When he reached her, Rainey flung herself into his arms and wept. After a while she lifted her head and he looked into her puffy, bloodshot eyes.

"Everything is going to be okay. I'll take care of you. I promise," he whispered.

Her heart was aching, but she was a girl who took care of herself and she was hesitant to let him watch over her. Still, she thought it sounded nice to have someone to take care of her, even for just a short time.

She pulled away slowly, wiped her tears, and looked up at him. “Thanks. I appreciate it,” she said with sincerity. “Would you mind driving me home?”

Chapter Sixty-Seven

Rainey walked into her gloomy rented room, where everything seemed much older and sadder than it had that morning. She was stricken by disappointment. She'd come a long way, but had been knocked flat on her back by the realization that she was still a person with real needs, real wants, and real feelings. Sitting on the floor with her knees to her chest, Rainey wondered if there would ever come a day when Ivy would love her again. As night fell and the room dimmed, she pulled her blanket off of the bed and draped it over her shoulders.

Her thoughts floated back to her childhood. She remembered the librarian who had fed them a few times and let them wash up in the library's bathroom. She thought about Buddy and how she had tried her best to help them. Then her mind turned to Aunt Sophie. Guilt compressed her diaphragm and her breathing was labored until she focused on controlling it. Rainey was desperate to see Rosemary, to spill out all of her troubles. The woman always knew what to say to relieve her anxiety.

The next morning, Rainey strode into The Sanctuary with purpose and found Rosemary in her office and closed the door.

"Morning, child," Rosemary said, looking up from the papers on her desk. "You look like you got rolled and plucked apart by a bunch of gang members. You okay?"

She shook her head and sat. "I have a confession to make and I don't have anyone I can talk to."

"Well, I ain't no saint, but you can always talk to me, sugar."

Rainey nodded. "Well, I have an aunt who lives in a nursing home. She's been in there for a long time. She doesn't know who she is or who I am. The only time I went there was before I was sent to juvie. I promised myself

I'd go back, but I haven't. I've been so busy trying to figure out how to live that I never found the time to go."

Rosemary rubbed her chin with her thumb and index finger. "I see. Well, was this aunt special to you? Or did she treat you bad when you was a kid?"

"Oh, no," Rainey said. "She was wonderful. She was the only person who took care of me. When she went away my life practically ended."

"So what's the problem I'm helping you figure out then?"

Rainey sighed. "It's not a problem. I feel like a bad person because I never go see her."

Rosemary sat back in her chair. "Ah, I see. Well, you're right. In that regard, you is a bad person then. Now, I'm sure coming to see you when you was a little girl was depressing for her, but she still did it. See here, when somebody's good to you, it's only right to be good back. That's the problem we got in this world. People are good at taking but they ain't so good at givin'. So when the tables are turned, like they have with your aunt, she gets it shoved up her ass. You see what I'm sayin'?"

Rainey groaned. "Yeah, I didn't come here so you could make me feel worse than I already do."

"Oh," Rosemary chuckled. "Did you come here so I could blow smoke up your white ass? That ain't me and that ain't you neither. You came here so I could tell you to get over yourself and go visit that woman. Not just once neither. You need to go see her on a regular schedule."

"Oh, right," Rainey said throwing up her hands. "I work at the motel, I volunteer here, and I spend time watching my parents' place trying to get a glimpse of Ivy so I know she's still breathing. I have no time."

"Oh, bullshit. You got plenty of time. See, the only thing you need to know about time is that you gotta spend it in a way that makes you happy. Sounds to me like you gots some work to do on that end."

Rainey slumped in the chair in front of the desk. She knew Rosemary was right. "What am I supposed to say to her? 'Hi. I'm your niece. You don't remember me but I remember you'?"

"Yeah, that's a fine start. Then you can tell her what you just told me . . . you can thank her for being the only person in the world who ever took care of you. And you can go back there every week and tell her the exact same thing and I bet you one day, she'll understand and appreciate what you're saying."

Rainey covered her face with her hands, the gravity of her inaction crushing in on her. "You're right. I'm gonna go there today."

Rosemary nodded, then leaned forward. "What brought this about anyway?"

"Oh, I saw my stupid parents yesterday. I had to pay them to bail my little sister out of jail for being drunk in public."

"And your sister? Did she thank you for helping her?"

"No, of course not. She acts like I'm the enemy."

Rosemary clucked her tongue. "Sounds like you need to stop being so nice to her then. Just 'cause things have been rough don't mean you should let her disrespect you." She wagged her finger at the girl, "You remember there are people in this world who mistake kindness for weakness. You need to give your baby sister a little reality check. You know what I'm sayin'?"

Rosemary's words struck her with the force of a freight train. Of course she didn't like the way Ivy behaved toward her, but she had lived inside the walls of that house too. She knew how hard life was made to be, and this made her overly sympathetic to her sister. "Yeah, I understand. But I think she has enough going on. Between my parents and dealing with Jiggy that's a lot for a kid to handle. I want her to know she's special and that she deserves more than what her life is right now."

"Special, huh? Okay, then maybe you need to give her a special ass-whooping the next time you see her on the avenue selling dope. That'll tell her how special she is. That child hasn't been through nothing that you ain't been through yourself. But enough about her, you need to get your ass moving and go visit your auntie."

Rainey nodded. "Okay, I'll call a cab."

"Where she at?"

"Ridley Park," Rainey said.

Rosemary's face puckered. "Ridley Park? Girl, that's all the way on the other side of the earth."

Rainey chuckled. "Oh, stop. It's only about thirty minutes away."

"Do you got any idea what a thirty-minute cab ride is gonna cost you? You didn't tell me all that when you was talking your heart out. Jerome is coming in thirty minutes. He can stay here and I'll drive you there myself. You need to get yourself a damn car and stop spending your money on your sister who treats you like shit that she can't wipe off of the bottom of her shoe, that's what you need to do."

Rainey smiled; she loved Rosemary's passion. "I know you're right. I definitely need my own car. But I really appreciate you giving me a ride

today. I hate taking the bus it takes forever to get anywhere, and cabs are too expensive."

Rosemary snapped her fingers. "See that? You already found the time that you can give to your aunt Sophie. Now, that there is progress."

Rainey moved around the desk and hugged the woman. "Aunt Sophie wasn't the only person who was nice to me. I seem to remember a woman who worked at the Dollar General who let me pick a candy bar out and paid for it. You know what that woman told me?"

Flattered, Rosemary beamed at the girl. "What she tell you, sugar?"

"Well, she told me, 'I don't want you to take no crap from nobody. Out here you stand tall. Fight if ya have to, but don't stand for no disrespect. We clear?' That was the best advice anyone ever gave me."

Rosemary giggled with delight. "Did I tell you all that?"

"Yep."

"Hell, I was smart back then too."

Rainey laughed. "Thank you."

"You're welcome. Kindness is free and I want you to remember that so you make sure you give plenty of that shit away. Now go get yourself together so I can take you to visit your aunt."

As Rainey pulled her hair back into a ponytail for the tenth time to exhaust her nervous energy, she was realizing how lucky she was to have met so many strong women. Each of them had taught her that respecting herself was more important than being respected by anyone else.

Chapter Sixty-Eight

To stop from fidgeting, Rainey shoved her hands into her front pockets, as the nurse walked her to her aunt. Her aunt Sophie was in the dayroom, sitting in front of a window. She was in a wheelchair and her shoulders and spine were curled over. Her long, blond hair had been cut short and was thinning, giving a view to her flaky red scalp.

"Hi, Aunt Sophie. It's me," Rainey said, leaning down and trying not to be shocked by her condition.

The woman looked old, but wasn't that old in actual years. Sophie remained in her crumpled position. The girl squatted in front of her and looked up into her face.

"It's me. It's Rainey. I'm sorry I didn't come to see you sooner. I haven't been here for a while because, well, I was away in jail. It wasn't my fault, though," she was quick to add. "The cops found drugs and a gun on me, but neither were mine. I bet you know better than anyone about Mom and Dad's drug problem. Anyhow, I got out when I was seventeen and haven't come to see you because well . . . because I'm a jerk and I don't have a good reason. But I'm sorry."

Rainey lowered her body to the floor and stretched her legs out in front of her.

"The thing is," she said, pulling at a thread on her pants, nervously, "I wanted you to know that what you did for me when I was a little girl changed my life. If it wasn't for you, I'd probably be just like my little sister, Ivy. I can see now that when you came to visit me, you probably hated coming into our house, but you came anyway. And that's why I'm a jerk. The last time I came to see you, Ivy was with me, and this place freaked me out. Actually, you freaked me out because you weren't the person I remembered. I didn't want to come back here after that visit."

Rainey dragged her eyes up to her aunt's face, searching for a sign, any sign, that the woman she remembered was inside the host body. Nothing. Nada. Zippo.

"Are you even in there anymore, Aunt Sophie? Can you hear anything I'm saying?"

Suddenly Sophie's fingers on her right hand bounced up and down several times, then vibrated out of control. Rainey's heart raced. She got up to her knees and called over to the nurses. "She's waking up. Her hands are moving," she said, quickly standing and pointing at her aunt's lap.

A nurse rushed over and offered Rainey a warm smile. "No, she's not waking up. This is normal for Sophie. This is a symptom of her Huntington's disease, where she has these spontaneous movements; it's called chorea. She can't move her fingers on her own. She takes antipsychotic drugs to help with the tremors, but there isn't much more we can do for her."

Rainey's eyes filled. "Does she ever talk?"

The nursed paused. "There are moments when she might grunt or shriek, but it's never anything we can understand. Of course, if she's trying to tell us something, we want to know what it is, but there's just no way of knowing for sure. When she tries to verbalize, we massage her hands and feet or rub her scalp. We've learned over time that those things calm her."

Rainey paused, trying to work out what the nurse was telling her. "So you think maybe she could talk but just doesn't?"

The nurse shook her head firmly. "No, I think if Sophie was able to speak, she would. We know that when she first came here Sophie was smart and capable. She was losing bits of her memory, but overall she was a delight."

Rainey's shoulders dropped and rolled forward. She felt immense guilt and sadness that she had missed this version of Sophie and that her aunt went through the transition without her being there.

The nurse touched Rainey's arm. "I'm sorry, I know it's not what you want to hear, but I don't want to give you false hope."

"Thank you," Rainey mumbled. She moved back to the floor in front of her aunt.

Rainey picked at the skin around her fingernails for a few moments. "Like I was saying . . . I remember some of the things we did together. Boy, I used to be so excited on the days you were coming to take me outta that place. I loved your house. It was neat and clean. We were always warm and you made me the best food. After you came here, I held onto those

memories for as long as I could. Then Ivy was born and I spent all my time thinking about her and how I could make her life better, but mostly I tried to keep her belly full."

Rainey stood and wheeled her aunt next to a chair where they could sit at the same height. She took Sophie's hands and looked into her face. She stroked her fingers. Looking down, Rainey realized that her aunt's hands were those of a much younger woman compared to the rest of her. Her long, sturdy fingers had easily gripped her camera and created beautiful pictures. She remembered the pictures hung with care on the walls of Sophie's room.

"You made the greatest things with these hands, Aunt Sophie," she said, gently massaging them. "I have to leave now, but I promise that I'm coming back to visit you very soon."

Ten minutes later, Rainey was stepping out into the spring air and afternoon sun. She tilted her face to the sky and made a wish that her aunt would have comfort and peace. Then she hung her head as she walked across the parking lot thinking of how fragile and unfair life can be.

"Hey, hot mama! You wanna go on a date?"

Rainey looked toward the familiar voice and saw Rosemary sitting on the hood of her car. She smiled and took a slow jog toward her.

"Is that how you got men to give you money?" she asked jokingly.

"Oh, no, girl." Rosemary slid off of the car hood and strutted around. Then she put her face close to Rainey's and in a low sensual voice whispered, "Baby, I think you and me have a date that's been destined to happen. I'll make you feel so good you won't even remember your name. There ain't nobody but you and me, you're the only person on this planet I can see," she purred.

Rainey's eyes widened and she laughed. "Wow, you're good. And why are you still here? I told you I'd take the bus back."

Rosemary took her hands. "I'm here because I figured you might need a friend when you got outta there. It ain't easy seeing something broken to pieces that used to be whole and perfect."

Rainey nodded, thinking back to her hour with Sophie. "I wish she could talk to me. I wish she could understand how much I still love her."

"Just 'cause she can't talk don't mean she can't tell you nothing."

Rainey rolled her eyes. "The nurse said that she can't control her movements either, so it's not like she can gesture or anything."

"See, you think that way 'cause you ain't never spent any time hooking. You know the best way to hear what a person is sayin'?"

Rainey smiled. "No, but I'm sure you're gonna tell me."

"Damn tootin' I am. See here, a person can be heard by feeling the beat of their heart. When my johns were getting what they wanted I could feel the rat-a-tat-tat of that muscle in their chest. When I wasn't doing so good for them, it was a steady beat. They never had to tell me nothing, I always knew by this," putting her hand over Rainey's heart. "When I was with a man I sensed was mean, I was sure of their meanness in the first ten minutes, 'cause their heartbeat didn't change no matter what I did."

Rosemary took Rainey's hand and put it over her own heart. "You feel that beat in your chest? It's moving quick 'cause you're upset. The next time you come to visit your aunt, you feel her heart. You can hear it in her breath too. When you hit the right note with her, she'll breathe real heavy like and that's still connected to the heart—that's right, that's the way Rosemary sees it."

Rainey loved the way her friend had a way of explaining things that made perfect sense. Gratitude washed over her to have Rosemary in her life. "You're a pretty cool lady, you know that?"

"Sugar, I've been called a lot of things in my life, but never a lady," she cackled. Then she steadied her gaze on Rainey. "I learned a lot about people by being a prostitute. I ain't sayin' that I think hooking is good or nothing, but I am sayin' that we all learn from our lives."

As they drove back to Kensington, Rainey hoped that someday she could be as strong and as helpful as the woman sitting in the car next to her.

Chapter Sixty-Nine

The next night, Rainey and Rosemary left the shelter and walked along Kensington Avenue.

"You wanna grab a burger?" Rosemary asked.

The girl smiled. "Sounds great. It's kind of lonely going back to Gladys's house. I just sit in my room and read or stare at the wall."

"Sounds like you'll need to find yourself an apartment of your own soon."

"Yeah, right. I don't have the money for my own place."

"Then I guess you need to get a better-paying job."

Rainey glanced at her. "I know, Rosemary. But it's not like I got any skills."

"You got people skills," Rosemary said matter-of-factly.

"And what exactly am I supposed to do with those?"

Rainey knew she was being negative, but the past few days had been hard on her. Ivy, her parents, seeing Sophie, and she hadn't heard from Lindquist since he'd driven her home from the police station, and now she was beginning to think she'd scared him off.

Rosemary threw her hands up. "Listen, I ain't got all the answers, I'm just telling you what you're good at . . . how about if you study real estate and sell houses to rich people? Those realtors make good coin."

"Yeah," Rainey said, realizing she had a point. "I could do something like that."

"See? You need to think outside those limitations you put on yourself just 'cause you spent time in juvie. I saved my money when I was hooking. Now mind you, nobody knew, but I had me a bloated savings account by the time I got outta the business and started working at the Dollar General.

Now I make enough from the interest on my money to pay all my bills and still have some extra."

"I hope I can be like you," Rainey said, looking at Rosemary. Every day she learned something new about her. Rosemary taught her valuable life lessons that she knew would guide her in making good decisions for a long time to come.

"Child, you can be anything you set your mind to. I'm proud to be your friend."

Rainey chuckled. "You have to be my friend at your own risk. I've been very close to four people in the past seven years. One is in prison, one I can't contact, and two of them died."

Rosemary flicked her wrist at the girl. "Oh, please. That ain't nothing. But you do sound like a truckload of bad luck."

Rainey's eyes cast down, her playful mood dissipating.

Rosemary swatted her arm. "Oh come on, girl, I'm just playing wit' you. See, the type of people we know are more susceptible to death, jail, addiction, and all kinds of crazy shit. Who are you talking about that you can't contact?"

"My friend Winnie. She moved to Florida with some guy named Henry. I don't know why, but I got a bad feeling about him and I told Winnie but she wouldn't listen. The last time I talked to her I drove her over to his house in West Philly with all of her stuff. When I call the telephone number that Henry gave me, which I've tried like a million times since Winnie moved, it rings but no one ever answers. I miss her."

"Henry, huh?" Rosemary asked. Her eyes were distant and clouded.

Rainey's pulse quickened. "Yeah, Henry. Why?"

"Oh, no reason," Rosemary waved her off. "I met a Henry once. Motherfucker was crazy, but that's another story for another day. There are plenty of Henrys in the world, some good, some bad, I'm sure."

The two sat in a booth waiting for their burgers to arrive.

"Have you heard anything from Kennedy?" Rainey asked, changing the subject. She'd been so preoccupied recently that she'd forgotten to ask about her.

The woman took a sip of soda. "Yeah, she's doing all right. She was sad about losing the baby. Brittney got her when she was released from the hospital."

"I knew they had a crush on each other," Rainey squealed. "I told you."

"Yeah, apparently you was right. Anyway, she's been living with Brittney in that tent. The one just off Kensington Avenue. She seems happy, came by the shelter just the other day, but maybe we should swing by when we are done eating here and see if we can get a read on things. I'd hate to see her fall into the wrong stuff."

"Why? Did she say something to you that's making you worry?"

Rosemary shook her head. "It's more of a gut feeling."

***

After finishing dinner Rainey and Rosemary walked Kensington Avenue until they reached McPherson Park, where a city of tents lined the sidewalk. Some were made of plastic and sticks tied together with rags. Other people lived in large cardboard boxes, with trash bags draped over the top and weighted down by stones.

"This is amazing," Rainey said.

"Yeah, they built a whole community," the woman responded, looking around at the people sharing a bite to eat or a few beers. "Problem is there are lots of drugs and crime here. The city wants to close them down, but they've been threatening that since the forties. There ain't nowhere for all these people to go. They'll move around some and end up back here again."

"It looks like hard living," Rainey said, still awestruck by the community. "But at least they have each other. I don't know what's worse, the way I grew up or living like this."

Rosemary huffed. "From what you told me sounds like your life wasn't much different than this," she said, waving her hand around. "You had no hot water, no food, and no bed. Sure you had a house, but it ain't the house that makes you comfortable it's all the other things that make our lives enjoyable."

Just then someone called out and Rainey looked to see Brittney waving. They weaved through the tents until they reached her. Brittney was rubbing her arms frantically and her pupils were so dilated her blue eyes appeared almost fully black.

Rosemary grabbed the girl's wrist and held it tightly. "What are you on?"

"I'm . . . I'm . . ." Her head jerked around and her eyes darted through the crowd of tents.

"It's okay, you're safe," Rosemary said, not letting go of her wrist. "Tell me what you took."

Rainey stepped forward and put her arm over Brittney's shoulder. She recognized the signs. "You took speed, that's for sure. Did you do some coke too?"

Brittney looked at her sideways and nodded.

"Where's Kennedy?" Rainey asked.

"I don't know, man. I don't know. I've been looking for her for a long, long time. Have you seen her?"

Rainey flinched and withdrew her arm and swallowed hard. "You should go into your tent and rest. You need to wait out your high. We're gonna go look for Kennedy, okay?"

Brittney nodded and disappeared inside her tent.

Rainey grabbed Rosemary's hand and tried to walk away, but she resisted.

"Where are we going?" Rosemary asked.

Rainey's eyes were blazing. "To find Kennedy."

Chapter Seventy

"You wanna explain why you're so mad?" Rosemary asked, jogging to catch up.

"I'm mad because Brittney's eyes looked like two black beetles. That's bullshit. And it pisses me off that these dealers keep walking the streets, feeding off of other people's problems by selling them drugs. After seeing Brittney, I'm really worried about Kennedy."

"Because it reminds you of your parents?"

"No," she fumed. "Because it reminded me that drug addiction ruins a lot more lives than just the users." She looked over at Rosemary and slowed her pace. Somewhere in the back of her mind, Rainey remembered something Kennedy had told her once. "I think I might know where Kennedy is."

"Sugar, this is a big city. I ain't so sure you'd know where she is."

"Rosemary, we can search out here all night, but I think she's over at the motel on Germantown Avenue. She talked about the place once; it's near where she grew up. She joked that if her life took a turn for the worst she could always go there."

"All right, all right," Rosemary said, holding her palm up. "Let's go get my car and we can drive there and see."

***

As they neared the corner of Germantown Avenue, Rainey saw the blue-and-white sign for the Freedom Motel. "There," she pointed. "That's the place Kennedy told me about."

Rosemary pulled her car over to the side of the road. "Holy hell, you know what that place is, right?"

Rainey nodded. "Kennedy told me all about it."

"And you ain't scared?"

Rainey shook her head. "Are you?"

"Girl, I ain't scared. I worked in these kinds of places for many years."

The two walked across the street and up the concrete stairs to the motel entrance, which was nothing more than a single blue door on the side of the building. Inside was a hallway with dark brown paneling and lights in the drop ceiling, but only a few were lit. The place reeked of hopelessness and depression.

"And I thought the Drop Inn was a shithole. It's a palace compared to this place," Rainey whispered.

"Wait until we see the rooms. I bet they're something you'd never clean."

At the end of the hallway, there was a small window made of bulletproof glass. Sitting behind it was a heavyset man dressed in a black T-shirt and jeans, shoving potato chips into his mouth.

Rainey's top lip was curled in disgust at the sight of him. He shoved another potato chip into his mouth and smacked his lips together, giving her a view of the yellowish, mushy cluster spreading over his thick tongue like a contagious disease.

When he noticed them, he leaned toward the window and sucked the salt from each finger, making sounds. Ten spine prickling popping sounds, Rainey thought. She cringed and leaned away, with the back of her throat burning from bile creeping to the surface. She let out a quick choking cough while stifling a gag.

He eyed Rainey up. "You looking for work?"

"No," she said firmly. "I'm looking for a friend."

"I can be your friend," he said with a greasy smile while bouncing his eyebrows.

"I'm sure you can, but I'm looking for a girl that I think is here."

"Oh, yeah? What's this girl's name?"

"Kennedy."

"Mmm. I might've heard of her. What do you want with her?"

Rosemary leaned in. At forty-five she was beautiful and her body was fit. "Baby, we just need to talk with her for a minute or two. See, her mama is real sick and we gots to find her so she can see her before she dies. You got a mama, right?" she asked in a sultry voice.

As a final push, Rosemary leaned over to make eye contact and gave him a glimpse of her cleavage.

The man grinned, but kept his eyes on Rosemary's chest. "Yeah, I know her," he said. She's in room fourteen. She's by herself now, but not for long. So you better hurry up, say what you gotta say, and beat it."

"Aw, thank you, baby. You're a sweet man," Rosemary purred.

Rainey took her arm and they walked toward room fourteen. "I don't know how you can flirt with someone like that. Didn't you want to knock his lights out?"

"Sure did, but that would only get us kicked out on our asses. Now, let's go find our girl."

Rainey jammed her hands into her armpits as they walked, reeling from the run-down condition of the motel and that Kennedy was actually in there. When they got to room fourteen, Rosemary knocked on the door and a few seconds later Kennedy swung it open. Rainey gaped at the sight. She was wearing a black lace bra, G-string with a garter belt, and high black heels.

Rosemary pushed past her, and Rainey followed closely behind. The room was small. There was a double bed in the center. The drop ceiling tiles, those that weren't missing, had rusty water stains that ran down the corners of the walls. The bottom half of the walls were covered in dark chocolate paneling that matched the hallways. A tattered blue curtain provided privacy to the bathroom, consisting of a toilet and a sink. The bedspread was a gruesome pink, gold, and green checkered print. Even for Rainey, who was raised in squalor, the room was shocking. She wondered how anyone could bear to be in it and how Kennedy tolerated spending another second in a place like that when she could leave.

Kennedy spun on them; annoyed, she glared from one to the other. "What are you doing here?"

"We came to get you outta this place," Rosemary said, trying to sound definitive. "Why are you here, Kennedy? You don't have to do this. Let us help you before you get in any deeper."

Kennedy hiked her hands to her hips. "This ain't none of your business. You don't know what I've been through."

Rosemary bit down on the tip of her tongue. "You're right. We don't know. What we do know is that Brittney is strung out on drugs and you're here selling your body. So I think we can assume you're supporting her habit. Am I right?"

"You don't understand!" Kennedy yelled. "I love her. Ain't nobody ever loved me like she does."

Rainey took a step forward. "Kennedy, we are standing here because we love you. We came all this way to find you and bring you back. Love comes at us in a lot of ways. If you're gonna be loved by someone who lets you do what you're doing to feed their addiction, then that ain't love, that's being selfish."

Kennedy scoffed. She opened the door and gestured for them to leave. "Oh, yeah? Then I guess you best look around . . . you might find something here that belongs to you," she spat at Rainey. "Maybe you need to spend more time showing your love where it's needed."

Touching Kennedy's arm, Rosemary leveled her tone. "Child, I was in this business for a long time. Eventually you'll meet that john who will hurt you—he'll give you pain that you never knew was possible. You're young and smart. I want you to come back with us."

Kennedy watched them for a moment, then gave a sharp head gesture for them to leave. When she closed the door, Rainey and Rosemary were left standing in the gloominess of the hallway.

Rainey was so mad that her green eyes glowed in the eerie lighting. "What do you think she meant by 'you might find something here that belongs to you'?" she asked, bothered by the girl's statement.

Rosemary shrugged. "Look, we don't know what's going on in her head. People will say all kinds of shit when they want you to leave them alone to make their own choices. For all we know, she could be using dope now too. We tried our best and we gotta move on. You can only save people who want to save themselves. Let's get outta here."

Rainey nodded, feeling numb as she followed Rosemary back out to the street. Rainey's gaze was detached and she glanced around with shifting eyes. Off in the distance, she noticed three girls standing together. She was about to look away when she noticed something familiar about the way one of the girls threw her head back and laughed.

"Wait," she said, Kennedy's words ringing in her ear. You might find something here that belongs to you.

Heart in her mouth, Rainey strode toward the girls, with her pace picking up along the way. Rosemary followed closely behind. They were almost upon the group when Rainey stopped dead in her tracks and gasped.

"Lord have mercy," Rosemary mumbled from over Rainey's shoulder.

Rainey stared in disbelief. This can't be happening.

Chapter Seventy-One

"Ivy! What are you doing?" Rainey yelled as she stood rigidly on the sidewalk.

The two girls with Ivy laughed. One of the girls taunted, "What? You mama come to take you home?"

Ivy walked up to Rainey and glared at her. "What are you doing here?" she growled through clenched teeth. Ivy glanced back to see if the other girls were still watching her.

Rainey was riding on an adrenaline spike. Grabbing Ivy's arm, she dragged her away from the girls. Ivy tried to resist, but her sister was stronger. She grabbed her younger sister by the shoulders and stared her down, getting a good look at her. She was wearing heavy makeup. She had on fake eyelashes, black eye shadow, and bright red lipstick. She wore a tube top over her flat chest and a short skirt. A pair of boots ran above her knees and to the tops of her thighs.

"This is not you," Rainey said, her voice shaking. "You do not have to prostitute. Is Jiggy making you do this?"

Ivy crossed her arms over her chest and looked away.

"Who is making you do this? Tell me. I want to know."

Ivy looked over Rainey's shoulder, refusing to make eye contact. "You better get outta here before Jiggy sees you talking to me."

Rainey shook her sister. "I don't give a flying fuck about Jiggy seeing me. I'm not afraid of him."

Ivy let out a sinister chuckle, slow and intentional. "You should be. He hates you. He tells me all the time how happy he is that I didn't turn out like you. He loves me and you're jealous."

"He loves you? You're standing in North Philly waiting for some pervert to bring you to that disgusting motel and pay you for sex. That is what

you're doing, right? Does that sound like love to you?" Rainey asked, breathing hard.

Ivy grimaced and a flush crept across her cheeks.

"Well?" Rainey pressed, hoping Ivy's silence meant she was getting through to her.

The young girl shrugged. "At least Jiggy stuck around to take care of me."

"You just turned twelve years old. The men who are paying you need to be put in prison."

"Not really," Ivy said, her demeanor turning callous again. "I tell them I'm eighteen."

Rainey pressed her palm to her forehead, unable to grasp what she was hearing. "And you think they believe you? You look like a little kid. You are a little kid. I don't care what happens, you're coming with me. I'll figure something out."

Ivy said nothing, staring defiantly over Rainey's shoulder and grinding her jaw, and in the darkness of the night, Rosemary was watching her.

"Child, you on speed?" Rosemary asked, stepping forward.

Ivy jerked her head sideways. "Shut up, you old bitch."

Rosemary was upon her in a second and snatched Ivy up by her wrists. "Ain't nobody gonna talk to me like that. I told you about this already. Now, you need to listen to your sister. She's giving you solid advice."

Ivy wrenched herself away and stalked back toward the other two girls, who were still standing a few feet away, gawking.

"Stay away from me!" she yelled back. "Or I'll tell my boyfriend and you'll be sorry!"

Rainey was stunned and unsure how to handle her sister. Her eyes were filled with pain as she glanced at Rosemary.

"I can't leave her here," Rainey admitted.

"You gonna drag her to the car?" Rosemary fired back.

Rainey clenched and unclenched her hands, then nodded. "Yeah, that's exactly what I'm gonna do." A look of frustration passed over her face. "I don't know all the answers. But I have to do something to help her. She says she wants me to leave her alone, but I don't believe that for one minute. I don't care what she says, I won't abandon her. I can't help it, Rosemary. I love her." Rainey jutted her finger at the motel, "She'll get killed in that place. Do you see how small she is?"

"I see everything you see, but I also see something you don't."

"What?" Rainey asked, desperate for whatever insight Rosemary could offer. "What do you see that I don't?"

"I see that even though she's only twelve she has lived a hundred years. That's what being raised by addicts does to a person. You know that . . . you were the same way. So that gives the child a free will that most kids her age don't have yet."

Rainey thought about it. Rosemary was right. When she was Ivy's age, she was raising a toddler and making her own decisions. Her sister had been her main focus and what had saved her. But after she was put in juvie, Ivy had no one.

Rainey sighed. "So I'm supposed to walk away from her?"

"I'm sorry to say that's all you can do right now unless you wanna call the cops and get her arrested. She's whacked out on speed, and who knows if she has more dope on her." Rosemary paused, then nodded. "Actually, there might be one other thing you can do."

"What?" She leaned into the older woman, biting her own lower lip gently.

"You can call our friend Lindquist."

Hearing Lindquist's name invoked an immediate sense of safety in Rainey, but when she thought about him seeing Ivy like this, she hesitated. "And say what? My sister is high and selling her body?"

Rosemary shook her head. "It's more delicate than that. You tell him you need his help, and see what he can do. Lindquist is a good man. I see how much he worries about these young kids on the streets. Honestly, I wish someone like him was around when I was a young girl selling my black ass out here."

Rainey hesitated. She worried that the little Sam had seen of her already was too much for him. "I'm not sure," she said. "I don't know if that's the right thing to do since this involves Jiggy."

Rosemary nodded, "That's a fair point." She took Rainey's hand and walked toward the car. "You need to sleep on it. The answer will come to you, I promise. It ain't like you won't be able to find her again. She's under Jiggy's watch and he never lets his bitches stray too far from those evil eyes of his."

"That's exactly why I'm worried about involving Sam." Rainey turned to look back at Ivy one last time, then turned to face Rosemary and heaved a deep breath. "Okay, I'll sleep on it. But I'm telling you right now if I don't

come up with a good answer, I will hunt Jiggy down and kill him with my bare hands."

Rosemary gave her a side glance but said nothing because even though she understood Rainey would never be able to get that close to Jiggy, she knew the girl meant it.

Chapter Seventy-Two

The next morning, Rainey headed straight for her parents' house the moment she woke up. When she opened the front door and stepped inside, Rainey was attacked with rancid memories slicing through her mind like bolts of lightning. Stepping over squatters, Rainey walked up the stairs and knocked on her parents' bedroom door. Without waiting for an answer, she turned the knob and let herself inside.

Her father lifted his head and peered at her. "Are you kidding? Get out."

"No, I'm not leaving. I need to talk to both of you."

"You need to remember the time you woke up in the Badlands. That could happen again real easy," Peter growled. "You remember that, don't you?"

"How could I ever forget what shitty people you are?" she stated with a level voice, remembering how vulnerable she was when they'd left her in that alley.

Miranda sat up, pushing her greasy, tangled hair from her face. "You don't quit, do you?"

Rainey shook her head. "No, I don't. We have to talk about Ivy."

Peter rolled onto his back, and a loud huff pressed between his rotting teeth. "What about her? Why are you always putting your nose where it doesn't belong?"

"Because I want the best for Ivy. She deserves to be with people who care about her and needs to be protected. I'm sure you know the things she's doing for Jiggy," she said, glaring at them.

"Things?" Miranda barked. "What things? Things you're making up in your head. There's nothing wrong with Ivy. She's a happy, healthy kid. Now go away so we can go back to sleep."

Her anger boiling over, Rainey stomped to the side of the bed and grabbed a handful of her mother's hair. She bent low and put her face inches away from Miranda's. Her mother's eyes widened and her breathing burst in and out as she struggled to free herself. But she was no match for Rainey, who was much stronger than her now.

"Get . . . get . . . o . . . off me," she sputtered.

"Get off you?" Rainey said, tightening her grip. "When I was paying your debts with my flesh you didn't tell anyone to get off of me—your child."

"Peter," Miranda moaned, and Rainey turned toward her father as he sat up wearing a wide grin and watched. His eyes were lit with amusement, but Rainey returned a cold, hard stare.

"Better listen to her, Miranda," he chuckled. "She's a badass now. I'd say she can definitely take you," he taunted.

"Shut up!" Rainey screamed. "Just shut the fuck up. This is serious. I want Ivy to live with me."

"Nope." Peter shook his head. "And, if you try to steal her, we'll call the police."

"What will it take?" she asked, her voice edgy as she let go of her mother's hair.

He shrugged. "Not sure. She's worth a lot to us. I mean, she's our kid and since we lost our first one to drugs, she's the only one we have left. If we gave her up, we'd be childless and that would make us sad."

"Just stop it. You don't mean any of that, it's always about what you can get," Rainey spat. "So let's get to it. How much for you to give me custody?"

"Well," Peter said, lighting a cigarette from the nightstand, "let's see. She's a natural businessperson. She brings a lot to the table."

"No," Rainey sneered. "She's a child who has been taught to do things that she shouldn't so you two can get high."

Peter wagged his finger at her. "You have your version of the truth and we have ours. Right, babe?"

Miranda rolled over slowly and nodded, but the fear in her mother's eyes wasn't lost on Rainey.

"She's worth more than you can afford," he said as he butted out his cigarette and picked up a glass pipe instead. He dropped a chunk of white rock inside and stroked his lighter. Rainey watched the smoke gather in the small chamber as he sucked on the end, pulling the toxic cloud into his

lungs. He held it for as long as possible before exhaling slowly. She watched as his eyelids fluttered and his head rested on the wall behind their bed.

Rainey's face gathered into a snarl. In a scathing tone, she said, "You need to think about what you want. It's in your best interests to let Ivy live with me. I want you to remember this, you crackhead: I will do what's necessary to get her away from all of you."

At this, Peter laughed and Miranda nervously smiled, reaching for the crack pipe. He pulled it away from her, and she moved forward. "Come on, Peter. I need a hit."

"Yeah, come on, Peter. She needs a hit," Rainey mocked.

***

"You went to their house?" Rosemary asked, grinning. "You got big balls for such a delicate thing," she cackled.

Rainey shook her head. "I had to try one more time. It didn't do much good. They wouldn't agree to let her stay with me."

"Well, at least you've taken one step forward. Just keep on looking ahead and leave the past behind you, where it belongs."

"You really think I should talk to Lindquist?" Rainey asked.

"I sure do. Just get you some advice. That's all."

***

Rainey considered Rosemary's advice as she lay in bed that night. In the end, she decided to call Sam and feel him out. The next morning, her heart raced as the phone rang.

"Hey," she breathed into the telephone.

"Hey yourself. How are you?"

"I'm doing fine. So I called because I need your advice on something."

"Sure. What is it?" he said.

There was a cheeriness in his voice, and Rainey suspected it was because he was glad she'd called him. "I need to get Ivy away from my parents and somewhere safe. She needs to be with me."

Lindquist didn't speak for a moment. "Mmm. That's a tough one, Rainey. The safest bet is to get your parents to agree to let her live with you."

Rainey was afraid he'd say this, and her heart felt like it split in two. "It's not that easy. They need her to stay with them."

"Need her? What does that mean?"

She sighed heavily into the phone, wondering how much she should tell him. She wanted to trust him but was still hesitant. "Look, you're a cop. I need to be careful about what I say to you. I think there's a line between what I can tell you, but I don't want there to be one."

"I get it. I really do. But if your sister is involved in illegal activity and you tell me, then I'm obligated to take action. I'd like to help, but I can't help either of you if I don't know the truth."

Rainey bit her lower lip; she couldn't tell Sam that Ivy had been selling drugs and now she was prostituting. Hesitating, she said, "I get it. Thanks for talking I'll catch up with you later."

Rosemary walked into the office. "What did Sam say?"

"If I tell him illegal things are happening, he'd have to do his job."

"What are you gonna do now?" the older woman asked.

"I've never tried praying before. Maybe I'll do that," Rainey said hopelessly.

"Ain't nothing wrong with askin' God for help," Rosemary said.

The images of Ivy the night before gnawed at Rainey. She raked her fingers through her hair and she prayed that in some way, somehow, she'd be able to help her sister.

Chapter Seventy-Three

Six months had passed since Rainey walked into her parents' house attempting to get them to let Ivy live with her. During that time, she had become much closer to Sam Lindquist, having lunch with him several days a week. At one of those lunches, where Rainey was focused on finding a new job, Sam gave her a grin.

"Okay, what do you see yourself doing?" he asked, smiling at her. Sam found Rainey to be independent and wildly sure of herself. He enjoyed those things about her.

"Well, I'm not sure. I learn quickly, and other than cleaning motel rooms I had a job once

where I delivered mail."

He squinted his eyes. "You delivered mail? For who?"

She peered up at him, grinning. "That doesn't matter."

"Okay, how about this? What kind of mail?"

"Just mail," she giggled. "You're not getting any more out of me than what I just told you, Sam. So you got any ideas?"

He gave her a curious look and nodded. "I think I know someone that can help."

***

A month later, she was working as a mail carrier at the post office. Rainey's fears that her record from juvenile detention would prevent her from getting a good job were washed away. Sam had informed her that her record was sealed because of her age and wouldn't show up on a criminal

background check. With her new work and pay, she was finally able to rent her own apartment.

On a Saturday morning in early March, she was sitting at a diner with Rosemary, excited to tell her about the place she'd rented the week prior.

"Look how far you've come," Rosemary said. "I'm so proud of you. What's your apartment like?"

Rainey grinned. "Well, it's kind of meh, but it's better than the one room in Gladys's house. I still can't believe I'm in my own apartment. It's a dump, but it's got two bedrooms, so when the time comes, I can bring Ivy to live with me. I'm saving up to buy a bed for her and a sofa for the living room. The last tenant ran out in a hurry, and left dishes, pots, and pans, so that's a break." She closed her eyes for a minute, envisioning her and Ivy living together as sisters again. "I went to the Freedom Motel last week, and Ivy was there. I watched her from a distance for a few hours. She was with three men in that time; all of them had to be thirty years old or more."

Rosemary shook her head. "Sugar, johns come in all ages, colors, and sizes. Some have all their teeth and some don't. Some smell like the inside of a garbage can and some don't smell at all. It's the nature of the beast. Did you ever think about not going there to watch? You're torturing yourself."

Rainey looked into her friend's eyes, and Rosemary saw her pain. "I can't stop going there. It's the only way of me knowing she's still alive. Not seeing Ivy, that's what would be torture for me."

The woman's heart clenched. "Are you going there tonight?"

Rainey nodded.

"You want some company?"

"Hell, yeah. If you drive, I won't have to take the bus and be harassed by every guy that walks by wanting a freaking date," she chided. "Besides"—she tilted her head and purposely blinked rapidly, so happy that Rosemary offered to go with her—"you're pretty good to hang with."

***

Approaching the motel that night, Rosemary parked her car and the two sat and waited. Rainey's eyes roved the street in front of the now-familiar building, but Ivy wasn't there. She sat back in her seat and turned her head to face her friend.

"Sometimes I wonder how I made it through most days when I was a kid. I've been thinking lately that when sober people talk about drugs it's all about the addict. But what about the people who have to live with them and put up with their shit? It seems like we are invisible. No one talks about what they've done to our lives or how they've ruined the family."

Rosemary clucked her tongue. "Ain't it the truth? Some of those people are bat-shit crazy when they're wigged out on dope. They do stuff that any sane person would never do."

"Exactly," Rainey said. "Then if someone judges an addict, we're told we have no compassion and we need understanding. But then when a doper complains about how hard their life is or about the lack of support from their family, they're given a pass for the things they've done because of their addiction. They rarely have guilt or pay consequences for their decisions." She moved closer to the front window to scan the street. "The way some people see it, those who never lived through it and don't know shit about addicts have a tainted view of things. You know?"

Rosemary nodded. "Lots of times people in society who ain't ever affected by stuff make decisions for all of us that just ain't right. For example, if your sister got picked up on prostitution, she'd probably go to juvie. Nobody considers there's someone behind her pushing her to hook. So the child who is the victim gets locked up while the pimp moves on to the next girl."

"I can't believe my little sister, the one I raised from a baby, is selling her body. She's so young and vulnerable, it really tears me up inside," Rainey said, reflecting on her innermost thoughts.

"Yes, she is. That child is too young to know the shit she's doing will affect her for the rest of her life. It's a damn shame. I was older when I started hooking. Yes, indeed, I was sixteen before I screwed my first john."

She looked over at Rosemary. "Sixteen is young too. Why did you start?" she asked.

Rainey asked questions in the past, but Rosemary always shut her down.

"Well, I guess this is as good a time as any to let you in," Rosemary said, leaning against the driver's door to face her. "When I was thirteen, my daddy left me and my mama. Less than a year later, she had another man living with us. He never messed with me, but he beat my mama black and blue, day in and day out. For the next few years, Mama had more broken bones and bruises than any human should ever have." Rosemary paused and shook her head slowly, recalling the awful memories. "She'd been to

the hospital so many times they knew her by name," she said, letting out a bitter chuckle.

Rainey placed her hand over her mouth, disturbed by the haunting images. "That's horrible. Did she fight back?"

"Well at first she did, but then he'd beat her worse. After he'd beat her, he'd chain her ankle to the bedpost and leave her there to suffer. One time after that bastard left the apartment, I went to her and said, 'Mama, let's you and me leave. You ain't gotta deal with this asshole. We'll find another way to live.' And you know what she said to me?"

Rainey braced herself, knowing that whatever she was about to hear would be bad.

"She said, 'Rosemary, you don't leave the people you love. I love Jerry and he loves me. He loses his temper 'cause I don't always do what I'm supposed to do. Once I do better, he'll beat me less. You remember that if a man beats you when you get older that means he cares.'"

"Why would she tell you something like that?" Rainey asked, not understanding how anyone could think that way.

"Child, because she didn't know any better; that's how she was raised. But when she said that, I was thinking, Mama, that man has beat you so much you lost the damn mind you were born with. About a year later, I was out with my friends and when I came home, I found Mama chained to the bed with her skull broken open . . . already dead by the time I found her. Worst damn day of my life."

"Oh, Rosemary," Rainey breathed, reaching over the seat and taking her hand. "That must've been awful. I'm so sorry."

"Thank ya, sugar, but that wasn't the end of it. Once she was dead and Jerry was on the run, I had to get my ass outta that apartment before child protective services showed up. I knew I didn't want to go into foster care, not with just two years left till I turned eighteen, so I left West Philly and found myself here. That's where I met my pimp, and after a few beatings he turned me out. So yeah, I took beatings, but never did I think I deserved to be beaten, not like my mama. No siree, I never bought into that bullshit that Mama was selling."

Rainey sat quietly for a moment, letting Rosemary's story wash over her. "Did you know you'd be a prostitute when you came here?" she asked gently.

"Ah, nobody knows they're going to be a prostitute. When you're out on the streets, you understand it's an option. I wasn't a virgin or nothing.

I'd slept with lots of boys by the time I was sixteen. Truth be told, I liked sex, still do. I figured if I could be paid to do something I like, then why the hell not?"

"What's it like to be a prostitute?" Rainey asked, really wanting to understand and knowing this was her opportunity to learn what Ivy was going through.

"First, I learned right quick that liking sex and selling sex are two different things. When you're selling sex there ain't no enjoyment in it. The man doesn't give a shit what you want. It ain't mutual. Plus you gotta do whatever they pay for, so if they want a blow job, that's what you do."

"What if you didn't want to do something?"

Rosemary shrugged. "I did it anyway. I had to or my pimp would beat my ass, then punish me by making me do to him and his associates whatever it was I refused to do in the first place. I learnt that one time, and from then on, I did whatever the john paid for."

"How did you get away from it?"

"Oh, honey, I aged out," Rosemary explained. "Once you get to a certain point the men don't want you like they did when you was young. The pimps don't want you either, 'cause you can't make him real money anymore. My key to getting out was that I stayed away from drugs and alcohol. Most prostis have a hard time staying sober with the shit these dirtballs put you through."

Rainey shifted in her seat, opened the window, and took a few breaths of fresh air. Her mind was filled with rotten images of men doing things to her sister.

"You okay, sugar?" Rosemary asked, watching the girl.

"Yeah," she said, pulling her head back inside the car. "That's scary stuff. Something I've never been able to get my mind around. I don't know how you did it. I don't know how Ivy's doing it. I have to get her out of this before it's too late."

"It may already be too late," Rosemary said, pointing through the front window.

Rainey's eyes followed, and her mouth dropped open.

Chapter Seventy-Four

Rainey reached for the door handle, but Rosemary grabbed her shirtsleeve and yanked her back.

"No, girl. Sit tight."

Rainey did as Rosemary said but kept her eyes glued to her sister. She watched a grown man who looked to be in his thirties slapping Ivy in the face with his open hand. Ivy fell to the ground on her hands and knees. The ogre pulled his foot back and kicked her in the ribs until the girl rolled onto her side and pulled her knees up to her chest.

"I can't sit here and watch," Rainey said as tears of rage burned her eyes.

Rosemary gripped her forearm. "Yeah, you can. If you go over there right now, he'll beat her more later."

Rainey flinched and her fury ignited. She watched as Ivy pushed back up to her knees and held her hands in front of her face.

"Who is he?" Rainey asked. "Do you know him?"

Rosemary nodded. "His name is Rooster. He works for Jiggy. Let's give it a minute or two. It looks like he's winding down."

"How the hell do you know that?" Rainey asked as Rooster grabbed Ivy by the hair and brought her to her feet. His face was a fleshy, bloated mass of fury that was inches from hers as he continued screaming.

Rosemary smirked. "I know, trust me."

"I'm going to rip that man to pieces," Rainey seethed.

"You ain't gonna do no such thing. You need to wait until the time is right and then you'll get her outta there. Ain't nothing you can do in this minute that won't get us both killed."

Rainey knew that she was probably right, but still it was hard to sit and do nothing. She pressed her back against the seat and watched until finally

Rooster stomped away. When Ivy stumbled backward, Rainey reached for the door handle.

Rosemary touched her shoulder. "You need to move slowly. Don't rush over there. Give Rooster a chance to get in his car and drive off. When you go to her, be prepared that she'll be angrier than you've ever seen her. There's a lot of shame with this profession, especially after one of your pimp's associates kicks the shit outta you on the street for everybody to eyeball."

Rainey hesitated a moment. She took several deep breaths and then pulled the door handle and stepped out of the car. Rosemary followed, remaining just a few steps behind her.

"Ivy, are you okay?" Rainey asked softly as she approached.

The twelve-year-old looked at her sister. Black mascara tears streaked her face. "What are you doing here? Leave me alone," she cried, adjusting her shirt and hiding her body.

"I've been watching and I saw what happened to you," she admitted. "I'm only here because I care about you. I want to make sure you're all right."

Ivy looked at her with droopy eyelids and shook her head. Her shoulders were hunched and she looked down at her feet. "I'm never gonna be all right," she cried.

Rainey's breath hitched; her sister's vulnerability was almost too much to handle. She bent down to lift Ivy's purse from the ground. When she did, a small bag of white powder fell out and her heart stopped for a full second. She looked at the bag and back at her sister. Can't ignore it now.

Rainey raised her eyebrows. "Are you using all the time now?" her words biting like fanged teeth into the night air.

Ivy's demeanor hardened. "Yeah, I am. I gotta do things with these guys and I hate it. I get a little high. So what?"

Rainey took a deep breath, trying to keep her cool and failing. "There's no such thing as 'a little high.' That's like saying you're a little pregnant. You can't do this to yourself, Ivy. You see what drugs did to Mom and Dad. I know you want more than this."

Rosemary stepped next to Rainey. "We have the shelter; we can try to help you."

"Why do you keep putting your big fat nose in our business?" Ivy screamed.

Rosemary's back went poker straight. She draped her arm over Rainey's shoulder. "Because this woman here is a good friend of mine, and I'd like to be a good friend of yours too."

Ivy reached in her purse, pulled out a cigarette, and lit it. She made direct, probing eye contact with Rainey. "Want one?" she asked defiantly, holding the cigarette pack out.

"No, I don't smoke and I wish you didn't either," she answered.

She blew a cloud of smoke out hard toward her sister's face. "If you say so."

Rainey steadied herself. "So I went to talk to Mom and Dad. I tried to talk them into giving me custody so you can live with me," she said, wanting so badly to give Ivy hope and to let her know that she was still fighting for her.

Ivy shifted from foot to foot. She pressed her fist against her heart and held Rainey's eyes. After a moment she said, "I don't know why you went there. I don't live there anymore."

After what she'd seen of her sister, Rainey hadn't thought Ivy could reveal anything shocking. "What?"

Ivy grinned, slightly amused by the look on her sister's face. "You heard me. I don't live there anymore." She stopped and waved her hand around at the hookers on the sidewalk. "I live in a place with some of the other girls. They're my family now."

"What are you talking about? How did this happen?" Rainey fired.

"That's what Jiggy wanted, so Mom and Dad agreed he could take me. They probably got free dope for the rest of their lives or something."

"Holy shit," Rosemary said under her breath.

Rainey tried to contain her rage. She walked several steps away from them and returned. Her tongue was poking at the inside of her cheek as she looked at Rosemary until the words finally formed. "What do we do now?"

"We get back in the car and go home," Rosemary said with seriousness. Then her eyes met Ivy's and she leveled her with a stern look. "You need to do what your pimp tells you. Why did that man whoop your ass tonight?"

Ivy glanced at Rainey and looked at the ground. "I took too much time buying dope."

"Yeah, well, don't do it again. Do what you need to do until we can figure you a way outta here," Rosemary said, her eyes hard. She turned to Rainey. "Let's go."

"Let's go? I can't leave her here."

Rosemary glanced at Ivy. "Yeah, that's what you gotta do for now."

Ivy shrugged and Rainey wrapped her arms around her. Surprisingly, the girl didn't push her sister away and now Rainey had a smidge of hope. "I'll be back for you. I know I told you that before, but this time I'm older and I don't depend on Peter and Miranda for anything."

Ivy rolled her eyes. "Yeah, sure," she said, twisting away from her.

Rainey grabbed Ivy's arm, pulling her close, and kissed her on the forehead. "I love you, Ivy."

Ivy said nothing, just crossed her arms over her chest, then turned away. Fighting back tears, Rainey walked to the warmth and safety of Rosemary's car, hoping she was making the right choice leaving her there.

Chapter Seventy-Five

By the next day, Rainey knew what she had to do. She needed a car of her own. A car would allow her to go watch Ivy more frequently. Plus, she'd been taking the bus to visit her aunt Sophie on Saturday mornings and a car would save her a lot of travel time.

While Rainey was making better money at the post office it still wasn't enough for her to afford her own car. Besides, she still didn't have a driver's license. After exhausting several options, she resigned herself to calling the one person she knew could help.

Picking up the telephone, Rainey dialed the number, then waited impatiently while it rang.

"Hello?"

"Hey, Boulder, it's Rainey."

"Well, well, this is a blast from the past. How've you been?"

"I'm doing okay."

After a few minutes of catching up, Boulder drew in a breath and said, "So, I know you're calling me for something. What is it?"

"Right, I'm calling because I, um, need your help. I need a car. I don't have enough money or credit to get a loan. I was hoping you could help me."

She hadn't spoken to Boulder since she moved out of Taz and Andrew's house, but she hoped he'd at least hear her out.

"What do you need the car for?" he asked.

"I'd rather not say." She could never tell Boulder it was to go see Ivy in the area of town controlled by Jiggy. She already knew how the club felt about getting involved with him. She thought about telling him it was to see her aunt but recognized that by not telling him the whole truth, it could lead to bad things happening between Jiggy and the Devils Angels.

"Listen, honey. You can't call and ask me for a favor then tell me you ain't giving me no information. I'll tell you what, come down to the club and we can discuss it in person."

"The club?" Rainey asked, feeling like she had made a mistake to call him.

"Yeah, the club. I'm sure you remember the place."

She hesitated for a moment, not wanting to go back there again and have to see Kiki and the other women. But having no other options, she reluctantly agreed.

***

Later that afternoon, she filled Rosemary in on her conversation with Boulder.

"You want me to drive you to the club, sugar?"

"No, I need to do this on my own. I don't want you to get involved with this one. I know Boulder would love to see you, but I need to work this out based on his trust in me."

"Okay, but when you get back, I need you to check in with me so I know you're all right."

"I'm not afraid to go there," Rainey said. "Boulder isn't gonna hurt me."

"You don't seem so sure about that," Rosemary said, looking at her closely.

"I'm not sure about anything, anymore. I've been getting unwanted surprises my whole life." She shook her head. "I know I shouldn't be surprised by the awful things my parents do. After all the shit I've been through with the two of them they let Jiggy take Ivy and I'm surprised? Think about that for a while."

Rosemary reflected on her thoughts from the night before. It was a shock to her too and she didn't even have a relationship with the kid. "Well, I was up most of the night thinking about your sister. I've been through a lot and know people who've been through hell and back. I hate to say it, but that child takes the prize for having the most fucked-up parents. But you already know that and it's a good thing you got outta there when you did. So you're going to the club to convince Boulder to loan you a car so that you can do what?"

"I decided that I'm going to the motel every night. I'll sleep there if I have to. I need to keep my eyes on her. I'm afraid someone is going to kill her."

Rosemary nodded. "Anything is possible on these streets."

Chapter Seventy-Six

Later that afternoon, Rainey took a taxi to the clubhouse. When she arrived, several members were outside fiddling with their motorcycles. All eyes turned and watched her.

"Rainey?" one man called out.

She turned, and a smile stretched across her face. "Snoopy, how are you?"

"I'm doing good," he said, walking over to her. "You know, I miss your ol' man. He was the best of the best." He lowered his voice. "What are you doing here?"

"I came to meet with Boulder. How are your kids?"

He nodded. "Doing real good. Thanks for asking. Hey, you better watch your back because Kiki has been on the warpath lately. Boulder's been eyeing up a couple of mamas and she doesn't like it too much," he warned.

She chuckled. "Thanks for the warning, but Kiki is always on the warpath. Oh, I don't think I ever got to tell you how much I appreciated you going with Andrew into my parents' house to make sure my sister was still alive."

"It wasn't a problem. I hope she's doing better; things were pretty rough when we saw her."

Rainey shook her head sadly. "Anyway, Boulder's waiting for me. Thanks again."

Inside the club, Rainey made her way down to the basement and spotted Boulder right away. Before she made it over to him, Kiki tapped her on the shoulder.

"What are you doing?" she asked with her face twisted.

Rainey kept her voice light. She wasn't looking for a fight. "I came here to talk to Boulder. That's what he asked me to do."

"Oh, yeah? Talk about what?"

Rainey sighed. "What do you care, Kiki? I seem to remember you treated me like shit the entire time I was here. Go back to your little cluster of bitches so they can kiss your ass."

When Rainey turned her back to Kiki, she saw that Boulder had been watching them. Good, she thought, that bitch won't dare start shit with me if he's watching.

Her smile brightened as she approached Boulder. She was relieved to see Andrew standing next to him.

Both men gave her a hug, and Boulder dismissed all the other men standing around them. He looked at Rainey. "So I was telling Andrew you needed to borrow a car."

"Yes. I was thinking I could pay you money every month to rent one or something."

Boulder smiled and shook his head. "I'll consider it after you tell me what you're going to use the car for," he said.

Rainey sighed. The last thing she wanted was to tell Boulder about Ivy. The second he got wind of his car getting mixed up in Jiggy's affairs, it would be over. "Why does it matter?" she asked.

"It matters because the cars are in my name, so if you get busted doing anything you shouldn't it comes back on me and the club."

She glanced at Andrew and he gave her a confirming nod. "Fine. I need it to go to the Freedom Motel at night."

"The Freedom," Andrew repeated, looking at her with confusion. "Rainey, if you're in a bad way we can help you out. You don't need to hook in a place like that. Stoker would haunt us if we let you do that."

"I'm not hooking." She looked down at her hands and paused. Okay, she thought, I'm going to tell the whole story and hope that Boulder will agree anyway. She lifted her head and met Boulder's eyes. "It's my little sister who's hooking . . . for Jiggy. She was selling dope for him, but I suspect he turned her out because she started using."

Boulder was looking at her, expressionless, keeping his eyes steady on her. She squirmed under his scrutinizing gaze, then gathered the courage to keep pressing forward.

"She's twelve years old," Rainey added.

"That's some fucked-up shit," Boulder said after a moment. "But you and me talked about getting involved with Jiggy; you know what that means. It could be an all-out war for the club."

"He doesn't need to know who the car belongs to. I'll never tell anyone."

"She's only twelve, huh?" Boulder mumbled.

Rainey pressed her hand against her heart. "Yeah, she's still a baby. The thing is, I don't know how much longer she can stay in her situation before it's too late."

Boulder nodded. "I'll tell you what, I'll lend you one of our cars. You can use it for three months, but after that you need to return it."

Rainey couldn't believe it. She had gone to see Boulder not knowing what to expect and now he'd just given her what she needed. Grateful, she gave him a genuine smile.

Boulder's legs weakened as he watched her. He still thought of Rainey often, and even as time had passed, he reflected on the afternoon they'd spent together. He looked over Rainey's shoulder to see Kiki glaring at them, and his face got serious.

"I wanna know where you're living so we can keep an eye on the car," he said.

Rainey wavered. She wasn't sure she wanted the Devils Angels to know her address. "Is that necessary? You don't trust me?"

Boulder let out a robust laugh. "The only people I trust are my brothers. Nothing against you, but that's the way it's always been and always will be."

Rainey shook her head and sighed. Truth was, she already knew that about him, so she wrote down her address and handed it to Boulder. As Rainey drove back to The Sanctuary her thoughts lingered on Stoker—how she'd loved him, but how he'd let her down. She had decided long ago that Stoker had been another soldier in the club doing whatever he was told. While she was sad that he was gone, Rainey realized good things had happened in the wake of his absence, and she was thankful for her new life.

When she parked the car in front of the shelter, Rosemary came to meet her outside.

"Look at this now," she crowed. "Ain't you fancy. You can talk an Eskimo outta giving you their fur coat in the middle of a snowstorm."

Rainey stood next to the car, giggling. "Yeah, hardly. I thought I was going to have to promise Boulder my firstborn. Anyway, he was pretty cool about it after I told him about Ivy. I think it was her age that got to him."

Rosemary nodded. "Yeah, I can see that. I've said it before, the one thing the Devils Angels don't dig is anyone abusing children. They come together over that topic and don't care who they gotta face."

"If that was true, then Boulder would've helped when I told him what Jiggy was doing to my sister when I lived with them."

"Ah, that Jiggy is a tricky one. Has Boulder ever seen Ivy?"

She shook her head.

Rosemary dipped her chin to her chest and peered up at her. "Sometimes we can't understand how bad things are until we see them with our own eyes. You get what I'm saying?"

The girl grinned. "Yeah, I get it. You're saying if I can get Boulder to see Ivy, he might help me."

The woman nodded.

"You're so smart, Rosemary."

Chapter Seventy-Seven

Later that afternoon, Rainey and Rosemary were preoccupied with a few things around The Sanctuary when the door opened. Neither of them looked up right away, so absorbed in their work they barely noticed when the bell rang over the door.

"Hello, ladies," a deep voice sang from behind them.

Startled, they both turned and grinned seeing Sam standing there.

Rosemary put her hand on her hip. "Well, if it isn't Agent Lindquist. Where you been?"

"Ah, you know, here and there." His eyes settled on Rainey, and she blushed. "Haven't you told Rosemary we've been meeting for lunch?" he said, smiling.

Before Rainey could answer him, Rosemary cocked her head and said, "Yeah, she's been telling me, all right. That doesn't answer why you haven't been coming in to see me."

Sam let out a robust chuckle. "You're right, Miss Rosemary. I apologize; it won't happen again. How are things going here?"

"Things are going just fine," Rosemary remarked, looking from Sam to Rainey, noticing the two of them watching each other and feeling the energy between them. "You hungry, girl? You need to go out and get you some lunch," she cackled.

Rainey kept her eyes on Sam's. "I'm starving."

"That's what I thought," Rosemary commented. She looked at Lindquist. "You better take this girl out and get her something to eat. I got work to do, so I ain't got no time for her shenanigans," she joked as she walked into her office and closed the door.

***

Rainey and Lindquist sat at a table in the local deli talking about their fondness for Rosemary.

"You know, we do eat a lot of lunches together," Rainey stated. She held her palm up to him, "Not that I'm complaining."

His face grew serious. "I know. A lot of my work gets done at night. That's when people seem to show up as their worst selves . . . they think no one can see them in the dark."

"That makes sense. As my derelict father likes to say, 'The best things happen in the dark when no one is watching.'" Rainey looked down at her turkey sandwich and picked off a piece of bread, thinking about her sister.

"You don't like your sandwich?"

She grinned. "The sandwich is fine."

"What's going on? Something on your mind?"

She pursed her lips and tilted her head.

"Ivy?" he pressed.

Rainey sighed and nodded.

"Have you seen her?"

She nodded again.

"Outside the Freedom Motel?"

Surprised, her eyes bulged. "You know?" Her mind racing, she wondered what else he knew about her sister.

"Yeah," he said. "I saw her there a couple of nights ago. We had to go there for some other police business and I noticed her outside. Our department doesn't mess with the women unless we know for sure that they're moving drugs."

"Well, she's not a woman," Rainey said, shaking her head sadly. "She's a child. Don't get me wrong, I'm not asking you to arrest her. That wouldn't be good."

"You don't have to worry. We can't arrest someone just for being dressed provocatively and standing on the sidewalk. Can I assume you've been spying on her and not telling me about it?"

"Of course I haven't been spying on her," she said, giving him a weak smile. "It's more like I've been stalking her. I'm so worried that something will happen to her, something worse than what she's already involved in."

Sam took a drink from his soda and cleared his throat. "I'm sorry this is happening and I wish there was something I could do to help." He had wanted to ask her something and thought a change of subject would be good. "I was thinking . . . well, um, I'd like to cook dinner for you at my place."

She gave him a wide grin, and her legs bounced on the balls of her feet under the table. In all of her struggles with Ivy, she'd been hoping to spend time with Sam in a more intimate setting. She liked him a lot and it seemed to her that he felt the same.

"Sure," she said, trying not to sound too eager, "but are you a good cook?" she joked.

His lips curled into a slow smile. "You have no idea how good I am."

"All right. When?" she asked, excited.

"Tonight."

"Okay. What can I bring?"

"Just yourself."

"That's great because I don't cook at all," she chuckled.

"Do you want me to pick you up?"

She shook her head. "Nah, I'll drive. A friend loaned me their car."

Sam narrowed his eyes. "A friend, huh?"

"Yes, Sam Lindquist. Just a friend."

"Do you even have a driver's license?" he asked.

Rainey took a bite of her pickle. "You know what your problem is? You ask too many questions. What time do you want me to be at your house?"

"How's seven?"

"That works," she said, picking up her sandwich. All she could think about was getting back to The Sanctuary and telling Rosemary that she was going to have dinner with Sam.

Chapter Seventy-Eight

Shortly before seven that night, Rainey parked her car in front of Sam's building on Nineteenth Street and looked down at herself. It had taken her an hour and seven outfit changes to decide what to wear, and in the end, not wanting to seem too enthused, she opted for jeans and a button-down blouse.

As she walked to the front entrance she took in the bustling, thriving neighborhood; the complete opposite of North Philadelphia. People were strolling through Rittenhouse Park, restaurants were busy, and couples and families walked the streets without looking over their shoulders. She took the elevator up to the fourth floor, and before she could even ring the bell, he pulled the door open.

"You found it," he said, grinning.

She smirked, nervous and excited to be in his apartment. "It wasn't that hard. This is a nice neighborhood you live in."

He smiled. "Yeah, come on in," he said, stepping aside.

She stood in the entryway, looking around, curious what Sam's home would tell her about him. The floor was white marble and the walls were painted the faintest shade of yellow. Painted portraits in heavy gold frames lined the walls. To her right was the living room and a wall of windows that looked out over Rittenhouse Park. To her left was an office with a mahogany desk.

"Wow," she breathed. "This place is beautiful."

"Thanks," he said, blushing. "The décor is all my sister. My taste in decorating isn't this good."

"Right, I forgot you have a sister. She's the one who bought me the clothes to wear to court, right?" she said, thinking everything coming out

of her mouth sounded clumsy. Being in his home was a big step, or at least that's what she had hoped.

"Yep, the same one. Come in and I'll show you around."

As they walked through his apartment and Sam chatted easily, she began to relax. Now she wasn't only amazed by him, but by where he lived too. Each room he brought her into was more stunning than the one before it. He had two bedrooms and two full baths, a kitchen, living room, dining room, and office.

After Sam's homemade meal of veal scaloppini and pasta and a long but wonderful story about his trip to Italy two years prior, they moved to the living room. They had light conversation sharing favorite sports teams, food, and places to eat. Then Sam moved to more silly questions, such as Would you rather be a vampire or a werewolf? What's your dream vacation? But her favorite question was, What superpower do you wish you had? As they talked and laughed and shared their answers, Rainey's worries about the evening were forgotten.

After a while, as Rainey was talking, Sam placed his arm over the back of the sofa behind her. She tried to act natural, but her pulse quickened and her hand flitted to her collar. She let out a soft giggle. Oh, please kiss me now, Rainey thought.

Sam looked down at her and smiled. "Listen," he said, and his voice grew gentle, "I just want to say that when you were in juvie, I wasn't crushing on you. I cared about you then because you were a kid who'd been dealt a bad hand. But when I saw you at the shelter and how you'd grown into a beautiful woman, I couldn't stop thinking about you. Not only did you overcome adversity, but now you're looking for ways to help others who have been wronged." He pushed her hair behind her ear. "After all of that, I saw you differently."

"Oh," Rainey said, blushing. "I never thought you were into me back then. And . . . well, thank you for saying all of that about who I am now. It really means a lot."

Sam's emerald eyes shimmered. "It's all true," he said.

Rainey's breathing got shallow as he moved his head toward hers. When he hesitated, Rainey took the leap and pressed her face forward the rest of the way until their lips met. At first it was a sweet kiss. But within a few seconds, when his tongue touched hers, it became hungry.

Sam pulled back and looked into her eyes. "I'm twenty years older than you," he said.

She shrugged, "I know. So what?" she said, leaning in to kiss him again.

"I'm a cop," he breathed.

"I'm a convict," she said, grinning. In that moment, Rainey was certain there was nothing Sam could tell her that would make her not want him.

He chuckled, but his eyes were fixed on hers. Their lips met again and he wrapped his arms around her, pulling Rainey to him.

This time it was Rainey who pulled back and, catching her breath, she said, "I like you, Sam. I don't care that you're older than me."

He kissed her neck, and her head dropped back. Her fingers burrowed deep inside his hair as she pulled his head closer. She sat back on the sofa and unbuttoned her blouse to expose her silky pink bra that she had picked specifically, hoping Sam would get to see it. A soft moan escaped him as he leaned over and kissed the tops of her breasts. She laid back on the sofa, and as he steadied himself over the top of her, she pulled his shirt off, bringing her lips to his firm chest.

"Wait," Sam said, panting. "Are you sure about this?"

She nodded, the lust bubble building inside of her ready to erupt. "Are you?"

He nodded. "Let's go into my bedroom."

She stood and he grabbed her hand and they walked into the next room. His king-size bed was covered in a soft blanket, which he pulled back. Still standing, he pressed his body against hers. She leaned into him as her desire took over.

Their eyes locked for a moment and their lips met.

Rainey's body was on fire. She wanted him as much as he wanted her. Sam watched as she unzipped her jeans and stepped out of them. Then she removed her bra and underwear. Once she was standing before him naked, he quickly slipped off his pants and boxers and took her in his arms, cupping her butt.

He laid her down on the bed and they slipped between the soft sheets. When Sam reached down between her legs, Rainey's world turned bright and all bad thoughts were erased. She never wanted him to stop, she wished she could live in that state of bliss forever. She pushed him on his back and straddled him. They kissed and rubbed against each other until neither could take it anymore and she helped him inside of her. They moved in a natural rhythm, as though they were created for each other.

"You're so beautiful," he whispered.

After holding out as long as they could, they both climaxed and fell flat against the mattress. Sam was smiling as Rainey giggled while she snuggled closer to him under the soft sheets.

He rolled onto his side and kissed her passionately, "I'm glad you're here."

"Me too," she confessed. "No one has ever made me feel this way."

"Well," he said, bouncing his eyebrows. "I hope that no one other than me ever makes you feel that way again."

Rainey's throat tightened and her muscles tensed, wondering if he really knew what he was saying, or if it was just in the moment. At her very core she wanted him to mean it.

"I'm pretty sure you'll change your mind after a good night's sleep," she chided, nervous that she'd be right.

Sam shook his head and looked into her eyes. "No, there's nothing that will change how I feel about you. I knew I wanted to be with you from the moment I saw you at The Sanctuary. I kept telling myself I was too old for you. Then after all those lunches we shared, I convinced myself that age doesn't matter. But the bottom line is, I couldn't get you out of my head." He was quiet then. All of his attention was focused on her. "Well?" he whispered.

Rainey knew what he was waiting for. He wanted her to tell him she felt the same about him, and she did. But she was frightened that she'd lose him like she lost Phoenix and Stoker. To protect herself, forcing her lips into a pout, she said, "I've been thinking about you a lot too," in a theatrical sultry voice.

He laughed. "I see. So I'm just a dude lusting after a young babe."

She rolled onto her side and they laid face-to-face. She sighed and didn't want to leave him hanging; it wasn't fair. "No, Sam. I'm playing with you. The only reason I came here tonight is because I was hoping that we could have something more than a friendship." She kissed his lips softly. "I never imagined a girl like me could ever be with a guy like you."

"A guy like me?" he asked, looking genuinely confused.

"Yeah, you know . . . no criminal record or gang history. A real job. A nice apartment."

In response, he lowered his mouth to hers. As his soft touch caressed her skin, she allowed herself to let go and enjoyed the comfort of receiving his love.

Chapter Seventy-Nine

It was close to one o'clock in the morning when Rainey slid out of Sam's bed and grabbed her shirt from the floor. For some reason, she thought staying the whole night would be too pushy.

"Where are you going?" he croaked.

"Home. Where do you think?" she whispered.

"Why not stay here tonight? I'll make you a great breakfast."

"I have things to do in the morning . . ." she said, giving him a sly look and feeling foolish now.

"Like what? Attend Sunday Mass? I want you to stay. Don't go."

She slipped back into the bed and was on her side now with her hands tucked under the pillow. "I guess it depends on what you're making for breakfast."

"Oh, does it now?" He smiled gently, gripping her waist and pulling her closer to him. He kissed her and stroked her hip with his thumb.

Rainey loved the way his eyes sank into hers. She loved the subtle way he touched her without being overtly sexual. She especially loved that he didn't want her to leave. And while she could take care of herself, it was nice to have the security of a man who lived a clean life.

***

After breakfast the next morning, Rainey drove herself back to North Philly. When she walked into her apartment and took in her drab surroundings, some of the lightness she'd felt faded. It was difficult not to compare Sam's beautiful home to hers. She still hadn't been able to afford

real living room furniture, except for a television and a futon she'd bought at a secondhand store.

She'd just gotten out of the shower when there was a knock at her door. Wrapped in a towel, she crept forward and looked through the peephole to see Rosemary standing in the hall.

Grinning and eager to tell Rosemary all about her date with Sam, she pulled the door open wide. "Well, this is a surprise!" she said, but her smile vanished seeing Rosemary's grim expression.

"Can I come in?" Rosemary asked.

"Of course," she said, her nerves kicking in. "Is something wrong?"

"Kind of. Your mom and dad showed up at the shelter this morning, looking for you."

Rainey's heart fell to her stomach. "Is Ivy okay? Did something happen to her? What did they say?"

Rosemary took Rainey's hand. "Sweetie, it's nothing about Ivy. Your aunt Sophie died."

Rainey was dazed as she covered her mouth with her hand. "But I just saw her yesterday morning. She was out of it, but she wasn't sick," she mumbled. Inside, her heart was breaking, and now her mind could only recall the woman she loved to be with, not the one who had laid in bed unable to speak.

"They said she had a stroke."

"Oh, no," Rainey said, a numbness settling over her. "I'm gonna get dressed and go to the nursing home."

"I'll come with you."

Grateful for Rosemary's friendship, she took a step toward her bedroom and turned back to the woman and gave her a long hug. "I don't know where I'd be without you," she said, tears streaming down her cheeks.

"The feeling is mutual. Now go on and get yourself together."

Rainey took heavy steps to her bedroom and dressed. Fifteen minutes later, they got into Rosemary's car and she drove them to Ridley Park. When they arrived at the nursing home one of the day nurses, Nicole, who knew Rainey from her visits with Sophie, rushed up to her.

"I'm so sorry about your aunt Sophie," Nicole offered.

Rainey gave the nurse a hug. "Thank you. Can I see her?"

Nicole nodded. "They took her downstairs, but your parents are in her room if you'd like to go see them first. Your aunt had your mother as her

emergency contact, so we called her, and they came back to go through her things. Your parents were so grateful they got to see her before she died."

"What do you mean 'see her before she died'?"

Nicole flipped through the visitor log. "Now, where is it? It should be right here," she said, pointing to a line on the page. "Anyway, they visited her last night; they must've forgotten to sign in." She looked up at Rainey, "It should give you some comfort to know that your mom got to see her sister before she died. So many people regret not having seen their loved one after they're gone," she rambled, not noticing the shock on Rainey's face.

"Okay, thanks," Rainey said. She turned away, swiftly walking to Sophie's room, ready to shred her parents to pieces. She opened the door and stepped inside, with Rosemary on her heels.

"What are you doing here?" she growled, wishing she could make them disappear.

With heavy lids, Miranda turned to her daughter. "What the fuck does that mean? She was my sister."

Rainey was practically vibrating she was so furious. "Up until last night, you haven't come to see her once since she checked herself into this place. You never do anything unless it benefits you in some way, so what's in it for you?"

As the words left her mouth, it was like someone flipped a light switch on inside her head. That was it. There was something for her parents to gain. Her eyes narrowed, looking from her mother to her father. "Well, what's in it for you?"

Peter swayed as he spoke. "It ain't like that, it's just that we know you want Ivy to live with you, and we thought this might be the right time."

"Oh, really? You mean, you're going to defy Jiggy and take her back from him? This isn't adding up."

Peter wagged his finger. "See, that's the thing. Once we pay Jiggy what we owe him we can give Ivy to you."

Rainey's face twisted with disgust. "Ivy is your child, not something you sell to the highest bidder. Do you know what Jiggy has her doing?" Her eyes shifted, drilling into her mother.

Miranda shrugged. "If she had controlled herself and sold the dope for him instead of using it, she wouldn't be hooking for him. Now, would she?"

Blinded by rage, Rainey charged her mother and put her hands around her neck, clutching her in a vise grip. If Rosemary hadn't rushed up behind her and ripped her off, Rainey may have killed her.

"Come on, girl. She ain't worth it," Rosemary whispered.

Miranda gave her daughter a shove. "Who the hell is she," she yelled, pointing to Rosemary, "your fairy-fucking godmother?"

Rosemary smirked. "Bitch, you're fucking with the wrong person. I suggest you go over there," she said, pointing to a chair in the corner, "and sit your blitzed white ass down."

Taking a deep breath to try to calm her nerves, Rainey fixed her hair and tucked it behind her ears. She glared at her father. "All right. Tell me what you want. Just get it over with already."

Chapter Eighty

Peter said nothing as he leaned against the wall with his lips pinched together.

Rainey glanced at the empty hospital bed where her aunt once laid, and then to her wheelchair on the other side of the room. Her heart seized at the thought that Sophie might be looking down on this vile scene of Miranda and Peter fingering her few belongings. Anger welled again and Rainey looked back at her father.

"Spit it out," she said, staring at him.

Peter sighed. "Well, Sophie had a will, but you're the only one getting anything from it."

At first she was confused; it took a second for what she heard to sink in. "Oh, really? How do you know that?"

"Because before she came here to shrivel up and die, she gave your mother a copy. Boy-oh-boy that pissed your mom off that she wasn't in it. Didn't it, Miranda?"

Miranda nodded. "Because she was a bad sister who cared more about other people than she did me."

Rainey's stomach flopped. She needed fresh air, she was suffocating in the small room with her rotten parents. "You both make me sick." She turned to her father. "So, what? You're expecting to get something from me? Tell me what it'll take to make you leave."

"Well, her estate attorney sold her house years ago and got four hundred thousand for it. Plus, she had some savings of about a hundred thousand. Then of course there are her photos, which are actually worth a lot of money, so those can probably be sold for, let's say, another fifty thousand." Peter paused. "All in, you're about to inherit half a million dollars."

Rainey gasped and she covered her mouth with her hand. The room spun and all the color in her face drained away. She reached out for Rosemary's arm to keep from falling. "You're kidding, right?"

"Nope. You know I'd never kid about money."

Feeling unsteady on her feet, Rainey backed away and sat on the edge of the hospital bed. Half a million dollars? How was that even possible? It was an unimaginable amount of money to her and it took several minutes for reality to kick in. Still sitting on the bed, she looked over at her father. "I see, this is why the time is right to give me custody of Ivy. So, how much do you want?"

Peter drew his lips back into an ugly grin. The gluttonous look in his eyes fed Rainey's disgust for him. "All of it," he said casually.

With the urge to pluck his eyeballs out of his skull, she rose to her feet and approached him. "Are you out of your mind?"

He shook his head, still giving her an ugly grin. "You always said you'd do anything for Ivy. Well, here's your chance to prove it."

Miranda giggled and her legs bounced up and down.

Unable to form words through the grief and anger that were tearing her apart, Rainey turned to Rosemary, who stepped forward and grabbed her hand. "She's gonna need a day or so to process everything. After all," she said, leering from Peter to Miranda, "this girl just lost a woman she loved. A woman who took care of her when she was just a pup. She'll be in touch."

Not waiting for a response, Rosemary guided Rainey from the room. When they reached the nurses' station, Rainey stopped and turned to face a nurse. Nicole looked up from her papers and approached the desk.

"I understand that my aunt had a will. Did she leave a copy here?" she asked, needing confirmation from someone she could trust.

Nicole shook her head. "Oh, no. We don't keep copies of wills, but hang on." She went into one of the filing cabinets and returned. "We always require an attorney contact when a patient does have one." She held out a business card. "You should call. I'm sure he'll be able to help you."

Rainey nodded. The only thing she wanted right now was to see Sophie. "You said my aunt is downstairs. Can I see her?" she asked, in a weak voice.

Nicole looked over at the head nurse, who tipped her chin up.

"Yes," she said. "I'll call one of the caretakers to bring you down."

The basement was made of gray cinder blocks that matched Rainey's sadness. Rosemary stayed beside her as they walked down the never-ending corridor to a double door. The room was cold and the overhead lights

were bright. The caretaker wheeled out the sheet-covered table and placed Sophie in the middle of the room. Without hesitating, he pulled the sheet back to the woman's shoulders. When Rainey saw Sophie's face her knees buckled and Rosemary propped her up and walked her forward. Sophie's face was contorted and her years of suffering were evident. The stroke she had was visible, with the right side of her face pulling up as the left remained low.

Staring into her aunt's face, Rainey imagined her young and vibrant. Given how similar they looked, it wasn't hard to see her that way. She stroked what was left of her hair, and the coldness of her flesh reminded her that Sophie was no longer occupying the body that lay on the metal table. She leaned over and kissed Sophie's forehead, then turned and left.

Outside, in the sunshine, she put her head back and absorbed the warmth on her face.

"I want to call her lawyer," she said, fingering the card in her back pocket. "Today."

"You okay, sugar?" Rosemary asked gently.

"I guess so," Rainey said, and as she said it, she realized it was true. She'd said good-bye to Sophie a long time ago. "I'm glad I came to see her a lot before she died."

"How about if we go back to the shelter? I'll get us something to eat and you can make your phone call."

"Yeah, that would be good." Rainey was glad not to have to make any decisions right now. It was nice to have the power of Rosemary with her.

On the ride back to The Sanctuary both women were quiet for a few minutes. Rainey's stomach was in a knot. Plagued by her parents and their cruelty, the acid in her stomach churned. Peter was vile and Miranda had seemed unaffected by her sister's death.

"Rosemary?" she said when she couldn't live with the thoughts of foul play gnawing away at her insides.

"Yeah?"

"Something isn't right."

"I know."

"You do?" Rainey said, turning to look at her.

"Of course I do. I know people, remember?"

"What is it then?"

Rosemary glanced at her sideways, then brought her eyes back to the road. "You think about it some more. You let what's in the far recesses of your mind surface. Don't do you no good if you can't think on your own."

Rainey leaned her forehead against the car window for several minutes, staring at the white line on the road as it whizzed by in a continuous blur. Then her head jerked upright.

"O my God!

Chapter Eighty-One

When they returned to the shelter, Rainey rushed into the office and left a message for the estate lawyer. Then she went to the library and did research on Huntington's disease. Two hours later, she called Sam.

"Hey, Sam. It's me," she said when he picked up. "I need your help."

"Okay," he said, his voice steady. "You sound panicked."

"I'm not, but I'm upset. My aunt Sophie died last night when I was at your place. You remember the one I told you about?"

"Yeah, I do. I'm sorry to hear that."

"Thanks, but there's more to it. She had Huntington's disease and that messed up her brain, but she died of a stroke."

"Okay, I'm not following."

"Well what I found out was, the most common cause of death when you have the disease is pneumonia. People with it don't normally die of a stroke. I mean, anything can happen, but it's not common. But do you know what does cause a stroke? I'll tell you: an overdose of cocaine."

"I'm sorry, Rainey. I don't understand."

She was wrestling with the thoughts in her head and how to articulate them to Sam. "All right," she said, taking a few loud breaths to calm her nerves. "Here's the thing. According to the nurse, my parents visited my aunt for the first time ever last night, and then they found her dead early this morning." She was quiet, letting her words marinate.

"You think your parents killed her?"

Rainey hesitated. "I think it's possible. My aunt had a will that they knew about and she left everything to me. This morning, they came to the shelter looking for me after the nursing home contacted my mom about my aunt. Then when I get to the nursing home they're there going through her stuff. That's when they told me about the will."

"Okay, but if your aunt left everything to you, then why would they care if she's dead?"

"Because they told me if I give them all the inheritance, they would sign over custody of Ivy to me. That means I can get her off the streets and bring her to live with me."

"Aren't they parents of the year?" he said sarcastically. "What can I do to help?"

"I need an autopsy performed on my aunt. I have to know what killed her. I don't know how to stop the coroner, who is picking her up tomorrow, from doing anything with her body. She's being cremated."

"Right. What's the name of the nursing home where your aunt's body is now?"

"Wooded Creek in Ridley Park."

"All right," he said. "Sit tight and I'll make a few phone calls."

"You can help me with this?" she asked, thrilled.

"Luckily, this is one thing I can do for you. I have a detective buddy who owes me a favor and I'll call and ask him to investigate. He's the best at putting together homicide cases."

Rainey's shoulders rolled forward and she allowed herself to cry. She didn't care that Sam could hear her. They were tears of gratitude. "I'd appreciate anything you can do. You know I don't care about the money," Rainey sobbed.

"I know. I know that you'd give them every penny if it would enable you to help Ivy."

She nodded. "Yes," she said quietly.

"Out of curiosity, because I know my friend will ask, do you know how much money you'll inherit?"

"I don't know for sure; I haven't talked to the estate lawyer yet, but according to my parents it's about half a million dollars."

"Wow," Sam breathed. "That's a lot."

"It is, I can barely wrap my mind around what it would be like to have that much money."

"Can I ask something more personal?"

"Umm, maybe."

"Do you know who Ivy's pimp is? I know who controls most of that area, but there are a couple of pimps who work their girls at the Liberty Motel."

She paused for several moments, trying to appear thoughtful instead of rattled. The thought of Jiggy and the problems he would cause prompted her silence. Think before you speak, she told herself. "No, actually I'm not sure," she said carefully. "Maybe she doesn't have a pimp."

"Okay, just thought I'd ask. I'll go make those calls." He paused. "Hey, how about if I pick you up around five tonight? We can make dinner together at my place."

Comfort washed over her as she welcomed the escape from everything that had happened that day. "That sounds nice."

"All right, then. I'll pick you up at the shelter or your apartment?"

"The shelter is fine."

"See you tonight. I should have some information for you by then. Bye."

"Sam?" she blurted before he disconnected the call.

"Yeah? Did you forget something?"

"Thank you for everything."

"I'm happy I can help. See you when I see you."

After they hung up, she sat at the desk, feeling both grief and happiness at once. Grief for losing Sophie and happiness for finding Sam. Eventually, Rainey settled on the hope that Sam could help her prove that her parents had killed Sophie.

Chapter Eighty-Two

Sam pulled out a stool at the breakfast bar, pouring a glass of cranberry juice into a wineglass for Rainey. "You sit here and watch me cook," he said, smiling at her. As he was chopping and stirring, she watched him contentedly. This is nice, just the two of us enjoying time together, peaceful happiness, she thought.

A while later, she put her elbows on the counter and rested her chin on her hands. "I'm dying to know if you heard anything about my aunt."

Sam cut into a loaf of bread and glanced at her. The hesitation in his eyes told Rainey she had been right to suspect them.

"So according to the nurses working last night your parents visited your aunt. However, they never signed the visitor book. But I spoke with three nurses who saw them and an orderly who spoke with them briefly. Also my friend Martin, the homicide detective I mentioned—he called the coroner and they're going to hold the body until you talk to the estate attorney. If your aunt gave you power of attorney, which is likely, then you'll be able to request an autopsy."

Rainey took a breath. "And if we find out that she died of an overdose, then will Martin arrest my parents?"

Sam's eyes shifted down and he shook his head. "It's not that easy. If she died of an overdose of drugs, then we'll need evidence that your parents are the ones that killed her."

"They were there the night she died. What other proof do the cops need?" Rainey asked, aggravated that her parents might get away with murder.

"That's the tricky part. I think you should take it one step at a time on this."

She leaned back against the barstool and looked up at the ceiling. "Hopefully, this lawyer will call me first thing in the morning."

Sam stopped cooking and went over to her. "You'll need to make funeral arrangements. Have you thought about that?"

She shook her head. "I don't know anything about funerals. When Stoker died, the club took care of everything. Doesn't the funeral place do all that stuff?"

"They do, but you need to be prepared to make decisions. I can go there with you tomorrow if you'd like. I had to make the arrangements for my uncle when he died."

"I'd like that." Rainey was overflowing with gratitude that Sam was there for her. She knew how lucky she was to have him in her life.

"Okay," Sam said, stepping back and clapping his hands together, "since that's settled we're going to eat and then I thought we could take a walk. How's that sound?"

Her gaze flitted around the kitchen as she pinched the skin around her throat and he turned to see why she hadn't answered.

"What? If you don't want to go for a walk," he chuckled, "you can say no."

"That's not it." She stood and went to put her arms around his waist and looked up into his eyes. "I want to go to the Liberty Motel tonight. I haven't been there in a couple of days and with everything going on it would make me feel better if I could see her."

Sam's stood up straighter and puffed out his chest. "Okay, I'll drive you there but we can't stay all night. Is that a deal?"

She laid the side of her face against his chest and nodded. "Deal. Thanks."

Sam put his fingers under her chin and lifted her head. His face came down and their lips met. He kissed her gently, stroking her lips with his tongue as she softly nibbled his bottom lip.

"Rainey Paxton, you are a hard woman to resist."

She got on her tippytoes and kissed him again. "I know. So don't resist me then," her voice rumbled with a mischievous grin.

"Oh, good, you're humble too," he joked.

Rainey shrugged. "Are we gonna eat or are you gonna keep talking?"

"Damn, girl, you're pushy."

Rainey went to his cutting board, grabbed a carrot stick, took a bite, and moved to the stove to see what was cooking.

Sam watched her, and in his eyes she looked like an angel. Her hard upbringing somehow made her seem a superhero to him. It wasn't easy to understand how she overcame the poverty and injustice that she'd been served. Yet there she was in his kitchen, seemingly at peace with the skin she lived in. He thought she was remarkable.

***

Sam's mind wandered to the conversation with his sister the day before.

"Sam, you're dating the girl that was a child when you busted her."

"I know, Eileen, but she's not a child anymore. Come on, she's twenty-one years old, soon to be twenty-two, I might add."

Eileen huffed intentionally so Sam could hear her disapproval. "Forget all of that, Sam. How do you know she's not using you for money or a place to live or something? I'm nervous that she'll bring riffraff into your life. You're a drug agent. You need to be careful."

"Always the nagging little sister," he teased. "I understand your concern, but you need to trust me on this. Rainey has been through many bad things, but she's remained a good person. She doesn't mess around with drugs and when she got out of juvie she worked a shitty job for years, cleaning motel rooms to support herself. Rainey is doing her best to take control of her life."

"She cleaned motel rooms?"

"Yeah, in a crappy area of town in a fleabag motel. You have to give her credit."

Eileen blew out a breath into the phone. "I give you credit and I trust you. Just be careful. Promise?"

He snickered. "Yeah, I'll be careful. You know, I want you to meet her."

"One day at a time, brother. I'm not sure I want you to date her, let alone me meeting her."

"Always the skeptic."

***

"Sam? Hello? Earth to Sam?" Rainey sang.

He shook his head like a dog shaking water from its fur. “Sorry, I had a moment.”

“I see that. As I was saying, it kinda looks like you might be burning the chicken, Mr. Gourmet Chef.”

“Oh, shit.” Sam jumped forward and turned the burner down.

Rainey grabbed two plates, and as she set the table for dinner, she thought of her aunt Sophie. It gave her great sorrow that the woman had died with her parents, the Devils backbone, at her bedside.

Chapter Eighty-Three

The next three days were busy as Rainey arranged for Sophie's funeral. She met with the estate lawyer, the funeral director, and the medical examiner between her shifts at the post office and trying to still spend time at The Sanctuary.

On Wednesday evening, Rainey was stretched out on Sam's sofa with her legs draped over his lap. "Aunt Sophie's lawyer confirmed most of what my parents told me. Her entire estate is worth about half a million dollars. I can't believe it. It's hard to imagine what that much money even looks like. Anyway, the medical examiner told me he'd have the toxicology results by the end of this week. Your friend Martin hooked me up."

Sam gently slid his hand over her thigh. "Yeah, Martin is a good guy." He leaned over and gave her a quick kiss on her cheek. "You've had a few rough days, haven't you?"

She held his gaze. "I know I haven't been the best date since this all happened. It's hard to concentrate when I have so many other things to worry about."

"Get that out of your head. You don't need to worry about me, on top of everything else. Have you told your parents about the service you're having for your aunt?"

She shook her head. "Why bother? It's not like they'd show. Plus, no matter what happens, I know they gave her an overdose and she would never want them there."

***

On Friday afternoon, finished with her mail route, Rainey was sitting on the floor in her living room when the phone rang.

"Miss Paxton?" an unfamiliar voice said when she answered.

"Yeah, who's this?"

"This is Dr. Madden, the medical examiner. I've concluded the autopsy and have received the toxicology results. I've determined that Sophie Anderson's death was caused by an overdose of cocaine. I'll be reaching out to Detective Martin Freeman who, as we discussed, initially contacted me. Given the state of Miss Andersen's physical and mental health, I've concluded that she would not have been capable of administering the drugs herself."

Rainey's chest and throat burned as the bile rose from the anger boiling in her belly. "How were the drugs given to her?"

"They were injected. I found a needle mark under one of her toenails."

Rainey cringed. Her hand flew over her mouth and she closed her eyes tight trying to block out the image of her parents killing her aunt.

"Whoever did this, did it intending to hide all signs that drugs were given. I'm sure Detective Freeman will be looking into what happened at the nursing home," Doctor Madden said. "Do you have any questions for me?"

"I don't think so," Rainey said, her voice cracking. "Thank you for calling me."

"Of course and, I'm sorry for your loss."

The minute she'd hung up with the medical examiner, she'd called Sam and told him everything. "I told you they did it. I knew it," she bawled.

"I'm coming over," Sam said, hanging up the telephone and immediately calling Rosemary.

Thirty minutes later, he was knocking at her door. She pulled it open and immediately collapsed against his chest as a sob broke free.

Sam pulled her closer, stroking her back. "You're going to be fine. You're not alone. I'm here now and Rosemary is on her way over."

Rainey let out a low, guttural sigh. Her arms dropped to her sides. In a strangled voice she said, "They killed her and I can't prove it. My parents murdered her." She pushed away from him and her arms flung wildly through the air. "I always knew they never cared about anyone else, but this? Oh, but wait!" she screamed. "They're addicts oh, boo-hoo-hoo, they couldn't possibly be responsible, since they didn't know what they were doing. I'm so fucking tired of them," she ranted. She folded her arms over

her chest and paced the small room. She stopped and glared at Sam. "Why am I always surprised at what they are willing to do to get high?"

"Because you've been waiting for them to come to their senses, to stop taking drugs and take responsibility for what they've done to you and Ivy. Sadly, that's never going to happen. But I think you've always known that they weren't capable. You've clung to this image of parents that don't exist. I see it all the time in my line of work. Families holding onto the pictures in their heads of what life was like before drugs or what it would be like if their family member stayed sober."

Rainey nodded; it was satisfying that he understood her so well.

"Why can't I just let it go?" she asked. "I already knew everything you just told me, but I keep tricking myself into having some hope that they'll change."

Sam sat on the futon and pulled in a long breath. "Look, being loved by our parents is a fundamental need for children. It's what every kid deserves. No child should have to dream about love or wish for it, that's the balance of life. Your parents denied you that balance, and it's not fair. Your parents, like other addicts, aren't capable of giving their children what they need. They never were. Their first love is drugs. Period."

"Does doing drugs give them a pass for being rotten people?"

"No, never. They chose to take drugs. They made a bigger choice to have children knowing that they have an addiction."

Rainey sat on the floor with her chin dipped to her chest. "That's it, then. They killed my aunt and now they'll walk away with all of her money and spend it on shoveling more dope into their veins. But in the end," she said more lightly, "I'll have legal custody of my sister."

Sam moved onto the floor next to her. "This is exactly why I do what I do. I've seen a lot of kids ruined by their mom or dad or both, like in your case. But you know what, Rainey?"

She glanced at him sideways, lifted her shoulders, and let them drop, exhausted.

"You made it through the other side without being ruined. You're more powerful than they could ever be. They didn't break you. That means there's a chance you'll pull your sister out of the dark hole they've buried her in."

"I hope you're right." Rainey didn't feel all that confident right then. When she'd seen Ivy at the Freedom Motel the other night, she looked

more gangly then usual and was staggering, barely holding her body up on the sidewalk.

He put his arm over her and she laid her head on his shoulder.

"Is that it? We have a funeral for my aunt and life goes on?"

"I don't know. Martin is investigating. If there's any evidence to indict them, he's the man who'll find it. I'm not convinced he'll find much, but we need to let him do his job."

She grimaced. "I hope he finds something." She lifted her head from his shoulder and looked down at her hands. "If I don't have hope then I don't have anything. My entire life was created on hope. Hoping that I could find enough food, hoping to raise Ivy right, hoping I'd have a better life outside of juvie, hoping that someday I'd find someone who believed in me . . . and I've found two people you and Rosemary. See? That's why I need hope in my life."

There was a knock at the door and Sam went to answer it. He let Rosemary in and she rushed past him. "Oh, sugar," she said misty-eyed as she sat on the floor beside her. "I'm so sorry. Sam told me what the medical examiner found. You listen, I think you need some time to absorb all this toxic waste that's been dumped on ya. After the funeral, we need to make a plan so you can reenergize."

"I'll be fine," Rainey said, offering her a weak smile. "I still have a lot to do after the funeral."

"Like what?"

Rainey looked at the ceiling and slowly shook her head. "I have to meet with the attorney and get the check. Then I have to contact those deadbeats and figure out how to make sure I get legal custody of Ivy before I give them the money."

She saw Rosemary give Sam a tight smile, which he returned with a curt nod. Rainey wondered what was being communicated between them but was too tired to ask.

"There's a lot to figure out," Rosemary said gently. "And your sister, she's deep into something that ain't gonna be easy to get her out of, it don't matter how much money you pay."

Rainey couldn't focus anymore; she'd reached her limit and needed everything to stop moving so fast. She stood up quickly and walked toward her bedroom. "Can I talk to you for a minute in private?" she said to Rosemary. She turned to Sam. "It's nothing against you, I swear."

Inside her bedroom with the door closed, she whispered, "Don't mention Jiggy. Sam asked me if I knew who Ivy's pimp was and I told him I didn't."

Rosemary scratched her cheek and in an uncertain tone, asked, "Why the hell would you lie to him about that? Did you ever think for one hot minute that he might be able to help you with that bastard?"

She shook her head. "No, maybe he'll put him in prison for a while, but that piece of shit will come out and find us to make sure he gets revenge for his prison time. I know it."

"He didn't come after you when you got outta juvie," she countered.

"He never went to prison. Besides, he had Ivy and knew the best way to punish me was to torture her. My parents have always known that about me and I'm sure they told him. Look," Rainey said throwing her hands in the air, "I just told you my reasons for keeping this information from Sam. Are you going to back me or not?"

Rosemary looked into Rainey's fiery eyes. "Of course I'll back you. I told you before, that I got you, no matter what. But you listen to me real good, child . . . you gots to be careful of that man Jiggy. He's a monster and he ain't got no soul."

"I know that, Rosemary. But that asshole will never outsmart me, ever!"

When they returned to the living room Sam eyed them both up and down. "Everything okay?"

Rosemary nodded. "I gotta go. I'm gonna plan a lunch for after the funeral. There's just a handful of us attending. Will you be there?"

"Yes, I'll be there," he answered in a somber voice.

"Your auntie is getting cremated today?" Rosemary asked Rainey.

The girl shook her head. "Tomorrow. I'm going to the funeral home in the morning to see her before they . . . they, ugh, turn her to ashes. I pushed the memorial service back to Sunday."

"You need me to tag along and keep you company?" Rosemary asked.

Before Rainey could answer, Sam took a step toward the two of them. "I planned on going with her. As long as that's okay with you, Rainey."

"That would be great. I'm nervous."

Rainey insisted on sleeping at her apartment that night; she wanted time alone to sort through her feelings. The next morning, Sam picked her up and drove her to the funeral home. She was quiet sitting in the car next to him, reflecting on her gratitude for the time she had with her aunt even though it was so long ago.

Chapter Eighty-Four

At the funeral home, the director led Rainey into a viewing room. Lying there in a coffin, bathed and dressed, Sophie wore a purple dress with white daisies that Rainey had bought. Her hair, what was left of it, had been combed straight down on either side of her face.

"She looks so different than how I remember her from when I was a little girl." She reached in her back pocket and pulled out the picture she'd taken of her aunt that last day they were together. The one she had snagged from her house that first night out of juvie.

"She was beautiful," Sam commented. "You look exactly like her."

Rainey smiled. "People always thought I was her daughter. I loved that I looked like her. I suppose my mom hated me more because of that; she and my aunt had a rocky relationship. Aunt Sophie didn't make excuses for my parents' drug habit or for neglecting me."

Rainey looked down at her aunt. She touched her face and laid her head on her chest. "'Bye, Aunt Sophie. Thanks for giving me a chance and helping me understand that there was more to life than those walls I was raised in. I swear to you, I'm gonna do everything I can to do the same for Ivy."

She turned and planted her face onto Sam's chest. A wail broke free and she sobbed. She cried for the loss of her aunt and the cruel way she'd died. Not just the cocaine, but also the years of deterioration of both mind and body. It didn't seem fair it would happen to a good person who took care of herself, unlike her mother and father.

She gathered herself and she looked up at Sam. "I'm ready to go."

That night, Rainey drove her car to the Liberty Motel. She got out and with fearless determination, walked the block and a half to where Ivy was

standing. As she got closer, she could see that her sister's eyes were stretched wide open and she was grinding her teeth.

"Ivy?"

It took Ivy a few seconds to recognize her. "What, man? What do you want?" she asked, her finger twitching and her head clicking to the side several times.

"Oh, Ivy. How much speed did you take?"

The girl's eyes were frantic, searching the sidewalk, looking for a john.

Rainey reached for her hand, but she yanked it away. "Stop. I need to make some money or he's gonna kill me."

"Who? Jiggy?"

She nodded. "He'll make Rooster beat me first, then he'll finish me off." Her head jerked in abnormal ways that appeared painful. "I've seen him do it before," she said, seizing her sister's attention with her protruding, unblinking brown eyes.

"I don't understand what you're saying. Tell me what's happening."

Ivy rubbed her arms. "I had a couple of johns tonight, but I used the money to buy dope."

Rainey's stomach clamped down as she observed her sister's bizarre behavior. *She is following in our parents' footsteps.*

"How much money do you need to give to Jiggy?" she asked, saddened.

Ivy's bulging eyeballs moved about like a ping-pong ball. Rainey looked on in horror at her grotesque, unnatural movements and sloppy demeanor.

"Ahhhh, I bought a hundred dollars' worth."

"Do you have any left?"

Ivy reached into her bra and pulled out a bag with a tiny bit of powder at the bottom. "I can't share it with you, though, 'cause I need it for later."

Rainey looked from her sister to the motel. "Okay, I'll give you the hundred dollars. Let's go to the motel and get a room."

"Sure. I mean, I never did a chick and you're my sister and all, but shit man, money is money."

Rainey snatched her arms with such force it made Ivy stumble in her high heels as she put her face up against hers. "I don't want to get laid. I came here to help you. Now, turn around and follow me into the motel. Keep your fucking mouth shut and let me do the talking."

Inside the motel, the same unkempt man peered at them. He looked Rainey up and down. "I know you from somewhere."

"No, you don't. I want a room."

"Really? You had to pick the youngest crackhead out there?" he said, scowling at Ivy.

"How about you shut your fat mouth and give me a room?" Rainey bit back.

The man scoffed. "Whatever you say, babe. Its twenty-five bucks a half-hour or forty-five for an hour. The hour is the better deal. What do you want?"

She rolled her eyes and slid enough cash for an hour through the tray below the window.

"Here you go," he said with a greasy smile, pushing back a room key. "Enjoy yourself with the little freak."

Rainey snatched the key, gripped Ivy's hand, and headed toward the room. She unlocked the motel room door and pushed it open. She stood back and let her sister enter first. Then she stepped inside and locked the door behind them.

"This place is disgusting," she remarked as her little sister lay comfortably on the bed. She walked over to the chair and grabbed Ivy's purse.

"Hey man, what are you doing?" Ivy whined.

"Shut up," Rainey spat, upset and annoyed by everything that was happening.

Ivy went quiet and leaned back on her elbows to watch.

Rainey turned the purse upside down on the bed. Her ears rang as she looked up at her sister, horrified. Her knees were rubbery as she tried to steady herself.

"No, please, no. Oh, Ivy."

Chapter Eighty-Five

Ivy let her head drop back on the hard mattress. "What the hell do you want from me?"

Rainey picked up the hypodermic needle. She grabbed the girl and pushed her sleeves up, taking in the marks on her arms. "Ivy, what have they done to you? What have you done to yourself? You've seen what drugs did to Mom and Dad."

Ivy pulled her arms free and rolled to her side, avoiding Rainey's intense, penetrating stare. "When I was selling dope for Jiggy, everything was fine. Then one night, he shot me up before having sex with me. Once I got a taste of it, I couldn't stop. So I started skimming from his stash. Then I kept taking more and more until he found out. Jiggy moved me to his house with some other girls and that's the whole dumb story. Are you happy now?"

Rainey walked around the bed and sat down. She brushed Ivy's hair back from her face. "No, I'm not happy," she said, keeping her voice calm. "I'm very sad and I don't know how to get you to listen to me. We have to get you help so you can get clean." She lifted Ivy's arm and looked at the track marks again. Tears bit at her eyes. "I know that things have been hard for you. The thing is if you don't stop using drugs now, you'll ruin your entire life."

"What life?" she grumbled. "I'm a prisoner. All I do is have sex and sleep. Sometimes there isn't even enough food at the house and all the girls fight over it. I'm smaller than the rest of them." She looked down at her track marks. "The other girls are a lot older than me and they smack me around."

Rainey's face flushed a bright pink with anger and her hands rolled into fists. "What girls? You show me who they are and I'll kick the shit outta them."

"Yeah okay, you wish. You'd never get near those bitches. Rooster and the other guys are always watching all of us. Those guys think it's funny when the other girls pick on me so they don't stop 'em."

"Oh, yeah? Well, they'll all be sorry one day."

Ivy gave her sister a side glance. "I know you say you're not afraid and that you mean it, but you don't know these people. They'll kill you."

"Look, I know that they're bad people who have no regard for life. But I got over my fear of dying when I was sent to juvie. I never left you, Ivy. The drugs belonged to Jiggy and they threatened to hurt you if I didn't do what they told me."

Ivy lit a cigarette and took a long drag. "Well, you did it all for nothing because they hurt me anyway. Ha! So dumb."

"I know they hurt you. I can see that and I wish I could've done something to help you before it got to this," she said, rubbing the girl's arm.

Ivy jerked her arm away. "So what are we gonna do here?"

"We're going to stay in here for an hour so you can rest. Then I'll give you a hundred dollars to take back to Rooster. In exchange, I want you to try to stop taking drugs so you can keep your mind straight," she said, reaching inside Ivy's bra and pulling out the small bag of powder.

Ivy jumped up from the bed. "Give me that, you bitch!"

Rainey stood, opened the bag and poured it onto the dirty carpet. As her sister dove to the floor Rainey ran her foot over the powder, smashing it into the fibers.

"Why did you do that?" Ivy cried, looking up at her from her hands and knees. "I needed it. I hate you. All you do is make everything worse for me."

Like a swift punch to the gut, Rainey's breath shot out. Then she lifted her little sister from under her armpits and looked into her face. "This ends here. This ends now. Do you understand me?"

Rainey wrapped her arms around her, but Ivy turned her head away and broke free. "Give me my hundred bucks. I need to get back out there before someone finds out that I'm in here with you."

"We have a whole hour," Rainey argued, but Ivy just jutted her hand forward again. Sighing, she reached into her pocket and gave her sister the money. "Please, Ivy, you need to be careful and take care of yourself. Make sure you give the hundred dollars to Rooster and don't buy more dope with it."

Ivy turned, grabbed her purse, and slid her feet into her high heels. "I ain't buying dope with it, I'm buying my safety. It was great doing business with you, big sister," she said, then opened the door and walked out.

Rainey slumped on the edge of the bed and pressed her hands over her face. No tears would come out. She had been crying for days over her aunt. And now Ivy was drifting farther away and she was scared it was already too late. Her mind was worn out. She was tired of thinking and worrying, but most of all she was sick of the anger. It was eating her up from the inside out.

***

It was almost two in the morning when Rainey tapped lightly on Rosemary's door. She knew her friend would be sleeping, but she needed to talk. A few minutes later, Rosemary pulled the door open, rubbing her eyes.

"What are you doin' here, darlin'? Is everything okay?" she asked, grabbing her hand and pulling her inside.

"I went to see Ivy tonight. I rented a room and spent some time with her," Rainey said flatly. "She's shooting dope now."

"O Lord. Come on and sit down," she said, gesturing toward the sofa. "I'll make us some coffee."

After Rainey relayed what had happened, Rosemary clasped her hands together. "It sounds like your little sister might already be too far gone." She held her palms up to Rainey. "I'm not trying to tell you what to do. And I know you don't wanna hear that about Ivy right now, but I care about you and I need to give it to you straight."

"But I think there's still hope. She's young and she hasn't been using for that long."

"You ain't got no idea how long she's been using. And you know better than anyone that using once is enough to use your whole life long. I think it's time for you to accept that she might not ever be coming home to you."

Rainey stood and shook her head. She raked her fingers through her hair. "No, I can't accept that. If that happens, then what's the point in me being here?"

Rosemary clucked her tongue. "Listen, Rainey. God didn't put you on this green earth just to save your sister. He put you here to do good for

yourself and others who cross your path. She ain't your only work to do. Now, I'm not saying don't try to help her, she is your sister, but you can't put the worth of your entire life into saving one other person. There are lots of people who need you. The kids at the shelter, Sam, and sure as I sit here, me."

Rainey scooted closer to Rosemary until their thighs were pressed together. "I know what you're saying is right, but I can't give up on her. You have to see it through my eyes, I always considered her my own child and I know the person she can be. She's my only family."

Rosemary nodded and patted her leg. "I'll be right beside you in battle, my friend. But keep something in mind. Family doesn't always come from a bloodline. You're my family and we ain't even the same race, but that doesn't matter none to us, does it?"

"Of course not."

"And you'd do anything for me, right?" Rosemary asked.

"You know I would."

"And," Rosemary wagged her finger, "I'd do anything for you, even if it was illegal."

Rainey turned and looked into the woman's face. She is serious. "Illegal?"

"Sure, why not? I did a lot of illegal stuff in my life. Now, don't get it confused. I won't do nothing immoral."

Rainey frowned. "I'm not seeing the difference."

"Okay. For example, I won't rob a bank 'cause that's just immoral, you know, people gotta work there and other people worked hard to save their money in that bank. But on the other hand, if I gotta break some rules to rescue a kid from a perverted child molesting prick, then I'm gonna do that and be happy about it."

The girl chuckled. "If that's your definition, then I'm all for it."

"Okay, so you wanna give it your best shot to save your baby sister. I got you. Do you have a plan?"

Rainey looked deep into her friend's eyes. She knew without a doubt she could trust her. "Yeah, I have a plan."

Chapter Eighty-Six

On Sunday morning Sam and Rosemary arrived at Rainey's apartment together. When she opened the door, she was wearing a long-sleeved, black chiffon dress that fell four inches below her knees. She had pulled her hair to one side and the long, blond mane was braided with a tasteful black bow securing the tip. She'd bought the dress at a consignment store and fell in love with it immediately. Rainey realized she'd never owned an article of clothing that was as beautiful or feminine.

Sam's head dipped after he looked at her. "Umm, this may seem highly inappropriate for a funeral, but you look beautiful."

Flattered, Rainey gave him a small smile. "Thank you. It's the first really fancy dress I've ever owned." She glanced at Rosemary. "I appreciate you guys coming for me. I'm ready to go. We just need to stop by the funeral home and pick up the urn."

After the funeral home, Sam parked his car on South Third Street in South Philly and the three got out and stood beside it. He and Rosemary stood back as Rainey opened the urn and pulled out a handful of ashes. She walked on the sidewalk and released a small but steady stream of ashes from her hand. After she circled the entire building, she stood with her two friends.

"This was our favorite place." She looked at the Oregon Diner. "We loved it here."

Rosemary held out her arms and they stood in a small circle, holding hands with their heads bowed. "Go on, child, say what ya gotta say to your auntie. We all listening and she's listening too, so tell her everything."

Rainey was quiet for a moment as she pulled her memories forward. "Aunt Sophie? I hope you can hear me. I remember the last time we were together here at the Oregon Diner. It was the day you told me that you

weren't coming to see me anymore because you were sick. I didn't know what that meant at the time . . . all I knew was that I was going to miss you. I was too young to realize the impact your absence would have on my life and on Ivy's life too."

Rainey was quiet for a moment, the images of her aunt running through her mind. Her shoulders curled over and a sob escaped her throat. Rosemary squeezed her hand and she continued.

"The last time you and me were here, I told you I was afraid to lose you because you were the only friend I had. And you told me I was going to have lots of friends. You said things would work out just fine . . . better than I could ever imagine." Her voice cracked and she pulled in a long breath through her nose. "You said I was easy to love, and I believed you . . . that meant everything to me. You must've known what my life would be like because you saw what was coming at me. You told me that I had to remember that I'm easy to love, especially when I feel like nothing is going my way. Maybe you heard my mom or dad tell me I was a hard child to love, they said it all the time. I can't say I've always been perfect at remembering what you told me, but I've tried my best. I have people who love me . . . like the two here with me today. One that I consider my mother, and the other, my best friend. You were so right. And you would love both of them too . . . I just know it."

She looked from Rosemary to Sam and managed a watery smile, her wet cheeks glistening in the sun. Sam made small circles with his hand on her back. "You are easy to love. Your aunt was right."

Rainey took several deep breaths and blew them out slowly. "Aunt Sophie, I will always remember what you did for me and how you stood up to my parents to take care of me as much as you did. Thank you for leaving me the inheritance and I want you to know that I'm using all that you left me to buy my sister's freedom and a chance at life. I know you'd understand why I'm doing it. I hope you have a better life where you're going. You didn't deserve the bad things that happened to you."

"Amen," Rosemary stated, reaching her right hand in the air as if she could touch the hand of God.

Rainey looked at Rosemary, then giggled and cried simultaneously. "You're very passionate about God for someone who had a sketchy profession," she teased.

"That I am! See, I think God guided me through my darkest days. He knows what I did, and I don't doubt for one second that He loves me

anyway. I always looked out for people and helped wherever I could. I think that's all He cares about."

Sam smiled at both women. "You two are good for each other."

Rosemary threw her arm over Rainey's shoulder. "You bet your sweet ass we are. Come on now, let's go inside and get us some food."

Inside the Oregon Diner, a few teenagers from The Sanctuary whom Rainey was especially close to were waiting. There was also a man in a suit who stood and greeted Sam.

"This is my buddy, Martin Freeman. He's the homicide detective looking into your aunt's death."

Rainey shook his hand. "Thanks for helping me with the medical examiner and everything. I can't believe you came here, though; that's super nice of you."

"Well," Martin said, giving her a grin, "you're the first woman this man has ever talked about," he said putting his arm over Sam's shoulder. "I wanted to pay my respects to you and your aunt, but truth is, I was also curious to meet the woman who stole his heart."

Sam flushed a deep crimson. "Dude, a little over the top. We haven't been dating for that long. You're going to scare her off."

Rainey gave him a lazy grin, tired from the heavy emotions of the past week and welcoming a bit of humor. "Wait. I didn't know we were dating," she joked.

Martin smiled broadly. "Oh, I like you already."

She smirked. "All joking aside, Sam's been great. He's been my rock."

"A-hem," Rosemary tooted behind her.

"Right, sorry. Sam has been one of my two rocks."

When the waitress came over to take their order, Rainey stared at the menu. "I'll have a burger and fries." She turned to the others. "That's what me and Aunt Sophie always ordered here." Sam looked around the table. "We'll all have the same thing in honor of Sophie."

By the time they were leaving the restaurant, Rainey was so exhausted she fought to keep her eyes open.

"You look tired," Sam said, taking her hand in his.

"I am. I haven't been sleeping well."

Sam ran his fingers over her head to the ends of her long braid.

"How about if you stay with me for a few days?" he asked. "I have to work, but I can still cook and it'll give you time to relax."

"That sounds like a damn good idea to me," Rosemary added, cocking her head to the side.

Rainey nodded. "But I don't have any clothes with me."

Rosemary held her palms up. "Don't worry about a thing. I'll go get some from your apartment and drop them off to you later. Maybe Sam can make me dinner while I'm there."

On the ride back to Sam's apartment Rainey's tired thoughts drifted to her sister. She had some work to do if there was any chance of saving Ivy. She hoped that the price to free her from Jiggy wasn't more than she could handle.

Chapter Eighty-Seven

One week later, Rainey got into her car and drove to the Strawberry Mansion section of the city. She parked and looked up at the house with concern. Spending the week at Sam's had been the break she'd needed, but it was time to work her plan on helping Ivy. Putting both hands on the steering wheel, she rested her forehead and took in the quiet, allowing it to seep inside her head. Then she opened the car door and walked up to the front door with purpose.

Much to Rainey's disappointment, Kiki answered the door. "What the hell do you want?"

Too tired to argue, Rainey said calmly, "I need to talk to Boulder. It's important."

Kiki cackled. "I think you better take your whore ass outta here before I beat it."

Thankfully, Rainey noticed Boulder coming up behind her. "Kiki," he growled, "you don't decide who I talk to."

Kiki's eyes narrowed at her ol' man, but she stepped back into the house.

"Can we take this down to the clubhouse?" Rainey asked.

Boulder looked over his shoulder at Kiki, turned back and nodded. When they reached the sidewalk, he said, "I'm surprised to see you here. I didn't think you'd return the car without me hunting you down," he said with a smile.

"I'm not here to return the car," she said, keeping her tone even. "I'm here . . . I'm here because I need your help. I'm desperate."

"Desperate, huh?" he said, giving her a side glance. "Well, let's see if there's something I can do then."

Inside the clubhouse, Boulder led Rainey upstairs to a bedroom that had been made into an office.

"Oh, I had no idea you had an office up here," she said.

He nodded and lit a cigarette. "We don't bring the ol' ladies up here. This is strictly for business and when I need to have private conversations." He sat behind the desk and she took a seat in a chair across from him. "So, what's on your mind?"

"My sister."

Boulder groaned. "Come on. How many times do we need to talk about this? Jiggy is off-limits."

"That's not what I wanted to ask you."

"Oh," he shifted in his leather chair. "Then go on."

"I need someone to go with me to the Liberty Motel and make sure she's okay. You know, I'm nervous to go there by myself," she fibbed, remembering Rosemary's words. Sometimes we can't understand how bad things are until we see them with our own eyes.

His gaze was steady, watching her carefully.

Rainey reached across the desk and put her hand over his. "I was hoping you'd go with me. I thought if some of the people working the area saw us together, I could keep going there on my own and nobody would mess with me."

Boulder's chest puffed out. "What makes you think people seeing me with you will make a difference?"

"Oh, come on, Boulder. Everyone on the streets knows you're the president of the Devils Angels. And you also know that people show you respect even if they hate you because of the power you have in this town." She sat back and watched him process the information.

"I can send one of my guys with you. They'll keep an eye out and make sure you're safe."

She shook her head. "That's not gonna work. I need people to see you. Nothing against your brothers, but they aren't you. Will you go with me?"

When he didn't answer quickly, she was worried he'd say no. So she added, "I would only feel safe if it was you who went with me."

His eyes moved up to hers, and Rainey's heart hammered, waiting for his answer. Boulder thought back to one of his last conversations with Stoker; the one where he was adamant that he needed to get his ol' lady's sister away from Jiggy.

"Okay, I'll go with you. When?"

***

Two days later, Rainey drove back to the Devils Angels' clubhouse, parked the car, and slid into the passenger seat of Boulder's van.

"All right. Let's do this," she said in a somber tone.

"You ain't gotta be worried. We'll be fine. I have a few of the fellas following us just in case any of those douchebags try anything."

She turned her head to the passenger window and watched the scenery roll by, hoping that Ivy would be at the Liberty Motel that night.

Once they were parked, Rainey sat forward and looked through the windshield. The street was more crowded than usual and a lot of hookers were milling about, when she finally spotted Ivy, and pointed. "There. That's her."

Boulder leaned forward, squinting. "Which one?"

"See the one in the red shorts and midriff top?"

"The kid with her ass hanging out?"

Rainey narrowed her eyes and glared at him. "Yes, that one."

He pulled out a cigarette and lit it. "Listen, you know the club has women working for us. This ain't nothing different than what they're doing."

"Except my sister isn't a woman. She's twelve, remember?"

Boulder nodded thoughtfully. "That's a shame for her. It's a hard life being a hooker, always having people telling you what to do."

They both sat silently and watched. Several minutes later Rainey saw Rooster approaching Ivy. He snatched her up by the hair, backhanded her, and she fell to the ground.

"What the fuck is he doing to her?" Boulder said, reaching for his door handle and charging out of the van.

Rainey followed Boulder toward the scene. By the time they reached Ivy and Rooster, who was now kicking her, Boulder was so mad that Rainey thought she could see the steam coming off the top of his head.

"You better take your hands offa that kid," Boulder growled.

Rooster turned and glared at him. "Who do you think you're talking to, bitch?"

Boulder stepped forward so the streetlight shined on him.

Rooster squinted for a few seconds, then his eyes grew large and his mouth was slightly open. He looked past Boulder and saw four Devils Angels standing several feet behind their boss.

Rooster lifted his hand in the air, and within seconds six of his men rushed behind him. He swayed his hips, “Your choice. What you wanna do? I suggest you think about it carefully ’cause Jiggy is on his way.”

Ivy gasped and Rainey’s heart pattered in her chest.

Boulder stood his ground.

Rainey looked on, holding her breath, afraid this wouldn’t end well.

Chapter Eighty-Eight

Rainey rushed to Ivy and lifted her to her feet. The girl's head rolled. She looked at her older sister and mumbled incoherently.

"Shit! You're stoned."

Ivy's eyes rolled back in her head. Then she let out a snorting giggle. Boulder's gaze moved to the younger girl, and his chest tightened.

"You see that kid?" Boulder yelled at Rooster. "Look at her. She's so high she ain't got any idea what the hell's happening."

Rooster's face was twisted. "Why the fuck do you think she was getting her ass beat? All that bitch wants to do is get high. She needs to work. That's what she's here for. This ain't no kindergarten. Her mommy and daddy know what she's doing. So you best butt out of this one, brother."

Boulder took a wide stance. His feet were set apart and his face was mangled with anger. "I ain't your brother. Call me that again and it'll be the last thing you ever say."

Rooster cleared his throat and in a quiet, unsure voice said, "I ain't afraid of you."

Boulder grinned at him. "Well, then you're dumber than you look."

Suddenly the prostitutes on the sidewalk were making noise. Some whispered while others cheered. Boulder looked out over the crowd that had gathered and saw Jiggy chugging toward them.

Jiggy walked past everyone, grabbed Ivy by the arm, and flung her toward one of his associates. "Get this bitch home."

Rainey was lightning fast as she snatched Ivy's other arm and planted her feet. With adrenaline coursing through her she looked up at Jiggy. He was as nasty as she'd remembered him. The difference now was she wasn't a young, scared girl waiting for him to violate her. She saw the real man inside of Jiggy, someone desperate to hang onto his power. A repugnant

bottom feeder who'd climbed to the top of his corrupt life through brute force.

He looked into Rainey's face, and she was glowering back at him with a fiery gaze and unflinching stance, Jiggy could tell much had changed about Rainey Paxton. But he was determined to feed her fear. He stepped so close to Rainey that his body grazed hers and she fought not to waver.

"You best let Ivy go," he said quietly. "You're making things much worse for her." He put his nose next to Rainey's head and took a long whiff of her hair, but she still held her ground. "Now," he sneered, "if you wanna trade yourself for your sister, then I'm willing to take you for a ride and give this piece of shit to Boulder."

Rainey's heart was thrashing in her chest and sweat was trickling down her back. But her love for her sister was stronger than her fear of Jiggy killing her right there on the sidewalk, with everyone watching.

Her eyes were locked on Jiggy's when a large hand seized his shoulder. "Nah, man. You get away from her. She's off-limits," Boulder sneered.

Jiggy turned away from Rainey and held his palms out in front of him. "Okay, I read you loud and clear. So now, you read me. You and your men get in your cars and get outta here. That way, we won't have no more trouble."

"That girl is a kid, Jiggy. Look at her," Boulder said, pointing to Ivy.

Jiggy turned and glanced in her direction. "Yeah, there was a time when that child was so tasty, but now she's just another strung-out addict. Ain't nobody even wants to pay top dollar for her ass anymore. When did you ever know of a youngster that can't sell her shit on the streets of Kensington?"

"I wouldn't know. We don't turn out kids."

"Oh, that's right. Suddenly you're the good guys. You take money from your prostis as long as they're eighteen. What do you do? Card 'em before you turn 'em out? Cut me a break, man."

Boulder's posture stiffened and his jaw was clenched. "This ain't a discussion about business. This is about a kid and I wanna know what it'll take to get her outta here."

Jiggy rubbed his chin with his thumb and index finger. A devious smile played on his lips. "I'll tell you what I'll do. You give me that sweet piece of ass," he said gesturing to Rainey, "and I'll give you that useless little girl. How's that for a deal?"

"I already told you that Rainey is off-limits. What? Are you hard of hearing?" Boulder grabbed Rainey's hand. "Let's go. We aren't getting anywhere."

Still holding onto Ivy's arm Rainey met Boulder's eyes. "I can't leave her."

He leaned in and whispered. "Let. Her. Go."

Rainey needed Boulder on her side and didn't want to piss him off further. She pulled her hand from his and hugged her sister, who was teetering back and forth. "I love you," she whispered as Boulder whisked her away.

Inside the van, Rainey kept her eyes on her sister as Jiggy dragged her by the arm to a parked car. She staggered and stumbled to keep up until he shoved her into the car and he got into the backseat next to her. Then the car peeled away from the sidewalk and out of sight.

Rainey rolled her head to the side and looked at Boulder, who was watching her intently. A cold chill passed through her. His eyes were hungry with unsatisfied anger and she rubbed her palms on her jeans to dry them.

"Thanks for coming here with me," she muttered. "Who knows what could've happened if you weren't here."

"Are you kidding me? Do you understand what just happened there? That bastard thinks he owns these streets and, in a way, he owns this section. We stepped over the boundaries. I just put my club in a bad spot; exactly what I told you I didn't want to happen."

"I never meant for that to happen."

"You never meant for it not to happen, Rainey."

Rainey shifted her body and leaned her back against the door. "You're right, but if you know that, then why did you come here? You knew it would be dangerous. Don't pretend like it's all my fault. I know you care about me and want to help me. I'm very appreciative of everything you did for me tonight."

Boulder rubbed his forehead. "I ain't blaming it all on you. Truth is, I came here knowing there was a possibility this could turn violent. Luckily, it didn't tonight, but the fires have been lit on both sides now. Just to be clear, I came here out of respect for Stoker . . . and you."

"I'm sorry for dragging you into this, but I couldn't think of any other way."

He looked out the front window. "I know. I knew that when you came to see me . . ." his voice trailed off.

She watched as his fingertips glided lightly across his jawline. His eyes were soft and bore into hers. She squirmed in her seat from the intensity of his gaze. She recognized that look . . . she'd seen it before . . . the day that she'd slept with him.

She finally spoke. "Listen, I don't know what's going on with you, but I have someone now. Someone I love."

Boulder straightened his posture and grabbed his pack of cigarettes from the dashboard. "I was hoping that you didn't. I've never gotten you out of my head."

"You're married to Kiki, and Boulder, she really loves you."

He nodded. "You're right, and I love her. But I could've loved you more."

She shook her head softly. "You're a great guy and you were a good friend to Stoker." She paused. "I think Stoker would've really liked my boyfriend, Sam; I think you'd really like him too. Maybe someday you'll meet him."

He turned his head and his eyes pierced hers. "If he's so great then why am I here and he ain't?"

She tucked her hair behind her ears. "Because he can't be here. He isn't you. He plays by a different set of rules than we do."

"I see." He chuckled. "Is that a nice way of saying he's a pussy?"

Her hand was resting on the base of her throat. "No, that's a nice way of saying that you aren't afraid to break the law, you do what needs to be done no matter who you help or hurt. I'm not saying what you do is good or bad, but that's how your world works."

He nodded. "That's true, fair enough. Let's get outta here before I'm forced to kill somebody." He heard her suck in a quick breath and looked over and gave her a warm smile. "I ain't afraid to break the law, remember?"

Chapter Eighty-Nine

The next morning, Rainey rushed through the door of The Sanctuary.

"Hey, Rainey!" one teen yelled and waved from across the room.

"Hey, Candace, where's Rosemary?"

"She's in her office. Said she needs to get shit done," she said, smiling and rolling her eyes.

"Okay, I'll see you in a minute. I have to talk to her real quick."

"All right, then. I'll be waitin' here for ya."

Rainey barged in and closed the office door behind her. "It worked exactly like you said it would," she said.

Rosemary looked up from her desk. "Shit usually works the way I say it will, but what are we talkin' about here?" she asked with a grin. "It's hard to remember all the stuff I say."

"Boulder. I got him to go to the Liberty Motel with me last night and we saw Rooster beating the shit outta Ivy. It was crazy. Boulder goes charging across the street, then Jiggy shows up, and before I know it, they're both facing off on the sidewalk. Boulder was wrecked when he got one look at Ivy. Of course, he knew it was my plan all along to get him involved, he told me that, but he wasn't mad at me."

Rosemary shook her head. "Mmm, mmm, mmm, get some testosterone flowing, insults flying, and men sure can go at it . . . ain't saying women are any different, we're probably worse," she mused. "So what happened? Where's Ivy?"

Rainey's head bent forward and she looked down at her feet. "Jiggy shoved her in a car and drove off. She was so high. Rooster told Boulder she's a heroin addict. I think that stuck in his gut."

"Wait. I thought she was shooting speed, now it's heroin?" the older woman commented.

Rainey shrugged. "I thought so too, but who knows? She's probably using anything she can get her hands on."

"Then you know where this is going with Ivy, right?"

She rocked her head from side to side. "Right, she's headed for self-destruction. But my plan is for Boulder to get Ivy out of there before that happens," Rainey said with uncertainty.

Rosemary nodded. "We'll sure as hell try, but it ain't easy to kick the needle. I've seen many good people turn bad right quick," she said in a serious tone. "Just curious, sugar, how was it seeing Jiggy after all these years?"

Rainey shook her head. "He's a horrible, rotten person, but he wasn't so scary anymore. I saw a weak man who feeds on innocent girls and women. It's hard to put it in words, but if I had to, I'd say that the world is a worse place with him living in it. Don't get me wrong, he's still a scary dude because he's ruthless, but I also see a man scared to death of losing his power."

"So you wasn't afraid like you was when you were a young girl. That's what I was hoping to hear. He could tell you're different now, you know that, right?"

Rainey shrugged, but inside she wasn't so sure, the way he smelled her hair and tried to take her instead of her sister. "It was hard to tell what he was thinking. He was the same asshole I remember, but I didn't care what he thought of me."

"Well, I'd bet my savings he sensed that you were unafraid, and that, my girl, is the way to shut him down. You need to take a victory lap," she stated, pushing her arms out and pumping her fists in circles.

Rainey's smile stretched across her face. "Look at me getting a win and not even knowing it."

Rosemary scrunched her face. "That ain't just a tiny win, girl. That right there," she said waving her index finger in the air from the girl's head to her toes, "that's progress."

Rainey laughed, feeling for the first time that week, one thing had gone her way.

Later that night, as she lay in bed waiting for sleep to release her, she thought about Boulder. Rainey knew she needed to let things settle before

she went back to him, to beg him to keep helping her until Ivy was freed. She drifted to sleep filled with gratitude for all that Boulder had done.

***

The following night, while sitting with one of the homeless kids at The Sanctuary, Rainey whipped around as someone burst through the door. In horror, she watched her mother and father stumble inside. They were dirty and disheveled, even more than usual.

"Where the hell is Rainey Paxton?" Peter yelled. "We need to talk to her."

Rosemary rushed from the office, but Rainey intercepted her and motioned for her to back off. Then she strode up to her parents aggressively; this was her battle to fight.

"You can't be here," Rainey hissed through clenched teeth.

"Oh, stop your bullshit," Peter fired back at her.

Rainey caught a whiff of them and her head jerked back. "You both stink."

Miranda, who was slightly swaying, licked her dry, cracked lips. "We got kicked outta the house. They said it was unhabit, uninabit—"

"Uninhabitable?" Rainey stated impatiently. "You're sickening. You're so stoned you can't even speak."

She stepped back and watched them as their eyes roamed around the shelter.

"You got kicked out. Where are you living?" she asked.

Peter lurched forward. "That's the thing. Right now, we're on the streets. We've been sharing an alley with some people we know. We came here because we need that money. If you want custody of Ivy, we gotta have it now."

She flipped her hair over her shoulder and planted her hands on her hips. "I don't have the money yet. These things take time," she said. What she did not say was that there was a homicide investigation, which had held up disbursement of the funds.

"You're a liar!" Miranda screamed. "You're just trying to keep all the money for yourself. That's my money. She was my sister, not yours." She moved her face inches from Rainey's and jabbed her index finger in her face. "You stole that money from me. I know you talked her into leaving it all for you, you greedy little bitch."

Without any sudden movement, almost in slow motion, Rainey grabbed her mother's finger and bent it backward. Miranda's knees buckled and her face contorted with pain. "Don't ever point your nasty, dirty finger in my face." She let go and took a step away from them. "Aunt Sophie left me all of her money because she knew you'd spend her life savings on getting high. You know, I can't give up hope that one day you'll wake up wanting to get clean and live a regular life."

Peter scoffed. "See, that's the problem with you people. You don't understand the thrill of the high. There's so much more to it . . . scoring the dope, getting the works to shoot up, melting it down, sucking it into that syringe, and then the ultimate escape. It's all of it. It's thrilling and exciting. It ain't some boring life where you go to work, go home and watch TV, and do it all over again the next day. Who the fuck wants to live like that?"

"I do," Rainey said. "I want to have good friends, food to eat, and a place to live. You make it sound so boring but it's a real life, a great life, not the life you have with pretend friends and scrounging around for your next fix. Always dirty and smelly with your teeth rotting out of your mouth and skin full of marks and scabs. I've seen your way of life and I hate it."

Peter waved his hand to dismiss her. "Whatever, we don't care what you like," he cackled. "When will you have our money?"

Rainey stared into her father's eyes. "You're a horrible father."

He gave her a big yellowed, tobacco-stained, toothy grin. "When, Rainey?"

Her body was on fire as though her blood were boiling inside her veins. She wanted them to stay away from the shelter, yet she needed to keep track of their whereabouts for the homicide investigation and to ensure that she could buy custody of her sister.

"I'll come and see you in a month. Where can I find you?"

"A month?" Miranda garbled, her eyes bulging out.

"Yes, a month. The estate attorney said it might take that long." She softened her tone, not wanting to lose track of them. "I'll come find you sooner if I get the check faster."

Peter wagged his finger at her. "Don't mess with us, you'll be sorry. Not a day more than a month. We're in the alley on Jasper Street off of Lehigh Avenue."

"Okay, I'll find you."

Peter's face pinched and he tugged at her hair. "One month, you better have a check by then."

As she watched them leave The Sanctuary, Rainey saw two people ravaged by their own bad decisions. They'd screwed up their own lives, which was one thing, but screwing up the lives of those who are supposed to be loved and cared for, that was unforgivable. She blamed her parents for the people they were and the monsters they had become, and for the first time, she transferred the heavy burden of her own guilt onto them.

Chapter Ninety

Three weeks later, after finishing her mail route Rainey was sitting on the floor in her sparsely furnished living room when there was a light tap, tap, tap on the door. She looked at the door as though it were a foreign object she didn't recognize. She wasn't expecting anyone. She rose to her bare feet, tiptoed over, and peered through the peephole.

She pulled the door open cautiously. "Hi, Martin. What are you doing here?"

The homicide detective had his hands in his front pockets. "I came over to talk to you. Sam is on his way; I'm assuming he isn't here yet."

Just then Sam rushed up the hallway behind him. Rainey noticed his eyes were set hard, creating deep crevices across his forehead. Curious, she pulled the door open wide and both men walked in. Sam gave her a quick peck on the cheek and stood back.

She was sweating and her hands were shaking. "What's going on?" she asked, looking from one man to the other.

Martin rubbed his palm across his forehead. "I have some news about your aunt's death."

"Okay," she said hesitantly. "Look, you're both freaking me out. Just say what you gotta say."

Martin nodded. "I was able to get security footage from the nursing home. Luckily, they have cameras in the hallways and there was one outside of your aunt's room. They left Sophie's door open and we have taped evidence of your parents killing your aunt."

"You have to tell me what they did to her. Please," she asked in a rush.

He glanced at Sam and back to her. "We have your mother pulling out a syringe and your father injecting the lethal dose of cocaine under her toenail. If he had administered the drug any higher in her body it wouldn't

have been caught on camera, but since he picked her toe to hide the mark, we got the whole thing."

Rainey's hand flew to her mouth as tears spilled down her cheeks. She could hardly believe it, the police actually had evidence of what she had suspected, what she knew in her gut to be true. They had killed her aunt Sophie, and for that she would do everything to make sure they paid for their crime.

Sam moved to her and put his arm over her shoulder.

She looked up at him. "I'm okay." She looked back at Martin. "What happens now?"

"Well, your parents were evicted from the home they were living in and we're looking for them, but haven't located them yet."

"I know where they are," she stated with satisfaction.

Sam drew back, looked into her face and a slow smile formed at the corners of his lips. "You do?"

She nodded. "They came by The Sanctuary about three weeks ago wanting Aunt Sophie's money," she said, looking at Sam. "I didn't tell you because I knew you'd worry about me staying in my apartment by myself."

"Umm, that's correct. What made you think they wouldn't follow you home?"

She touched his cheek. "It's fine. I just didn't want you to worry. They took so much from me already and I won't let them take any more. They don't scare me, Sam." She turned back to Martin, and after relaying their location, asked, "What's going to happen to them?"

"They'll be arrested. We have enough evidence to charge them with murder. That'll keep them in prison. If the judge sets bail, they can get out if they have the money."

Rainey frowned. "They don't have any money. You should've seen them," she said, turning to Sam. "Filthy, smelly—they both have teeth rotting out of their mouths. Their clothes were covered in dirt and dried-up puke. It was awful, even for them."

Sam looked at his buddy. "Will you let me know when they're in custody?"

Martin nodded and walked to the door. "Take care of yourself, Rainey."

When Rainey and Sam were alone, he took her in his arms, put his lips to hers, and kissed her tenderly. Pulling his head back, he looked into her eyes and grounded her with a serious gaze. "I don't like you not telling me about your parents going to The Sanctuary. You could've gotten hurt."

She smiled and shook her head. "Nah. I could kick both their butts at the same time," she kidded.

"Well, looks like there's a good chance you'll get to have Ivy live with you. You're her only living relative."

She gently pulled away from him, almost too scared to let herself believe she'd finally be able to take her sister home, but it came with deep concerns and problems. "I know, Sam. But she's in a bad way. You know as well as I do that she's hooking and using dope now."

He nodded, slowly. "I know. But that doesn't mean you should give up."

Rainey shook her head. "I never said I was giving up. Once my parents are arrested, I'm gonna fight for her harder than I ever have in my life."

"And her pimp? Did you ever find out who she's under?" he asked.

"No," she bold-faced lied. "But it doesn't matter because soon I'll have my aunt's money, and hopefully I'll be able to buy her out of it."

Sam gave her a weak smile. "The people who run the streets of Kensington aren't impressed by money. They're impressed by power. They have plenty of money between drugs and prostitution, but power, that's much harder to come by."

Rainey's eyes grew dark. She'd never thought about it that way. For a moment, thoughts of losing Ivy to Jiggy forever swirled in her mind and she shut her eyes to rid herself of them. Wanting to change the subject, she looked toward the bedroom and smiled up at Sam.

"I was thinking maybe we could have a sleepover," she said, giving him a hopeful look.

He paused. His instinct was to take Rainey back to his place, but he knew she had a sense of pride about living on her own and didn't want to disappoint her. "Sure," he said, wrapping his hands around her waist and lifting her off her feet. "I love sleepovers."

***

Later that night, after eating dinner, the couple moseyed into the bedroom. Sam placed her on the bed. He slid her jeans off and kissed her inner thighs. Then he lifted her shirt and pressed his face between her breasts. Unsnapping her bra, he placed his mouth over her nipple, licking softly. He moved down to her stomach, kissing and touching each part of her. His fingers slid gently between her legs and she let out a throaty moan.

He worked his way down until his tongue was between her legs. Rainey's back arched and she reached down and laced her fingers through his hair. His lips and tongue moved smoothly until she climaxed and her back eased down onto the mattress.

"Holy shit, Sam," she breathed. She looked down and he was beaming back from between her legs. "Come here," she said pulling him up.

He laid on top of her for a second before she rolled him over and straddled him. He put his hands on her breasts and massaged them gently as she guided him inside of her. Finally, Sam's head and shoulders pushed into the mattress, and when it was over, they lay in a tight tangle of arms and legs.

As Rainey lay with him having released the tension of the day, she thought how lucky she was to have found the amazing people who were in her life.

Chapter Ninety-One

Two miles away, while Rainey and Sam made love, Detective Freeman grabbed Peter's left hand, cuffed it, and repeated the same on his right. Miranda was on her knees while a female officer performed the same police procedure on her.

Peter struggled against the handcuffs. "You can't arrest us. We didn't do nothing. Just because we are using doesn't give you a right to haul us into the station. We have a disease; do you hear me?"

Detective Freeman bent at the waist and looked into Peter's dilated pupils. "You and Miranda Andersen are being charged with the murder of Sophie Andersen."

Miranda's head jerked awkwardly in the detective's direction. "Who told you that shit? Our asshole daughter? She's a liar. Look at her record, she spent time in juvie. You can't believe a word she says!"

The detective glared at Miranda, then his eyes moved to Peter and back to her again. Both watched him intently, waiting for the handcuffs to be removed.

In the quiet of the alley, Detective Freeman's voice boomed, "You have the right to remain silent. Anything you say can and will be used against you in a court of law . . ."

Chapter Ninety-Two

With Miranda and Peter locked away, Rainey focused her efforts on getting Ivy out from under Jiggy. She sat alone in the borrowed car watching her little sister catcall men on the corner. Her stomach lurched when Ivy disappeared into the Liberty Motel with a six-foot-tall man who looked to be at least three hundred pounds. Ivy, who is just shy of five feet tall and ninety pounds fully clothed, followed him inside.

Rainey sat back in her seat and waited. An hour passed and neither came out of the motel. Her knuckles were white from the death grip she had on the steering wheel. Finally, the man thudded outside. He was still fastening his belt as he reached the sidewalk and kept on walking.

Rainey moved to the edge of her seat. Her face was close to the front window and her eyes scanned the entrance and surrounding area of the motel. Come on. Please come out, Ivy.

Thirty minutes later, she heard sirens blaring their warning that something was wrong, that someone's life needed to be saved. The ambulance barreled past her and stopped abruptly in front of the motel. Paramedics rushed toward the entrance, wheeling a gurney. Rainey was near hysterics as she leaped from her car. Before she could make it across the street, a black sedan screeched to a halt and blocked her. The back door swung open and Jiggy's hand clamped on Rainey's wrist before she could process what was happening.

"I thought you were gonna sit in that car forever. Lucky for me, you got out," he whispered.

Rainey's heart stopped beating for a full second.

"You know, after a while, people get to know your car, and well, you made it too easy for us."

Panicking that he would overpower her, she yanked several times but couldn't break his death grip. She looked to the motel as the paramedics raced the gurney toward the ambulance.

As the ambulance sped off, she steadied her gaze on Jiggy. She took in his carrot hair and loose, white facial skin. His thick sideburns ran to the top of his double chin. Her eyes scanned all the gold jewelry he wore: the jewelry paid for by the flesh and bones of her baby sister.

"Let me go," she said, fighting to keep her voice even as fingers of fear clawed up her spine.

He chuckled. "Get in the car," he said, pushing her toward the sedan.

She planted her feet and twisted her arm but still wasn't able to break free. Rainey feared that once she was inside the car, no one would ever see her again. She imagined them shooting her up with drugs, as they did to Ivy, and her life being over.

One of Jiggy's goon boys stood on the other side of Rainey to keep her from running. Her eyes tightened as she used her strength to break free from his grip, but Jiggy grabbed a handful of her hair and held tightly. Her head leaned into him as he pulled her closer.

Jiggy moved his face close to hers. "I've been wanting to have you for a long, long time. Tonight I finally get to take a bite outta you, literally." He pressed his fat nose on her breasts and sniffed. "Damn bitch, you smell so good." He opened his mouth and sunk his teeth into the top of her left breast, not letting go until her knees buckled under the intense, fiery pain.

When his jaw unleashed, she composed herself. While on the outside she was trying to keep her cool, inside, her guts were twisted and her heart was beating so fast she was positive it would explode in her chest. Her bravado waned as she looked into the eyes of the deceiver . . . the enemy . . . the evil one. His eyes were small and beady. Like two dark pencil holes poked into his blubbery face. He stared at her with bad intent as he pushed his lower jaw out. His thick tongue came out like a serpent and licked her face, from her chin to her forehead.

"Mmm, now that's some tasty flesh right there."

With dread settling over her she tried to wrench his fingers out of her hair. But he laughed and licked her neck. Then he backhanded her. His goon boy pulled her wrists tightly behind her back. Jiggy grabbed the collar of her shirt and ripped it in two. Her breasts, covered by a black lace bra, sat in front of him. "Oh, man," he muttered, burying his face between them.

Rainey dry heaved as she watched. She shook her shoulders, trying to shake him off of her.

"Put her in the car," Jiggy demanded, rubbing his crotch with his open palm.

Goon boy forced Rainey closer to the open car door. She straightened her body and planted her feet. The burning pain in her arms made her wince, and then suddenly there was no more pain.

Chapter Ninety-Three

Rainey pulled her head back as a fist smashed into the side of goon boy's face. As he fell, his hands unleashed his hold on her arms. She was thrown to the pavement and used her hands and feet to back away quickly, like a crab scurrying on the beach disappearing into the cover of sand.

Her mind whizzed as she processed the punches and kicks being exchanged. Her eyes darted to the back of the sedan, where Boulder was now holding Jiggy on the trunk of the car.

"What did I tell you about going near her? Huh?" he growled, banging the back of Jiggy's head on the trunk a few times. Then Boulder lifted his fist and brought it down into the center of the devil's face.

Rainey cringed, never having seen this violent side of Boulder. She watched as Jiggy pulled his legs in and slammed his shins with full force against Boulder's chest. It set him back a few steps, but Boulder grabbed the waistband of Jiggy's jeans, ripping him off the hood of the car, and letting him hit the ground. Jiggy landed flat on his back and Boulder flopped down hard on his chest and snatched the collar of his shirt.

"This ends here," Boulder seethed, as spittle flew from his mouth and landed on the devil's face.

"Nah, you're wrong. This is where it begins," Jiggy said, giving him a sadistic smile with blood-streaked teeth. "I'm just getting started. You crossed the line. You wanna battle? You got a battle."

Boulder remained focused. "Okay, we can do it that way. But, to be clear, you will lose. So you better make sure your boss knows about it before it happens . . . or I can tell him for you. I know that scumbag too."

Jiggy released a sinister laugh and spit bloody saliva into Boulder's face, which he wiped away with the back of his hand. He lifted his fist and

slammed it into his jaw, Jiggy's head flung sideways, leaving him dazed and sputtering. Then Boulder made his way over to Rainey, cupped the back of her head, and pulled her to him. "You are so fucking lucky I've been following you. I knew Jiggy would come for you and you should've known that too. What? You got a death wish or something? Now get in the goddamn car and go."

Rainey opened her mouth to explain, but he held his hand up to her face. "We aren't talking about this right now. Do as I say."

At that moment, Andrew came up from behind Boulder and whispered something in his ear, then turned to Rainey. "They took your sister to the children's hospital. You need to go there right now."

Stunned into silence, Rainey nodded and got into the car. When she arrived at the hospital, she rushed into the emergency room and asked for Ivy. After several questions about their relationship and personal information about the child, the nurse sent her to the waiting room with a promise that a doctor would talk to her when they knew more.

In the waiting room, she called Rosemary and asked her to find Sam. An hour later, Sam and Rosemary hurried through the doors of the waiting area.

Rosemary pulled Rainey to her feet and gave her a tight hug as relief washed over her. "Don't you worry, sugar, we're here now. We got you."

When Rosemary let go, Sam took over. He held her for several long moments, and in that time the two became one. He said nothing, and, more importantly, he didn't let her go.

***

A few minutes after arriving at the hospital, Sam found a nurse, and after showing her his badge, the three were escorted into a private room. Rainey's legs bounced wildly; the unknown was the darkest, ugliest side of life for her and her most dreaded state of mind.

A few minutes later, a doctor walked in and closed the door behind him.

Rainey leaned forward on her elbows. "What's wrong with my sister? Is she alive?" she asked.

He gave her a curt nod, and after introducing himself, said, "She was brought in with a stab wound to her pelvis area. We rushed her to the operating room and were able to stop the bleeding. She's been badly beaten

and she has lost a lot of blood, but she's stable now. We have her in ICU. Someone will be in to take you to see her soon."

Rainey stood, ready to go see Ivy, but the doctor turned to Sam. "Are you the detective on this case?"

Sam shook his head. "I'm with drug enforcement."

The doctor nodded. "Good, because there was a significant amount of heroin found in the child's system." His eyes pivoted to Rainey. "I assume you're aware that your sister has a serious drug problem. She has needle marks over several areas of her body."

Rainey cast her eyes downward as her ears burned. "I am, but it's not her fault."

"I see. Okay, I'll send a nurse in to bring you up to ICU shortly." Then he turned, continuing to ask Sam a few more questions. Rainey took Rosemary by the hand and led her to the other side of the room.

"The doctor thinks it's her fault she uses drugs," she whispered, outraged.

Rosemary raised her brows. "It's okay, sugar," she whispered. "You told me Jiggy forced dope into her arm the first time. She never chose to start, but after that first taste of heroin the drug made all the choices for her. As long as you remember how it happened it don't matter what anybody says."

"Yeah, but the doctor doesn't know that and neither does Sam."

Rosemary squinted her eyes. "That don't make no difference and this ain't the time to discuss it neither. We need to go see your girl and figure out how we can pull together to help her outta this heap of shit she's sittin' in."

Rainey nodded. "You're right."

"I usually am," Rosemary said, trying to inject a touch of humor.

Rainey smiled. Rosemary's words were not lost on her. She thought about Ivy and her addiction. It was true: Jiggy had made her an addict. But now Ivy willingly took drugs to ease her painful life, only causing her more pain. The drugs were a temporary release from her circumstances and a standing threat of ruining her life.

Chapter Ninety-Four

Ivy was placed in a coma to allow for healing and sent to the ICU where she spent two weeks. After that time she was moved to a room on the surgical floor where the doctor lessened her intravenous pain medication.

Ivy had only been on the surgical floor for twelve hours when her eyes fluttered open. The first thing she saw was Rainey's face looking down at her. Her eyes moved over the hospital room and she almost didn't see Rosemary sitting in a chair in the far corner.

"What happened?" Ivy croaked.

Rainey was ecstatic to see Ivy awake again. She grabbed a cup of water and placed a straw between her lips and Ivy took a sip.

"That last guy you went into the motel with almost killed you," Rainey said in a gentle tone.

Fear registered on Ivy's face and her eyes widened, suddenly realizing how close she'd come to death. Then her thoughts rapidly flowed to her pimp. "Does Jiggy know where I'm at? He'll think I ran away. He'll hunt me down and kill me."

"No, he won't. You're safe here. I'm with you."

Ivy's heavy eyelids blinked in slow motion. "You're so dumb. You have no idea what Jiggy will do to me," she mumbled.

Rainey was instantly annoyed that her little sister thought of Jiggy so soon after coming out of her coma.

"Anyway," Rainey said in a huff, "You're in the hospital and once you're better, you're coming to live with me. I have an apartment and you'll have your own bedroom."

The dim light in Ivy's brown eyes shone brighter. "How? What about Jiggy?"

"You don't need to worry about him. Leave that to me." She winked. "I have hard-core friends too," she said, thinking of Boulder, who had reached out to her several times over the two weeks, while Ivy fought for her life in the ICU.

Ivy looked at the IV in her hand. "Can you tell somebody to give me more dope for my pain?"

"Listen to me," Rainey said, keeping her voice soft. "They gave you narcotics while you were in the ICU. That helped you heal and get you through the worst of your withdrawal. However, since you had heroin in your system, and I told them you're an intravenous drug user, they won't give you narcotics now that you're awake and past the worst of it."

Panic rose in Ivy and she steadied her eyes on Rainey. "Get a nurse."

A few minutes later a nurse popped into the room. "Oh, good. You're finally awake. We've all been waiting for you to join us," she sang.

Rainey watched as Ivy transformed for her new audience. She flinched and produced a painful, tight-lipped smile. "I'm in a lot of pain. Can you give me something?"

The nurse glanced at Rainey and back down at Ivy. "Of course. Let me go see what the doctor prescribed for you."

Ivy gave her sister a sly grin, but Rainey held back. She knew exactly what the doctors' instructions were; they'd talked about it more than once.

When the nurse came back into the room, she had a syringe and alcohol pads with her. Ivy laid her head back on the pillow and waited for the head rush that she craved so desperately. Rainey watched, wondering if she should say anything as the nurse cleaned the IV area with alcohol, twisted the syringe into the line, and slowly injected the clear fluid. A few seconds after the nurse was finished, Ivy lifted her head from the pillow, her face pinched with annoyance.

"Something's wrong," she said. "I don't feel anything. I probably need more."

The nurse tilted her head. "Do you still have pain?"

She pouted and gave a nod.

"I can call your doctor. He prescribed IV Tylenol for you. Let's give it a minute. I'm sure you'll get relief soon."

Through clenched teeth, Ivy said, "I need something stronger. Give me morphine or something. I don't know, whatever you have, but Tylenol ain't gonna work."

"Stop it," Rainey said assertively. "You're being rude."

The nurse glanced at Rainey and gave her a small smile. Then she put her hands on the bedrail and leaned just slightly into Ivy's space. "I know you don't feel well, but we need to manage your pain with your drug addiction. Do you understand what I'm telling you?"

She paused for several seconds, giving Ivy a chance to respond, but her lips pressed into a straight line as she defiantly held the nurse's stare.

The nurse took a deep breath and looked away. "The doctor will be in to see you soon and I'm sure he'll explain everything to you," she said, speaking into the air, then making eye contact with Rainey.

After the nurse left the room, Rainey pulled a chair beside the bed. Ivy's eyes were dark and serious. Her face was red and covered in a sheen of sweat. She shoved the covers off and flinched from the pain in her pelvis.

"I hate this hospital. I wanna leave. I ain't staying here and taking Tylenol. Why won't they give me something better for my pain?" she ranted. "Why don't you tell them to give me something stronger? You always say you wanna help me, so do it!"

Rainey took in a deep breath; it broke her heart to see Ivy this way. "You're not getting anything stronger. You're fighting a losing battle. You're a drug addict. And they aren't about to feed your addiction," she said firmly. "The doctor can now manage your pain without narcotics. These people saved your life and I'm not going to sit here and let you treat them like shit."

Tears burst from Ivy's eyes, and this time Rainey believed they were real. "But you don't know how bad it hurts. I need something stronger. Will you talk to the doctor? Please, Rainey. You promised to take care of me," she begged.

"That's what I'm doing, Ivy," Rainey said evenly. "I'm taking care of you, and part of that is to have you clean and sober. The part of your life that involved drugs is over. You don't need them anymore. You're never going back to the streets or the Liberty Motel or Jiggy."

Now that Ivy understood that leaving Jiggy also meant leaving drugs, she frowned. "You can't make me do anything I don't wanna do."

"You're right," Rainey said, "but I can try. I've already filed for legal custody of you. I'm not going to argue with you about this. You need to rest and get well so I can take you home."

"You can't do that. Mom and Dad won't let you."

"Mom and Dad can't stop me," she said, then stopped before saying too much, wanting to wait for Ivy to get stronger before she told her about their arrest.

Ivy turned her head away. "Yeah, okay. Well. You have no idea how crazy they can be."

"I know Mom and Dad better than you think. They only care about themselves. That's why all this bad stuff happened to you."

Ivy whipped her head in Rainey's direction. "At least they let me get high. Not like you. You're a stiff-ass just like they told me. You don't care about nobody but yourself." Her lips turned downward and her brow scrunched as she turned away from her sister.

Rainey looked over at Rosemary, who had been sitting in a chair across the room this entire time. Rosemary lifted her eyebrows and gave her a nod of encouragement. Rainey sat next to her little sister in silence. Her heart shattered as she stared at the back of Ivy's head, knowing that her baby sister, the one she would die for, had surrendered to the possibility of death by injection.

Chapter Ninety-Five

After another two weeks in the hospital, Rainey and Rosemary arrived to bring Ivy home. They found her out of bed, sitting in a chair dressed in jeans and a T-shirt that Rainey had bought for her.

"Morning," Rainey sang, attempting to be cheery, wanting everything to go perfectly for Ivy today.

Ivy gave Rosemary a withering look. "Does she follow you everywhere you go? Why is she always around?"

Rainey put her hands on her hips. "You better get used to it. I see Rosemary every single day and so will you. She's the best friend I've ever had. She's stuck by me through a lot of crap, including you almost dying."

"I didn't almost die," Ivy spat.

"Okay, Ivy, whatever you say. Are you ready to go?"

"Not really. I don't want to live with you. I wanna go back to Jiggy."

Rainey went dead still, mortified by the words her sister had just spoken. After all the suffering he put Ivy through, how could she ever want to see that man again?

"Listen, you little turd," Rosemary snapped, stepping forward, unable to keep her cool or her mouth shut any longer, "your sister has gone through a lot of trouble to be able to take you to her apartment. Now, why you'd wanna go with that no-good prick Jiggy is beyond me. I get the dope part, girl, I do. But Jiggy? That doesn't make no sense." She turned to Rainey. "Are you sure the doctor didn't say nothing 'bout her getting a brain injury? 'Cause this child is just yammering a bunch of nonsense."

Rainey bit the inside of her lip to keep from smiling; her friend had a very direct way with words. She turned to Ivy to see if Rosemary's words had any effect.

"Mind your own business," Ivy said, jabbing a finger at Rosemary. "I don't care what you say, you don't know nothing about me or Jiggy. He loves me."

Rainey gripped the wall to steady herself. She wasn't prepared for this . . . Ivy wanting to be with Jiggy or her loving him. Stunned into silence, she gave her sister a hard stare.

"Child, first of all, don't point that finger at me if you don't want me to break it off. Second of all, I know Jiggy right well. I sold my ass on the streets for years. I was older, mind you, not a baby like you just barely outta diapers out there trying to catcall a john. Shit, you don't even know what you're doing."

Ivy's eyes widened, and she looked the woman up and down. "You're too old to be a prosti."

"I said I was one for many years. Clean your ears out, will ya?"

Ivy's expression softened slightly, and Rainey wondered if Rosemary had gotten through to her. Rosemary was tenacious and pushy, a woman who had been on the darker side of life and it showed in her attitude. Ivy skimmed her fingers along her jawline, silenced by the woman and looked at Rainey. "I'm ready to go."

***

Inside Rainey's apartment, Ivy looked around. Now that Sophie's money had come through, Rainey had been able to purchase a sofa and furniture for both bedrooms. She'd even splurged on new dishes, pots, and pans. Although Sam and Rosemary encouraged her to buy the things she needed, Rainey was frugal with her money. "After all," she'd told both of them, "Aunt Sophie saved this money for me and I need to keep it safe, so one day I can do things with it that she'd be proud of."

Rainey showed her sister the small apartment and brought her to the room that would be hers. There was a single bed with a purple and white checked quilt and a matching pillow sham. The headboard, dresser, and nightstand were all white. She'd bought a few pictures at a department store in center city that carried the color scheme through adding pinks, oranges, and yellows.

Ivy looked around the room, and Rainey could tell she was impressed. "This is mine?"

Her sister nodded. "You like it?"

"Sure, it's okay," Ivy said, flopping on the bed. "What's in the dresser?"

Rainey opened the drawers. "I got you some clothes. I think you'll like them."

Ivy approached, and her hand gently drifted over the new items. "Cool, thanks."

"I'm not the best cook, but I'm making cheese omelets for dinner. It's one of the things that I've learned how to do because it's kinda hard to screw up eggs," Rainey chuckled.

Ivy looked at her. "Yeah, that sounds good. The food in the hospital sucked."

Rainey smiled. "I'm going to take a shower. My boyfriend is coming over to have dinner with us. He wants to meet you. Just relax and hang out."

Ivy sighed, flopping back on her bed and closing her eyes.

"Did you hear me?" Rainey asked. For a while now she'd been nervous about Ivy and Sam meeting and wanted Ivy to be as excited.

Ivy turned her head and faced her. "Yeah, whatever. I met him a while ago at that house you lived in," she stated.

"Oh," Rainey breathed sadly. "No, that was Stoker; he died. This is a guy I've been dating for only a short time now."

Shock registered on Ivy's face. "Oh, Stoker died? That's totally sucks; I liked his motorcycle." She looked away and paused. "Okay, so your new boyfriend is coming over. What am I supposed to say? Oh yay, I can't wait to meet him. You only care about yourself. What about my boyfriend? I'm not allowed to see him."

Sickened that Ivy kept referring to Jiggy as her boyfriend, Rainey sat on the edge of the bed. She attempted to stroke her sister's hair, but Ivy pulled her head back.

"Look," Rainey said, calm but firm. "Jiggy is not your boyfriend. You are a kid and he's a grown man. He used you, beat you, and hurt you in so many ways . . . he's done all kinds of horrible things. I don't understand what you're thinking."

Ivy leaned up on her elbow. "You weren't there," she said, but this time her voice wasn't accusatory, just quiet, small. "I was so hungry . . . and Jiggy, he'd come to my room and hurt me, but he'd bring me food or soda sometimes."

Rainey was sad listening to Ivy's thoughts and beliefs about Jiggy. She wanted so much for her sister to understand that there was no good reason

for what happened to her and that no amount of food or soda would make up for the pain she was made to endure. "I know how Mom and Dad neglected you. They did the same with me. I was hungry all the time too, but a grown man having sex with a child isn't right. You said he hurts you. Do you think that's okay?"

Ivy averted her sister's gaze. "That's just how he shows love. I swear, he gets so happy when he bites and pinches and punches and stuff."

Rainey shook her head, sickened by the pictures that formed in her mind. "That's not how a good person shows love. When a person cares about you it shouldn't hurt. Did Jiggy tell you the way he treats you is love?"

She nodded. "Yeah, and it's true too. He tells me I'm his girlfriend and that I need to do whatever he says. At first I was scared so I told Mom, but she told me that Jiggy was right." She ran her hand up her forehead and over her black hair. "Sometimes when we had sex it hurt so much, but after a while I learned to block out the pain. Plus, he would give me dope, and that always helped."

Rainey shook her head, understanding now that Ivy needed much more help than she originally thought. "You and me have a lot of stuff to work through together."

Ivy laid on her back. "I don't know what stuff you're talking about, but I'm doing fine. I know how to take care of myself."

***

In the shower, the hot water eased Rainey's stiff muscles and her thoughts settled on Jiggy. He was hurtful and cruel. He caused Ivy so much pain and suffering, yet she was devoted to him. Ivy believed that he loved her and she understood it would be difficult to undo all of the damage that had been done. Ivy had been brainwashed, broken, trained into thinking she needed to serve Jiggy. Rainey thought back to when she was her age and didn't understand how being loved and cared for worked either. She'd been lucky to have a brief time when the window of her life opened and love showered upon her from her aunt. But Ivy had been only five when Rainey was sent away to juvie, too young to remember the love she had given her. She needed to figure out how to teach her little sister the difference between love and abuse. She knew that most people saw them as two very different

things, but not so much for the child convinced that love is supposed to hurt.

Chapter Ninety-Six

When Sam arrived at the apartment later that evening, Rainey nervously called out for Ivy. When she finally came in, she sauntered into the living room with her hair disheveled and wearing only her bra and underwear.

Rainey groaned. "Um, go put some clothes on," she said, glancing at Sam, embarrassed.

Ivy eyed Sam up and down, and in a voice much too old for her age, she said, "Why? He ain't never seen a woman in her underwear before?"

"Actually," Rainey said sharply, rising and grabbing her sister's arm. "He has seen a woman in her underwear, but probably not a little girl."

Ivy whipped her arm away. "You're so annoying!" she yelled.

Rainey pointed toward Ivy's bedroom. "Go. Put. Clothes. On."

After Ivy stomped off, Rainey turned to Sam and sighed. "I had this image of her being so happy to be here with me. In my mind, I thought she'd finally feel like she had a home, a safe place to live where the two of us would rebuild our lives together." She shook her head slowly. "But it's not like that at all, she's so angry." She lowered her voice to a whisper. "She doesn't want to be here."

Sam lifted her chin and kissed her forehead. "You have to give it some time. She's been programmed and manipulated since she was a little girl. Think about how difficult it was for you to let your guard down."

Rainey paused. "I have thought about it a lot. And I was desperate and disappointed, even scared, but I didn't carry the anger that she does. The things that Ivy has been put through, well, I escaped most of it by being in juvie. I wanted to have friends and be loved and accepted." She chuckled. "Thinking back, I'm surprised they didn't kill me in juvie. I had no idea what I was up against." She put her hand on her hip and cocked her face

to the side. "I did break Tootsie, though; that in itself was a miracle. Now, don't get me wrong I was ready to battle, but I preferred kindness. I felt sorry for myself in the beginning and carried a lot of guilt about leaving Ivy with my parents, but I wasn't bitter."

"Well, like you said, you also didn't have the same experiences Ivy has had. She's experienced heavy drug use and well, prostituting is hard on the body, mind, and soul. She's learned things that will be difficult to unlearn."

Rainey shook her head thoughtfully, knowing it was the truth. "That's because my parents are scumbags." She pressed the side of her face against Sam's chest. "It scares me to think about how things will work out with Ivy and me, and as you know, not much scares me." She pulled away and looked up at him. "What if I never reach her? What if I can't help her save herself?"

Sam tightened his grip on her. "Then you'll have to recognize that you're as human as the rest of us."

She pushed off of his chest gently. "What does that mean?"

"Well, you do tend to think you're invincible. Going to the Liberty Motel alone. You know, doing things that another woman or even a man your age would find dangerous and terrifying."

"Well, most women my age never woke up in an alley in the Badlands when they were seventeen, or spent three years in a juvenile prison because their parents wanted to protect their dealer. I could go on, you know," she said with a sly grin.

"Right there," he said, pointing at her. "That no-nonsense stance you have . . . Ivy has it too. Her experiences were different from yours, but each of you has an edge because of what you endured. Now, enough of this stuff. What did you make for dinner?"

She giggled. "Cheese omelets, but I haven't made them yet because I was waiting for you to help me in the kitchen."

"Oh, I see. You need me to crack the eggs or something?"

"If 'something' includes scrambling and cooking them too, then yeah, I need you to do that something."

Sam let out an exaggerated huff. "Fine. You go get your sister and I'll get to work in the kitchen."

She kissed him tenderly on his lips. "I still can't believe I'm making it with a cop."

He smacked her lightly on the ass. "Yeah, well, I can't believe I'm making it with a convict."

Rainey was smiling as she walked away to check on her sister. She managed to convince Ivy to get dressed and come out for dinner a few minutes later.

"When are we eating?" Ivy asked, looking from Rainey to Sam.

Rainey shrugged. "Twenty minutes?"

Ivy slumped into a chair at the kitchen table. "Do you sleep here?" she asked Sam.

Sam was scrambling eggs in a bowl and looked over his shoulder at her. "Sometimes, but not very often. Why?"

Ivy rolled her eyes. "I was just curious. At my house people sleep there all the time. But I ran into my mom and dad a while ago and they don't have that house anymore, but lots of people know them in Kensington." She scowled at her sister. "I'm gonna find them so I can move out of here and go stay with them."

Sam shot Rainey a look, and she nodded. She needed to tell Ivy the truth.

"So there's something I want to talk to you about," she said, sitting down beside her.

"O God. What?" Ivy whined, throwing her hands up. "I'm sick of you always wanting to talk to me about stuff."

"Do you remember me telling you about our aunt Sophie?"

Ivy picked at the skin on her cuticles. She glanced up at Rainey. "Not really."

"Well, Aunt Sophie was Mom's sister and she had a disease that affected her brain. She hadn't talked in many years and she couldn't remember anything."

"Did she ever see me?" Ivy asked.

Rainey nodded. "I took you to the nursing home to meet her once, but you were too young to remember."

"Okay. So what?" Ivy asked impatiently.

Rainey glanced at Sam and back at Ivy. "Well, I need to tell you that Mom and Dad are both in prison. They'll probably be in there for a long time."

Ivy squirmed in her chair. "What did they do?"

"Mom and Dad shot up Aunt Sophie with cocaine and it killed her. They did it because she had money that they wanted and now they're being charged with her murder."

Ivy blushed deeply and she glanced at Sam. She pulled her legs onto the chair and wrapped her arms around them, the gravity of what her parents

had done hitting her hard. "After I left home, they didn't have any money left to buy . . ." Ivy's voice trailed off.

Rainey filled in the blanks. "Once you were gone, they didn't have any way of buying their drugs. It's okay to say whatever you're thinking."

"I know that, I guess," she mumbled the second part to herself. "When things first got bad, I didn't understand but once I started getting high then I knew why they loved it so much."

Sam turned to her unable to keep silent any longer. "Getting high is not an excuse to do bad things to other people, especially kids."

The young girl dipped her head to her chest and paused for a moment. She looked back up at her sister. "What did Mom and Dad do to you?"

Rainey's shoulders tensed; she didn't expect to have to explain everything about herself with Sam there, but knew she had to keep their conversation going. "First, they let some jerk named Freddy have sex with me. Then they gave me to Jiggy, but right when he was about to rape me, the police came into our house and I had all this heroin around me and . . . a gun. They both belonged to Jiggy, but Mom and Dad wanted me to tell the judge the drugs and gun belonged to me, that's why I was sent away."

Rainey glanced at Sam, and finally learning the truth, he looked as though his heart was breaking.

"Jiggy and you?" Ivy screeched with a furrowed brow. "I don't believe it." She got up and stepped toward the doorway. "I'm really tired and I wanna lay down. I'm not that hungry anyway."

Rainey spun to Sam, confused. "What just happened?"

He assessed her for a moment. "Well, I think that you hit a nerve when you said your parents gave you to Jiggy."

Rainey put her hand over her mouth. "Or maybe she's upset because I told her about our parents going to prison. I mean, they were her escape plan—to find them and live with them again."

Sam shrugged. "Honestly, I'm not sure which it is, maybe it's both. She's been with Jiggy for quite some time. More than a year, right?"

Rainey nodded then her eyes met Sam's. "Hey, wait a minute. I thought you didn't know who Ivy's pimp was."

"Oh, yeah? I thought you didn't know either, but you don't seem too surprised."

She nodded. "I should've known you already knew." She gave him a sad smile. "So what does this mean for Ivy?"

He bit his bottom lip. "It means she has a long, bumpy road to travel if she wants to take control of her life."

"She keeps protecting Jiggy. She won't say a bad word about him," Rainey said.

He slid his hand down her back. "We know Jiggy likes young girls. We also know that he's rotten to his core. My guess is that he trains young girls to think that his abusive behavior is normal and he convinces them it's all out of love. I'm not a psychiatrist, but I think she probably has Stockholm syndrome."

"What's that?"

"It's when a victim has feelings of sympathy or love toward their abuser. Oftentimes, the abused, like Ivy, feel sorry for their abuser and try to protect them. She's become dependent on him to fulfill all of her needs—food, shelter, drugs, you name it."

Rainey put her head back and let out a loud moan. "I hate that guy and I'm worried that he'll come looking for her here."

"Yeah, I thought of that too. You need to keep your eyes and ears open. If anything strange happens, I need to know about it immediately. No secrets, okay?" He looked at her, and his eyes were dead serious.

She nodded. "Okay, I promise," she vowed, and meant it.

***

The following week, Rainey took Ivy to a restaurant to celebrate her thirteenth birthday.

"This is the first birthday party I ever had," Ivy said, looking around the restaurant.

Rainey beamed, proud to be doing something special for her. "I bought you a present too," she said, reaching into her purse and handing her sister a small wrapped box.

Ivy's eyes feasted on the gift for a moment before tearing the paper away and whipping the lid from the box. "Ohhhh, it's so pretty," she said, pulling the gold necklace with a heart pendent from the velvet lining. "Thank you."

Rainey sat back, thinking that she'd finally reached her sister.

***

Over the next two weeks Ivy was filled with unspent energy and spent hours staring out the window or sitting on the steps outside of the apartment building, her eyes constantly scanning the streets, as though she were waiting for a loved one to return home.

Rainey had gotten temporary custody and enrolled Ivy in the junior high school half a mile from their apartment. The problem was Ivy had no interest in going back to school and fought her return every step of the way. When the first day of school finally came, Rainey walked with her to the new school and watched as she entered the building. She tried to be affectionate with her, like when they were younger, but Ivy was reluctant and never let her defenses down.

A week later at the shelter, while Ivy hung out in the common room, Rainey sat in the office with Rosemary. She looked toward the girl and back at the older woman. "I think Ivy's settling in," she said. "She just finished her first week of junior high and she's not as angry all the time."

Rosemary's eyebrows lifted. "Sugar, you ain't outta the woods. That ain't how this works. You ain't never worked the streets and you ain't never had a pimp. For youngins like your sister, a pimp is like a moth to a flame; don't make no difference that you'll burn your wings off, it's too hard to stay away from the warmth."

"What are you talking about?" Rainey asked, confused. "She hasn't said a word about Jiggy recently. Are you seeing something that I'm not?"

Rosemary nodded. "I know that people always want to go where they feel like they belong. Now, this ain't nothing you're doing or not doing, this is all about what's in her head, what's familiar to her, and everything she's been taught. And believe me, it don't matter if it's a place that will cause them great harm. We all human and get wrapped up in our emotions and I hate to say it, but sometimes we look to the wrong people to find the answer. That's a trademark of hookers and addicts."

At first, Rainey was crushed by what Rosemary was telling her, leaving her feeling inadequate. Then she really considered the woman's explanation. She ran through the past several weeks in her memory, trying to pinpoint any events that supported what Rosemary was saying. And although nothing came to mind, she knew that the woman understood more about what happened on the streets than anyone else she knew.

Chapter Ninety-Seven: One Month Later

After work, Rainey stopped at The Sanctuary to get Rosemary and they walked to her apartment to cook dinner together. Inside the apartment, laying on the sofa was Ivy, with her arms and legs sprawled out and her head hanging off of the side. Rainey rushed over and grabbed her hands, her eyes landing on the fresh track marks on her arm. She put her ear to her mouth and was relieved to find she was breathing, but very lightly. Being driven by panic, Rainey grabbed Ivy's shoulder and screamed into her face, "Open your eyes!"

Thankfully, she opened them briefly in a groggy stupor, grumbled incoherently, but then shut them again.

Rosemary, who had been watching, walked to the kitchen and filled a bowl with cold water. She returned to the living room and threw it into the child's face.

Ivy flinched and her eyes flew open. "What the hell, man? What's your problem?" she slurred.

Rainey pulled Ivy's arms out straight and pointed at the track marks. "Hell, Ivy. What have you done? You were doing so good."

Ivy gave her a sloppy smile. "Yeah, I do feel good," she sang.

Rainey leaned away from her and a choking sound escaped Ivy's throat. Rainey looked at Rosemary with unwavering eyes and said, "I'm going to put her in her bedroom. Can you go through her duffel bag and make sure she doesn't have any more dope?"

After getting Ivy settled in bed, Rainey sat next to her friend on the sofa. "Did you find anything?"

Rosemary held up a bag with white powder.

Rainey shook her head and rested it on the back of the sofa. "I don't understand. She doesn't have any money. How can she buy it?"

Rosemary turned to face her. "Really? You forget that fast. Try to think back to the Liberty Motel."

The images of Ivy at the motel flitted through her mind, and a sickening realization that her sister was hooked on drugs was dizzying. She'd been so dumb, so naïve to think that Ivy had beaten her addiction so rapidly. She imagined Ivy as a small infant, innocent and sweet, but now Rainey's shoulders rocked forward as she let her tears break free. Hopeless, she glanced at Rosemary and said, "I thought she beat it, I really did. I believed everything she told me because it's what I wanted to hear. She duped me. I knew better than to let my guard down."

Rosemary nodded and placed her hand on the girl's leg, "Sugar, you need to take care of yourself too. You've been taking care of her, doing everything to make Ivy happy, and not giving a shit about your own self."

Rainey lowered her head, deeply disturbed. Ivy was more like her parents than she wanted to believe, stopping at nothing to get her next fix. The air in the room seemed thick, and for a moment she wished she possessed secret powers to change her sister's life.

***

The next morning, when she walked into Ivy's bedroom, the teen bolted upright in bed and covered her face. "Leave me alone."

"No, I'm not going to leave you alone. You were fucked up last night. What happened? Why would you do that after being sober for all this time?"

Ivy put her pillow over her head. "I don't know. If you leave me alone, I won't do it again. Okay?"

Ivy's hair was tangled and her eyes were bugged out. Her face had blotches, and the way her body twitched turned Rainey's stomach. She had all the telltale signs of an addict.

"I'm sorry, Ivy. But I can't believe anything you say anymore."

She removed the pillow. "But I just promised. Didn't you hear me? If you'd get off my back, I wouldn't need to take drugs. Besides," her tone cocky, "it was just one mistake, you're being dumb."

"Hey Ivy, don't be rude to me, and another thing," Rainey said, raising her voice, "I won't fall for any more lies. I've heard them all before, remember? Now, where did you get the money to buy it?"

Ivy cringed and stared at her sister with wide eyes. "Does it matter?"

"Yes, to me it does. Did you have sex with someone for it?"

"It's not a big deal," Ivy said, her voice calmer now. "I know you don't understand it, but it doesn't bother me like it used to in the beginning."

"Selling your body is not something you should ever get used to, Ivy. You have so much to offer the world. There is so much more you can do with your life."

"Yeah. Okay, can I go back to sleep now?"

Rainey crossed her arms over her chest. "Umm, no. You need to get ready for school."

"I can't go today, I'm sick," she whined, throwing her body back onto the bed.

"You're not sick. You have a heroin hangover. Get up and get yourself ready."

Ivy looked around her room. "Where's my backpack?"

"The one where you stashed the rest of your dope? It's in the living room."

Ivy gave her a pained stare. She grabbed fistfuls of her hair and pulled on them. "What did you do with my shit, man?"

Rainey was physically jolted by her erratic behavior, and her body stiffened. "I flushed it. Did you think I was going to let you keep it? My God, Ivy, who are you?"

Ivy jumped out of bed and tore around the room like a wild lion confined to a cage. "It wasn't yours. You had no right to take it!" she yelled.

Rainey was trying to keep herself together, to calm the nerves bouncing around her body, threatening to make her lose her cool. "I have every right," she said evenly. "You're my little sister, my responsibility now, and I'm not going to let you become our parents."

Ivy halted, her eyes narrowed, and her mouth pinched. "Why can't you just mind your own business? Huh? You're not the boss of me."

Rainey cocked her head to the side. "Actually, I am the boss of you. I would like for us to have a normal, decent sister relationship, but you don't seem to get that. I'm offering you a chance at a better life, a clean life, a life where you don't have to give sex to perverts or be beaten by that piece of shit Jiggy."

Ivy stormed past her to the bathroom, slamming the door closed.
"We're leaving in fifteen minutes for school. Make it quick!" Rainey yelled after grabbing her keys and standing at the front door.

Chapter Ninety-Eight

One week after the argument with Rainey, Ivy dodged school and was walking in a more dangerous area of the city. As she approached a house, a few of Jiggy's associates saw her.

"'Bout time you came back, bitch. Where you been at all this time? Shit, you're lucky, another couple of weeks and we would've come looking for you to drag your nasty ass back here," one of them said as she climbed the rickety wooden stairs. "If I was Jiggy I'd kick your ass real good."

Ivy flinched. She was accustomed to Jiggy's associates being rude and rough with her. What am I doing? Why did I come back here? she asked herself for a split second, then brushed it off.

As she looked around her, Jiggy came to the door. "There's my girl. I knew you'd come back to me." He moved onto the porch and put a vice grip on her neck, backing her up against the brick wall. "I didn't think it would take you this long, though. You know, I don't like waiting for my whores. I expect them to come running to me."

She used both hands to loosen his grip on her neck. Looking up at him she said, "I missed you."

He released his hold on her, cupped her butt, and pulled her to him. "There's my girl." He looked into her eyes. "You look good, baby. All clean and pretty . . . smelling good. I was lonely while you was away. I was getting tired of waiting for you to come back to me. Good thing I didn't have to come and get you."

Ivy got on her tippytoes and kissed him. She pulled him closer to her. "It was awful not having you around. I was in the hospital for a while and then I was trapped in my sister's apartment." Her eyes grew big. "I almost died . . . you know, from that guy who stabbed me at the Liberty."

"Yeah, I know, Jiggy knows everything. Now, about that asshole who fucked you up at the Liberty, you don't need to worry about his sorry ass no more. I took real good care of him. He ain't never gonna bother you or any of my whores again."

Filled with flattery, she giggled. "Thank you. I mean, that's the reason I didn't come back to you sooner. I was worried that john would kill me the next time."

"Nah, come on now. Jiggy's got you. You know that. I ain't gonna let nobody hurt you ever again," he said, lowering his mouth to hers. "Come inside and show me how much you missed me."

Jiggy lay on the bed, naked. "Okay, bitch. Go on and undress."

He watched as Ivy's hands shook while she removed her jeans in jerky movements.

"You nervous or need a hit?" he asked.

"I need a hit. You got any smack?"

"'Course I got some." He sat up on the edge of the bed and prepared a needle for her. He pushed it toward her, and when she went to take it, he pulled his hand back. "Now, just a little taste to bring those jitters of yours down. You'll get more after you show me that you love me as much as I love you."

Pulling her down on the bed, Jiggy tied off her arm, inserting the needle into a vein, pulling back, and pressing forward. Her eyelids fluttered and her body went limp.

"That feels real good, doesn't it, baby?"

One side of her mouth lifted and she nodded in bouncy movements.

"Good. Come on. Stand up and take the rest of your clothes off. Where'd you get that ugly outfit, anyway? You barely showing an inch of flesh," he remarked.

"My sister. She's a prude."

"You ain't no prude, though, are you?"

She shook her head. "No."

Ivy stood and lifted her shirt over her head. She was wearing a white bra, practically institutional-looking.

Jiggy pulled her between his legs. "That's the nastiest damn bra I've ever seen," he said, snapping the elastic in the back. His hand slithered down her stomach and stopped at her scar. "Is this what that prick did to you?"

She looked down at the healed stab wound. "Yeah, it hurt real bad, Jiggy."

"I bet it did," he said, pulling her to him and sinking his teeth into the skin covering her ribs. Reeling from the pain, she threw herself back on the bed, stifling a scream as she gave herself over to him.

Within two days of returning to Jiggy, she was back working the streets. At first she was fearful that someone would try to hurt her, but he had assured her through his words and a steady stream of heroin that no one would ever harm her again.

***

In the days following Ivy's absence, Rainey paced her living room at night. She knew enough to understand that Ivy would be unsettled and craving drugs. Her disappearance happened in an instant. She'd walked her sister to school one morning, and she hadn't returned in the afternoon. So the battle had started.

In Rainey's heart, she knew that Ivy had gone back to Jiggy and was certain she was prostituting for him again.

Against Rosemary's advice Rainey had made several trips to the Liberty Motel, but Ivy wasn't there. She walked the streets of Kensington at night, looking for her. She drove to various areas of North Philly and called local hospitals, but it was as though she had disappeared into thin air. Rainey racked her brain trying to think of any place she could have gone. She even went to their old home where they grew up, but it was boarded up and empty.

Rainey was coming to terms with the fact that she may have lost Ivy forever. It was a devastating moment. She had worried and fought for so long that she'd forgotten how to live her own life. Pushing thoughts of herself aside, she had to keep looking until she knew for sure that there was no way her sister was coming home again.

A week after Ivy had been missing, Rainey's desperation grew and she decided to make one last attempt to find her. That's when it became abundantly clear what Rainey had to do.

Chapter Ninety-Nine

At two in the morning Rainey stood on Boulder's doorstep, knowing if anyone could help find Ivy, it was him. When he pulled his door open, he was in his boxers, rubbing sleep from his eyes.

"What the hell, Rainey? You can't come here at a normal time of day?" he grumbled.

"I'm sorry. Can I come in?"

He looked at her closely, and noticing the stress in her face and the way she was wringing her hands together he knew that something bad must have happened. He stepped aside, "All right. Come on in. You look like shit. When's the last time you slept?"

Kiki stood in a silk robe in the doorway of their living room. "Are you kidding, Boulder? What's going on here? This is outta hand now."

He held his palms up and strutted over to Kiki, put his arms around her waist, and kissed her to put her at ease. "I know, babe. It'll be fine. Can you make a pot of coffee?" he asked nicely, glancing at Rainey, who was hunched over on the sofa with her legs bouncing. "I think I'm gonna be up for a while." When Kiki left the room, he turned back to Rainey.

"So," he said, sitting down across from her, "I take it you didn't come here to give me my car back in the middle of the night. Funny how three months turned into whenever the hell you get around to returning it," he said, half serious.

Rainey managed a weak smile. "Boulder, I need your help."

He yawned loudly. "Let me guess. Your little sister?"

She nodded but couldn't meet his eyes, ashamed that she was begging him for help with the same problem. An uncontrollable moan escaped her mouth. "I know I'm always talking about her and worrying about her, but

you don't understand. I consider Ivy not only my sister, but also my child. Someone needs to help her, needs to care, and I'm the only one who can."

Boulder leaned forward. "I get it, but at some point you need to figure out a long-term plan with this kid. What is it you need from me?"

So nervous she could barely speak the words, Rainey raked her fingers through her hair, and heat rose into her chest. "I can't find her. She was doing good . . . had been sober for over three months, was back in school, and then bam, she disappeared. She hasn't been home in a week, and tonight I reached my limit and came here." She looked up at him with red-rimmed eyes. "I can't stand not knowing where she is or what's happened to her. She's young and stupid but she's mine, and I want her to be safe."

Kiki came in then with a mug of steaming coffee and handed it to Boulder. He looked up at her and smiled. Then she turned to Rainey. "You want a cup?"

She looked up at the woman who had never extended an ounce of decency to her. "Yeah, sure, I'd love one."

Kiki nodded and went back to the kitchen. She'd overheard the conversation and saw the girl as less of a threat to her relationship with Boulder. Now Kiki recognized that Rainey was a young woman struggling to save a child she considered her own.

"You're asking me to help you find her?" Boulder asked, lighting a cigarette.

"Your club is anywhere and everywhere. You always know what's going on."

He blew out a cloud of smoke. "Save the flattery. I'll help you, but this is the last time. Do you have any idea who she's hanging out with?"

Rainey's teeth locked down on her lower lip and she rubbed the back of her neck. "Hanging out with? You mean like friends from school? She didn't have any. I'm pretty sure she's back with Jiggy."

He let out a harsh laugh. "You're fucking kidding me, right?"

Rattled by his reaction, she rubbed her palms on her pant legs and shook her head. "I know you don't want the club involved with him . . ." Her head dropped to her chest and a sob escaped her throat. "I don't have anyone else to ask for help."

Kiki returned with coffee for Rainey, then sat beside her and draped her arm over her shoulder. "Boulder, isn't there anything we can do? At least find out where the kid is?"

Rainey, both shocked and confused by the small act of kindness, looked into Kiki's eyes. "Thank you," she whispered.

"O Christ! Now I have the two of you up my ass. That's all I need is for you two crazy broads to join forces." He sat back and took a loud slurp of his coffee. "All right. Let me talk to the guys and see what we can find out. I've already had it out with Rock, Jiggy's boss, for knocking the shit outta him. I'll go back and see what he tells me and come up with an arrangement for the information."

"An arrangement?" Rainey asked, alarmed by what that could mean.

"Yeah, when I initially went to Rock, he wanted me to hand you over to Jiggy. Once he realized that wasn't gonna happen, I gave him a piece of territory—you know, a few streets— where his girls could work. This one is gonna cost me big 'cause people like Rock don't give up information on their own that easy." He looked up at the girl. "I'll try and find out where she is and let you know, that's all I can do. You understand me?"

"Yes, yes, I understand. Thank you," Rainey said in a high-pitched tone.

She stood and walked unsteadily to the door. Kiki caught up to her. "Why don't you come here for dinner tomorrow night when you're done work?" Kiki asked, then turned to Boulder. "You can talk to Rock tomorrow, right?"

He gave his ol' lady a curt nod.

"Thanks, I'll see you tomorrow."

On the ride back to her apartment, she was fixated on finding her sister. The child she once nourished and took care of was no longer the same person, and it was hard for her to sit with that reality. As she drove farther into Kensington, her hope of finding Ivy intensified. If there was anyone who could do this it was Boulder. Rainey vowed to be forever grateful to him for helping and to Kiki for having her back.

Chapter One Hundred

Two days later, Rainey walked into Rosemary's office.

"Where you been at?" Rosemary asked in an accusatory tone. "I went by your house and you weren't there so I called Sam and he said he ain't seen you neither. We was both worried. He found out you showed up for work and that's the only way we knew you was alive."

Rainey slumped down in the chair across from the desk. "I was at Boulder's house. Kiki invited me over for dinner."

"Kiki? Did that stone-cold witch have a change of heart about you?"

Rainey let out a chuckle. "Yeah, I have that effect on people." She paused and looked down at her sneakers. "I went there the night before last to ask Boulder to help me find Ivy. I can't give up. I have to know she's okay. I'm thinking maybe if she's back to hooking she'll see how good she had it and want to come home."

Rosemary, unblinking and not saying anything at first, stared at Rainey. A pencil was resting behind one ear and poking through her short afro. She slid the pencil out and held it between her fingers. "See this?"

Rainey tilted her head and nodded. "Yeah, it's a pencil. No one in the world uses pencils anymore besides you."

She lifted her chin and pinched her lips together in a show of defiance. "That's right. I always use a pencil because ain't nothing in life ain't riddled with mistakes. So I keep a pencil handy to erase mistakes and start over. The same holds true for people, sugar. When they become more trouble than you can handle, then sometimes, no matter how much they mean to you, you gotta erase them from your life. Those kinds of people always find someone else to lay their problems on. They're what I call soul

suckers. They'll steal your very being right out from your core if you ain't protecting yourself."

Rainey tried to blink back tears, Rosemary had hit the very heart of what was happening between her and Ivy. Yet it was so hard to let her sister go. "But I love her. She's a baby. I can't erase her from my life. I wouldn't be able to live with myself."

Rosemary moved around the desk, pulled Rainey into a strong hug, and said in a hushed voice, "Ivy ain't the baby you raised no more. I know she's still a child, but her experiences changed everything about her. I know it ain't her fault that your mama and papa didn't care for her properly, but it ain't your fault either. You can't carry that weight on your shoulders and you ain't gonna ever stop her from doing what she wants to do. Eventually her addiction will ruin her life and yours too if you can't find your boundaries."

Rainey let out a sob, the woman's words ripping her heart in half. She rested her head on Rosemary's shoulder. "I thought that after she almost died it would've woken her up. Make her want to live life the right way."

Rosemary pulled her head back, still rubbing Rainey's back softly. When she spoke, her tone was firmer. "That's what you ain't getting. Ivy thinks she is living her life the right way already. She believes her pimp is her family and that he loves her unconditionally, even when she's using heroin. That's how it works on the streets. You gotta understand and accept that she goes to him for comfort and security. As sick as it sounds, that's the downright truth."

Rainey put her hand to her mouth, and her stomach retched. She raced for the bathroom and was just in time to hit the toilet as she vomited the horrors and truth of Rosemary's words.

It didn't take long for Boulder to discover Ivy's whereabouts. In exchange for the information, Boulder had promised Rock not to interfere in Jiggy's business and give him two dozen handguns. When the deal was done, Boulder called Rainey to give her the update. She had received the news about her sister with almost no emotion.

A few nights later, Boulder and Kiki picked her up to take her to see Ivy. Rainey brought Rosemary along for support, not wanting to face this next chapter without her. When they arrived at the Jackson Motel in the Badlands, Rainey spotted Ivy almost immediately.

"There she is. She's the one in yellow," Rainey breathed, pressing her face to the window.

Ivy was dressed in a short yellow spandex dress. The healthy weight she'd gained and the wholesome glow she had acquired while living with Rainey were gone. Her ribs and hip bones protruded through the fabric, and her face was nothing more than a skull draped in skin. She shimmied up and down the sidewalk, stalking the cars that drove by slowly.

Boulder turned to the backseat. "She's alive. That's what you wanted to know and what I promised to find out for you."

Rainey nodded, still looking at her sister. "Thank you for finding her. I've seen enough. I wanna go home."

Rainey didn't get back to her apartment until almost one in the morning, and once inside she couldn't wait to leave again. Packing a few things, it was almost two hours later when she knocked lightly on Sam's door. He pulled the door open and took one look at her face. Tenderly grabbing her by the wrist, he pulled her into him as her anguish was released.

"I'm sorry. I know it's late," she said into his shirt. "I didn't know where else to go."

Sam stroked her hair. "You came to the right place. This is where you belong." He led her to the sofa and covered her with a soft blanket. He sat next to her while she cried.

"It's over," she said. "I can't make her stop taking drugs or keep her from being a prostitute. I just . . ." She burst into tears and took staggered breaths.

"You just what? Finish what you were saying."

"She's back with Jiggy . . . working in the Badlands." A sob broke free and Rainey took in several long breaths to control herself. "Nothing has been the same between her and me since I got out of juvie. Ivy's never happy to see me and she can't wait to get away from me. I miss the baby who wanted me even though I had nothing to give."

"Well," Sam said gently, "maybe you should look around because there are other people who love being with you. I understand it's not the same thing, but your memory of your relationship with your little sister and the reality of many years gone by will never align."

She nodded. "I know that now. But it's so hard to let go of those memories."

He took her hands in his. "You should never let those memories go. You should cherish them until the day you die, but those memories are in the past. You need to realize that you can't re-create them in the present. You've

tried hard to do what's right for Ivy and we've watched you battle for her life." He paused, and a look of apprehension crossed his face. "There is one thing you can do, but I don't think you'll like it."

Rainey felt her insides lift for a moment. "What?"

"You can call child protective services and tell them where she is."

"And then what? They'll bring her back to me and she'll run away again?"

"No, not necessarily. Since you have legal custody once they find her, they'll force her to leave her current situation. She'll be placed in a facility that's prepared to deal with her addiction—not just her drug addiction, but also her unhealthy addiction to her pimp."

Her expression was somber and pensive, thinking about all that Sam had explained. "And she wouldn't live with me?"

"Yes, that's what I'm suggesting. Let her grow up in a controlled environment where you can build a relationship with her over time. There are places you can send her to live until she's eighteen. They're pricey, but you have money from your aunt that can help her."

She rubbed her forehead. She liked everything Sam had suggested and was trying to process this approach. "Sorry, I wasn't ready for this, but I think you're right. It's not a hard decision. I'd rather see her have a chance at life than fulfill my own dreams of rescuing her. I've been selfish trying to do it on my own. Will you help me call them?"

"Of course," he said, kissing her cheek. "We'll call first thing in the morning. You get some sleep now, okay?"

Rainey nodded. Then she laid across his lap and within minutes she was fast asleep.

Chapter One Hundred One

The next morning, Rainey and Sam made the call to child protective services. They took turns explaining the events that led to Ivy falling victim of prostitution and drug addiction. The woman on the phone was empathetic and assured her that they would look into it and get back to them within the next few days. When they hung up Rainey turned to Sam with a smile. "This is the right thing to do. Thank you. I finally feel like I'm doing something that moves her and me forward."

"Good," he said, kissing her forehead. "I was thinking it might be a good idea for you to stay here with me this week. You know, in case there's any news but really to give you a change of scenery. What do you think?"

Vulnerable and a little nervous about how things would play out, she nodded. "That sounds like a good idea."

Three days later, the two were sharing a spaghetti dinner that Sam had "slaved over," according to him, when his phone rang.

Sam answered the phone. "Helloooo," he sang, still chuckling.

His smile dropped and his eyes shot to Rainey, who was still looking down at her plate, trying to master swirling her spaghetti with a fork and spoon. She finally did it and her eyes popped up at him with a huge smile on her face. His grave expression startled her and she dropped the utensils onto her plate, her heart racing.

"What happened?" she asked, bracing herself for the worst.

Sam held up a finger, finished the call a minute later, then gently laid down the telephone. "That was Rosemary," he said. "A man named Boulder called The Sanctuary looking for you. There's been a car accident and Ivy was involved. We need to go to the hospital right now."

Rainey nodded, shoved her feet into her sneakers, and ran out the door with Sam on her heels. On the way, her mind swirled with worst-case scenarios as Sam tried to keep her calm.

***

Rosemary rushed toward the couple when she saw them coming into the emergency room. The mood was bleak as the three of them sat together, waiting. The nurse had told them that Ivy sustained major injuries and was in the operating room. Rainey paced the waiting room as they waited for an update from the surgeon. They'd been there for more than an hour when Boulder charged through the door with Kiki. Rainey rushed to them, and Kiki held her tightly. Sam came up behind her and extended his hand to Boulder.

"You must be Boulder. I'm Sam, Rainey's boyfriend."

He gave the agent a sturdy nod. "We wanted you to know what happened," he said, turning to Rainey.

"Did you see it happen?" she asked.

Boulder's eyes swept over Sam, then he shot a look at Rainey. "A friend of ours was there and they recognized Ivy and called me."

Rainey shifted her stance, too distracted to pick up on his subtle cues. "Well, what happened?" she asked.

Boulder was looking directly at Rainey, "Word has it that Ivy was out of it. She was staggering around the sidewalk and . . ." he glanced at Sam again. "How about we take this conversation over there?" He pointed to a corner across the room.

She waved him off. "It's okay. Sam knows everything. He can hear this."

"Okay." He hesitated for a moment to think about how to say it. "Well, it seems like she had been battered around by her pimp and he pushed her off of the curb and into an oncoming car. The driver tried to stop, but it was too late. She was hit at a high speed and landed headfirst into the front windshield."

"O my God . . . O my God . . . O my God," Rainey howled, shaking her hands out, picturing her sister with her head split open. "Did anyone talk to her? Did she say anything?"

Boulder shook his head. "According to my source there was a lot of blood. That's all he told me. Did the doctor talk to you yet?"

Rainey let out a strangled scream, too horrified for words.

Rosemary threw her arms around her. "Okay, sugar," the woman cried. "You're gonna be okay. You're gonna make it through this. Come on now, you gotta be strong. Let's wait until we talk to the doctor."

Sam wrapped his arms around both women as he and Rosemary felt the undeniable, raw sadness of the woman they both loved.

They led Rainey over to a seat and then waited with her for the next four hours while Ivy was in surgery. While the two fought to stay awake, she coasted on pure adrenaline.

When the surgeon finally appeared, Rainey was standing in the center of the waiting room with her arms crossed tightly over her chest.

"Rainey Paxton?"

She rushed forward. "That's me."

He held his hand out. "I'm Dr. Finley, I performed the surgery on your sister. Let's go somewhere private and talk for a few minutes," he said, leading her through a set of doors.

She looked back over her shoulder to make sure her friends were behind her. Dr. Finley ushered them to a small room, and she thought she would come out of her skin waiting for him to speak. Finally he clasped his hands on the table in front of him and said, "Ivy made it through surgery."

She let out a loud breath and lowered her head. "Thank God."

Dr. Finley put his hands up. "She's very critical. Her spleen was ruptured and we had to remove it. She had extensive internal bleeding. My team has done everything we can at this point and we will monitor her over the next seventy-two hours—"

"I don't understand," Rainey rasped, cutting him off. "I thought she hit her head."

"She does have a cut and bruise on her forehead, but her scans showed her brain is fine. The driver of the vehicle and witnesses were questioned by the police and we understand that someone pushed her a fairly far distance into the street in front of the car. The left side of her body took the major impact, and that's most likely how her spleen was ruptured."

The doctor leaned back in his chair as he watched her absorb the information. She looked to Rosemary, then Sam, and back at the doctor.

Rainey's eyes filled and her voice cracked as she asked, "But she'll be okay, right?"

Dr. Finley paused for a moment. "We aren't sure. I know you're upset and want answers; I don't blame you. But the spleen is what provides us our

immune response, and without one she is susceptible to infection. She's sustained other injuries and it's hard to say if she'll be able to overcome them."

"Okay, what else can you do for her?" Rainey asked, raking her hand through her hair.

"We will watch her closely and monitor any changes." He put his hand over Rainey's. "I'm assuming you know about her drug use."

Rainey nodded; glad he didn't make her bring it up first.

"Well, that gives us another hurdle to overcome. She's abused her body pretty badly. I suspect she was quite young when she began using." He paused. "You told the registration nurse she's thirteen?"

She nodded. "Just recently, yeah. We just celebrated her birthday. It was the first party she ever had, even if it was only the two of us," she said sadly.

He gathered his papers. "That's all the information I have for you at this moment." Dr. Finley stood. "Do you have any other questions for me?"

"When can I see her?"

"She's still in the recovery room. Once she's brought up to ICU one of the nurses will let you know and you can go up."

After the doctor left, the room was filled with a deafening, debilitating silence. Rainey's elbows were on the table and her head hung over them. Her hair hid her face from the others. Her shoulders shook as she sobbed, trying to empty the sadness and frustration consuming her body before it destroyed her.

Chapter One Hundred Two

Rainey stayed by Ivy's bedside, stroking her hair and holding her hand. She willed her to open her eyes. Dr. Finley was cautiously optimistic after the first twenty-four hours had passed, and hope surged through Rainey's very being. Ivy had been in the ICU for nearly a day and a half when her eyes finally opened and she smiled at Rainey like she had when she was a baby. She searched Rainey's eyes, noticing her dark circles and deep lines on the sides.

"I'm glad you're here," Ivy managed. "I don't blame you—" she said, breaking into a dry cough, and Rainey held an ice chip to her lips. Ivy let the water slide inside her mouth, then made eye contact again. "I didn't have anyone to blame for what happened to me, but I know it's not your fault." She gave Rainey's hand a limp squeeze. "I know you love me," she said and hesitated. She looked away and looked back at Rainey again. "I love you too."

Rainey's breath hitched and she leaned over Ivy and kissed her face softly. She pulled back and looked into the girl's eyes; her innocence seemed to magically be restored. Rainey was filled with gratitude accompanied by a surge of joy and peace.

The sides of Ivy's lips lifted into a pained smile. "Tell me about when I was a baby," she said in a weak voice.

Rainey's heart took flight as she rubbed her sister's hand. "Well, when Mom and Dad first told me they were having another baby, I wasn't too happy. Not because I didn't want a brother or sister, but because they already didn't take care of me, so how could they take care of another kid? I was only nine when you were born and I was so scared of not being able to raise you on my own."

Ivy's eyes widened. "You knew you'd have to raise me?"

She nodded. "Of course. I had been taking care of myself already. Oh, but I remember the day they brought you home. I looked into your brown eyes and my breath got caught in my throat because you were so beautiful. All my worries about taking care of you slipped away and I realized that I finally had someone to love and share my life with . . . it was the happiest moment of my life."

"Was I crying?"

Rainey grew distant as the images of years gone by played in her memory. She shook her head softly and gave Ivy a sweet smile. "Oh, no. You were happy. You smiled at me right away. I remember how good you smelled," she said, closing her eyes. "The nurses must have bathed you right before they brought you home. Pulling in your scent was so nice, I loved it. I was afraid if I touched you, I'd get you dirty," she chuckled. "But once we were alone, I opened your blanket and inspected your feet and hands, you were so tiny. I stared at you for hours and one thing was for sure, you weren't just my little sister, you were my baby, my child."

Ivy closed her eyes for a minute and reopened them. "Don't stop," she croaked.

"By the time you were one and a half, you were teetering around; trying to walk and say words. You had two little chiclet teeth right here," she said, opening her mouth and pointing to the middle of her bottom gums. "When you were really hungry and we didn't have much to eat I would let you press those little suckers into my finger. Every time I said 'ouch' you would laugh so hard. It was a game we played so I could distract you from being hungry."

Rainey looked down at her sister and brushed her black hair from her face. "You were the best baby. You were happy and it gave me a reason to go on. You know?"

Ivy gave her a dim smile.

"In all the shit I've been through the hardest moment of my life was when I was hauled off to juvie and had to leave you behind. I didn't tell you this before, but Sam was the arresting officer."

Ivy's eyes got large. "Really?" she whispered.

Rainey nodded. "He's been there for me. You know?"

Ivy's mouth dropped open and her breathing got raspy.

Rainey put her cheek to her sister's. "I'm sorry about everything that happened to you. All I ever wanted to do was protect you." She looked

into Ivy's face; her eyes were closed and she took in a shallow breath. "I will never love anyone in this life as much as I love you."

Rainey sat back in her chair, holding Ivy's hand for a while, until the silence of the room started to feel wrong, too silent. Not even the sound of a breath. Rainey's pulse quickened as she looked at her sister.

"Ivy?" Rainey put her ear to her mouth. Nothing. "Ivy? No, wait, Ivy. No, no, no, you can't leave me. No, please." She placed her hand over Ivy's heart, but her chest was still. Then the machines she was connected to screamed an urgent message that Rainey couldn't comprehend. A group of people rushed into the room. One nurse directed Rainey to the door, but she couldn't leave, she had to stay. It was her responsibility to take care of her sister.

The nurses and a doctor worked on Ivy for almost twenty minutes before Dr. Finley walked in. He went over to the side of Ivy's bed and the staff gave him a quick update on the medical procedures they performed. He held up his hand to the nurse who was hand-pumping the bag valve mask and she looked into the young girl's face and stopped.

Rainey was surrounded by sorrow and clamped her hands over her ears to block out the lonely sound of nothingness caused by grief. Her eyes riveted to Dr. Finley, and she pulled her hands away from her ears.

"Time of death . . ."

***

All of her fears of losing Ivy and never regaining her slipped away. Rainey's heart was left with nothing. There was an emptiness to the core of her being she believed she would never fill again. A part of her was lost; a piece of her heart had died with her sister. Rainey stood there, in a daze, until she felt herself falling.

Rosemary was just getting to the ICU when Rainey hit the floor hard. She helped a nurse put her into a nearby chair. Rosemary looked around at all the chaos in the room; her hand floated to the base of her neck and she turned to the nurse closest to her.

"What . . . what . . . happened here? Did our baby girl die?"

The nurse's doleful eyes spoke volumes and she nodded in response.

Rosemary put her hand on her forehead. "Lord, have mercy." She looked at Rainey awakening on the chair. She rushed over, grabbed her under the

arms, and took her out of the room. She was half dragging, half carrying Rainey down the hallway when Sam stepped off of the elevator.

His eyes took in Rosemary and Rainey, but his body failed him for a moment; his feet were stuck, as if in dried cement. Then his brain caught up with what he was seeing and he sprang forward. Rainey was barely coherent. Rosemary met his eyes and gave her head a solemn shake.

As they brought her into the family waiting area of the ICU and sat her down, Sam knelt before her and put his hands on her knees.

"I'm so sorry," he said, bowing his head.

She stared straight ahead. "Ivy's gone for good."

He looked up at her. "Yes, she is."

"I was talking to her when she died," she said in a zombie-like state. She broke from her trance and looked at her friend then back to Sam. "Ivy told me she loved me. She said she never really blamed me for what happened to her."

"She was right," Rosemary said, trying to reinforce what was obvious to everyone except Rainey.

Rainey nodded. "She wanted me to tell her about when she was a baby. I think she knew she was going to die. When I looked at her right after she passed, there was the smallest smile on her lips—like she was finally at peace."

Rainey's shoulders shook and her head lowered as her sorrow rode out on a stream of tears.

Chapter One Hundred Three

The morning of Ivy's funeral Rainey was sitting in her apartment with Rosemary. She peered out the window at the gathering blackness of the sky, matching her mournful mood.

"It's going to pour," she said glumly. "This day is hard enough; I don't need a storm."

Rosemary shook her head and reached for her hand. "No, sugar. You shouldn't see it that way."

Rainey hung her head and mumbled, "Sure."

"Let me explain," Rosemary said, lifting the girl's chin with her fingertips. "I see it different. I've been to a few funerals in my day, and those dark clouds, well, that's God letting you know he's sad for you." She pulled the curtain back and pointed to the sky. "See there, those clouds that block out the sun? Well, He gave you that so you know He understands your pain and suffering. But the rain, see now that's different." She dropped the curtain and stroked the girl's back. "The rain is God crying tears of joy that his precious child is coming home to him."

Rainey looked up at her sharply, her rage rising to the surface. "If God is doing all of the things you're saying, then why the hell did He let those horrible things happen to my sister? Huh? She was a little girl. And why did He let her get killed?"

"Oh, no." Rosemary wagged her finger. "You're confusing things. God's the sorta man you'd be willing to marry, Miss Rainey. He don't ever try and tell nobody what to do. He gave us free will, and if we fuck it up, then bad things can happen to innocent people . . . even children."

Rainey shook her head. "What about Ivy's free will?"

"Ain't easy for a child to use their free will when adults dance with the devil. See, that's how it works. Some people are weak, weaker than you can

ever imagine. And instead of using their free will to do something good with their lives, they open the door for evil as soon as the devil knocks. Do you know why?"

She shook her head, desperate for Rosemary to tell her the reason Ivy was gone.

"Because the devil entices us to be with him. We learn from when we're young it's so much easier to hate than it is to love. We're taught to look out for ourselves and so we have a lot of negative thoughts that center around jealousy and anger against other people. If we give in to that way of thinking, we become the people that do the hurtin' to others and being hateful becomes a source of power."

Rosemary put her hand over Rainey's heart. "God is right here inside you, child. And you can bet He carried you through all the bad things in your life. Your parents, juvie, losing people you love, and now, losing your baby sister. Try to remember all the blessings He's sent you." She pulled her head back and plastered a cheesy smile on her face. "Like me, and that man standing over there," she said, pointing to Sam. "He has loved you since you were a girl. He loved you different back then when you were in juvie, but now that love has grown into something the two of you can share. You see what I'm telling you?"

Rainey nodded and held onto Rosemary. "Thank you for being the mother I never had."

Rosemary pointed to the ceiling. "Don't thank me, thank Him. He put us in each other's lives. I thank Him every day he gave you to me. Never did get a chance to have a baby of my own, always wanted a girl too," she said, running her hand over Rainey's hair.

Rainey burst with pride and love for this woman. It was true, Rosemary was the mother she never had, but to hear her acknowledge that the feeling was mutual was both uplifting and self-affirming.

Later that morning, at Ivy's funeral, Rainey sat in front of her coffin. She watched her sister closely, waiting for her to sit up and take a deep breath. She supposed it was normal for people who lose kids tragically to expect a miracle, either that or she was going crazy, she'd told herself.

Rainey looked around and spotted Sam and Rosemary on the other side of the room with a few kids from the shelter who had come to show their support. She was disappointed so few people had shown up to the funeral. Not that she knew many people, but in her mind a lingering remembrance of when she was in juvie surfaced. When her cellmate Phoenix was buried

by the state after being killed; with only a few people attending the mass burial. She wanted to know that people had loved her sister. She lowered her head as she recalled those final moments she'd shared with Ivy and she was filled with warmth and love.

From behind her, several voices broke through her thoughts. Rainey turned to look and her heart swelled as she watched Boulder and Kiki leading the Devils Angels into the funeral home. The couple stood before Ivy's coffin and bowed their heads in respect. Then they turned to Rainey, and as she stood, the two converged on her. The other members followed and soon she was standing inside an enormous circle of leather, denim, wallet chains, and love.

The members took turns standing before the coffin and bowing their heads in a show of respect for Rainey and her deceased ol' man, Stoker. Bikers filled most of the empty chairs behind her as a priest stood at the front, reciting his final words about the child he had never met. But he was both sad and touched by the outpouring of love from the hardest-looking people; it shifted not only the priest's perspective but Sam's as well.

When the priest finished, Boulder turned to Rainey. "We're having a party at the club right after the cemetery to celebrate your sister's life. You know that's how we do it. We'd like you to be there."

A smile spread over her face, and Rainey felt immense respect for him. "Yes, I'd love that. My friends will come with me, too."

Boulder leaned into her and kissed her cheek.

The funeral procession was filled with a few hundred motorcycles. As a show of solidarity, they escorted a dead child who lost her life and her innocence to the violence of the unsavory streets of Kensington. As Rainey sat in the back of the limo driving slowly through Kensington with Rosemary and Sam on either side of her, she held each of their hands and took great pride in the motorcycles groaning out a mournful song.

***

The party at the clubhouse was crowded with bikers as Rainey made her way down to the basement. Boulder and Kiki met her at the bottom of the stairs. Boulder gave her a quick hug, and she pulled her head back. "What about Jiggy?"

"What about him? There's nothing to talk about," he said, then abruptly walked away.

Wordlessly, Kiki put her arm over Rainey's shoulder and took her to a quiet spot in the corner of the room. "I lost my only child to cancer ten years ago," Kiki said, looking intently into Rainey's eyes. I was only a teenager and it was hard. I think I know what you're going through."

Rainey wrung her hands together. "I'm so sorry, Kiki. I had no idea," she said, as a lightbulb went off in her head. "That's why you made Boulder help me."

Kiki nodded. "I knew what you were going through; watching your child slip away and there's nothing you can do to change the outcome. It was a long time ago, and honestly it still hurts me. Now, about Boulder's reaction a few minutes ago—"

"Yeah, I think I might've upset him when I asked about Jiggy. It's only because I was wondering if anything would happen to him since he killed my sister."

Kiki nodded. "Let's put it this way. Boulder took care of everything," she said.

Rainey tilted her head to the side and knotted her brow, "I don't understand."

"Between you and me?" Kiki asked.

Rainey raised her right hand in the air. "I promise."

Kiki pressed her lips together and leaned back, looking at her with uncertainty.

"I swear, Kiki. I'll take it to my grave."

Kiki looked down and Rainey followed her gaze to her missing pinky, and for a fraction of a second Tootsie's face popped into her mind's eye.

Kiki continued, "If I ever find out that you tell anyone what I'm about to tell you, I'll hack those other four fingers off with a dull butter knife."

Rainey flinched from the visual. "I won't say a word. Pinky swear." She smiled, pushing the hand with the missing pinky forward.

Kiki smirked at her. "So here's what happened . . ."

Chapter One Hundred Four

Kiki leaned in closer to Rainey so no one else could hear. "Boulder was owed a favor from a Latino biker club out of New Jersey. Those mean bastards went in, snatched Jiggy right off his own porch, and drove away with him."

Rainey wasn't sure whether it was relief or bliss that rushed through her. But either way the news was delightfully shocking. "What? No way. I mean, but won't Jiggy's gang go after them?"

"Hell no, girl. New Jersey has some heavy-handed biker clubs. And that particular club spans across the whole damn country. Word is those Latinos are in cahoots with a few of the mob families in New York, New Jersey, and Philly," she said bringing her voice to a faint whisper. "They do most of the dirty work for the mob"—she bounced her eyebrows—"if you know what I mean."

Rainey was unable to pull her eyes away from Kiki. "Yeah, I know." After several seconds of silence, she couldn't contain herself. "Well, are you gonna tell me what happened to Jiggy?"

Kiki smirked and her eyes roamed to the ceiling. "Let's see, they forced him into the car . . ." she tapped her chin with her index finger, delaying, enjoying Rainey's incredulous look.

Rainey playfully swatted at her and let out a giggle. "Come on. Knock it off. It's been a rough week. Spit it out already."

"Okay, so they drove Jiggy to an abandoned mill and stripped his ass naked. Then they put a football helmet over his head to keep him from dying too quick, tied him to the bumper of a pickup truck, and drove his skank ass over the gravel like a Texas rodeo. They dragged him around that parking lot a dozen times before they stopped." She shook her head. "I'd imagine it hurt really bad," she said, smiling.

As gruesome as it was, Rainey let it all sink in, but if anyone deserved this fate it was Jiggy. "You're telling me they dragged him to death?"

Kiki shook her head. "Not quite."

Dread flushed through Rainey's stomach. "He's still alive?"

Kiki held up her hand. "Let me finish. When they stopped dragging Jiggy's ass around, they untied him from the bumper, took his helmet off, and sat him to the side. They let him think it was all over. Then one of the bikers jumped into the truck and drove to the other end of the lot while four dudes grabbed him up by his arms and legs. As the truck barreled toward them, those dudes tossed Jiggy in front of it." Her face got serious and she lowered her voice. "Just like he did to your sister."

Rainey pressed her hand over her mouth as she imagined the scene unfolding. While the act sickened her and made her stomach flop, she was relieved that Jiggy had been handed a death sentence similar to what he gave to her sister. She nodded and turned her head to Kiki. "Thank you for telling me."

"Girl, I ain't done."

Her eyes opened wide. "Oh, there's more?"

"Well, a little. So they put his raw, busted-up ass in a kiddie pool that was filled with wood soaked in gasoline. They lit that bitch on fire, and Perez, the president of the club, told Boulder that the bastard still wasn't dead and started screaming until he was burned alive."

Rainey grimaced. "O my God, that's horrible."

Kiki pointed her index finger at her. "See, now you're just talking shit. That ain't horrible; that right there is payback. He suffered the painful death he deserved until he pulled his last breath—that burnt-ass, fire-breathing, skin-peeling prick."

Rainey couldn't help but laugh. Her emotions ran wild. She was elated to know Jiggy paid the price for what he'd done, but sadly it had taken her sister's life for him to be stopped.

Chapter One Hundred Five: One Year Later

Several months following the funeral, after much coaxing from Sam and badgering from Rosemary, Rainey moved into Sam's apartment. While Rainey knew his plush home would be much more comfortable, she worried about losing her freedom. But Sam proved to be a man of his word and soon she realized that he had no intention to control her, only love her.

***

It was a warm morning in April. Sam was driving Rainey and Rosemary to the courthouse. After weeks of trial proceedings, the day had finally arrived when Miranda and Peter would receive their sentences from the judge.

"I swear it took forever to get to this day," Rainey said, sitting in the courtroom between Sam and Rosemary. The jury had found Peter and Miranda guilty of first-degree murder of her aunt Sophie two weeks prior. Anxiety tightened her throat as she waited for the judge to announce their sentences.

Peter and Miranda stood side by side at the defendants' table. With deadpan eyes, neither showed remorse as they watched the judge. They'd both put on weight without access to drugs. Peter had lost most of his hair and Miranda's was cut short. They looked like older, uglier, heavier versions of the people who had caused Rainey so much pain.

The judge scanned their faces, lifted her eyebrows, and gave her head a quick shake. She looked down at her notes and back up. "Peter Paxton, on the guilty verdict of first-degree murder, the court sentences you to life in prison without the possibility of parole."

There were murmurs from the media sitting in the courtroom. The case had become quite a scandal on the local news, especially after Ivy died, and they got the rest of the story from Rainey. Peter stood erect and stared at the judge as if he hadn't heard her.

The judge turned to Miranda. "Miranda Andersen, on the guilty verdict of first-degree murder, the court sentences you to life in prison without the possibility of parole."

Miranda's shoulders slumped forward and her court-appointed attorney grabbed her under the arm to prevent her from falling onto the table. Rainey sat stoically for a moment as a sense of justice pulsed through her. She believed her parents got exactly what they deserved, and it was immensely satisfying. She looked at Sam, then at Rosemary. They all held steady smiles as they got up and left the courtroom.

Chapter One Hundred Six

Berwick, Pennsylvania, State Correctional Institution for Women

Miranda was transferred to a state correctional institution two and a half hours west of Philadelphia to serve her life sentence. She'd been distraught since the judge sealed her fate. Her black hair was matted to her head and her brown eyes were flat and lifeless. They escorted her in handcuffs to her cell, where she came face-to-face with her cellmate.

Miranda's cellmate was a tall woman. Her broad shoulders and muscular biceps indicated that she was a bodybuilder. She had a vine tattoo that ran from below the V-neck of her prison uniform and that crawled up her neck and over her cheeks. Attached to the vines that covered each ear were skeleton heads. The tattoos didn't bother Miranda, tattoos were commonplace on the streets, it was the woman's strong physique and grizzly bear demeanor that rattled her.

The woman glowered at Miranda. Then she gave her a tight smile that showed her crooked, mangled teeth. "Welcome home, you piece of drug-slugging shit."

Miranda's eyes bugged out and she turned to the guard, who gave her a shrug in response. The guard unlocked the handcuffs and without making eye contact or reacting to the woman's words she left them alone in the locked cell.

"The other women call me Stella. You are never to say my name. You can call me Queen. If I ever hear you say my name, I'll beat the hell outta you." She walked in circles around her so closely that Miranda could feel the heat coming from her body. "Here's how it's gonna be," she said.

Miranda cowered and shoved her shaking hands into the front pockets of her uniform to steady them. With her shoulders hunched over, she peered up at the woman.

"You're gonna do whatever I want if you don't want a beating every day and even if you do what I say, the odds aren't in your favor," she cackled and shook her head knowingly.

Stella leaned against the bars of their cell as she smiled and waved at the other women. The women were acting like a pack of wolves waiting to tear the flesh off of their prey until there was nothing left but bones picked clean.

Then she glanced at Miranda, who was looking around frantically. She snapped her fingers. "Hey! Hey! Pay attention. You need to keep up." Miranda's eyes were bulging from their sockets. "Now as I was saying, seeing how the others out there wanna give it to you real good, you're gonna have a hard time living in this shithole. See, we're all criminals in here, but you're the one who killed your disabled sister and we heard you gave your thirteen-year-old to some drug dealer who pimped her out so you could keep getting high. Your kid died. Did you know that?" Not waiting for an answer, she leaned in closer. "We get the news on the TV in here. That's some fucked-up shit you did."

Miranda froze, afraid even to breathe too loudly.

Stella walked to the metal toilet. "See this shitter here? Don't ever let me catch you using it without my permission. You understand?"

Miranda's eyes filled as her mouth dropped open.

"Oh, great," Stella cackled. "You're a fucking mouth breather? It keeps gettin' better and better." She watched Miranda for a few moments, taking in energy from the woman's fear. "Let me tell ya a little about me. See, unlike you, I protected my family. I killed my mother for letting her boyfriend and his disgusting friends rape my little sister. My mom was strung out on heroin, just like you. Makes me sick to my stomach even looking at you. You see, I was twelve years older than my little sister; she was only eight at the time. Can you imagine being eight and having a bunch of men jump your bones? No, I don't think you can, 'cause if you could, you wouldn't have let the same thing happen to your daughters. You remember, the one who died and the older one who told the media all the other shit you did. Did you ever think about what your kids were going through?"

Torn open by the sharp claws of terror, Miranda's blood rushed through her veins until she became light-headed. She forced herself to focus on the woman.

Stella stepped into Miranda's space. "I guess the answer is no, you didn't think about what your kids were going through, probably 'cause you were too high." She turned her back to Miranda before wheeling back around, her eyes wild. "Back to my mother, 'cause I know you gotta be curious. I beat the shit outta her, then I filled the bathtub with water and drowned any life that was left outta that bitch. I sure did and I was happy about it too. You let that sink in for a while. See, I don't care how messed up you were on drugs, and neither do any of the other women in this place. 'Cause even me, an ordinary murderer, knows the difference between right and wrong, you scumbag."

Stella walked to the other side of the cell and touched a picture of a young girl taped to the cinderblock wall. "This here is my sister. She lives with my aunt and uncle now. She's safe."

Miranda tucked herself tightly into a corner, watching in horror as Stella strutted over to her.

"Let's get some things straight," Stella said, punching Miranda in the gut. "Don't expect me to feel sorry for you and what you did 'cause you're a drug addict. We all heard that 'Oh, I was on drugs and didn't know what I was doing' shit that you fed to the jury. Luckily, they all saw through it too. There are lots of addicts in here that don't do what you did to your sister and kids."

While Miranda was bent over holding her gut, Stella lifted her fist into the air and brought it down on the back of her head. "You don't do anything in this place without my permission. You don't sleep or eat or shit or piss or speak or stand at the bars of this cell if you don't get my approval first. You're nothin' but a piece of stinkin' shit."

Miranda shook her head. "I didn't kill my sister. It wasn't me. My boyfriend killed my sister and he's the one that sold my daughter, not me, I swear."

Stella pulled her arm back and slapped Miranda across the face, sending her into the wall. "Don't you ever try to manipulate me. I ain't stupid, and remember, my mother was a junkie too, so I know what you'll do to get what you want. Besides, like I said, we all seen stuff about you on TV and ain't nobody in here thinks you're innocent. Hell, bitch, they got you and that moron boyfriend on camera offing your sister. What was her

name?" She poked Miranda's forehead repeatedly with her index finger, "Yeah, Sophie. The poor woman couldn't even defend herself, couldn't speak or scream for someone to help her. There ain't no hidin' it here and I know a dirtball when I meet one."

Miranda shriveled into herself and pressed her back against the wall, wishing she could go back in time and close Sophie's door so they didn't get caught. Stella stood over her glaring, as she bent down with a dirty syringe in her hand. "Seeing that you like to shoot up and kill defenseless family members so much, we all thought it would be a good idea to give you a proper welcome. The thing is, we all took a vote last night. We're gonna call you Needle-dick. We think it's fittin' given how much you love your needles and how big a dick you are for ruining other people's lives. Besides, this way you can never forget what you did to your family. You heroin-using, blackhearted, soulless prick."

Miranda looked up at Stella with eyes pleading for mercy, but there was no forgiveness from the woman towering over her.

Miranda got to her knees. "I want us to be friends. I'm not a bad person, I swear."

The woman smacked her on the top of the head. "What did I just tell you about getting permission? Did I say you can speak?"

Miranda mumbled, "I'm sorry."

"See now, you aren't sorry about nothing. That's the problem with people like you who don't care about what you do to other people." She stooped down and looked into Miranda's eyes. "It's kind of like worshipping the devil your entire life, then asking God to help you when your time on earth is coming to an end." She pointed to the ceiling. "See, my God don't work like that. So save your 'I'm sorry' and your tears and blaming your rotten boyfriend. It's too late."

Miranda's mouth opened slightly.

"You got something you wanna say?" she challenged.

She peered up at Stella. "I wanted to tell you I think we got off to a bad start. That's all."

Stella laughed. "Let me tell you something. We ain't off to no bad start. This is prison. You should've thought about what could've happened to ya before you did what ya did. Now, I ain't about to be your friend, and I ain't gonna help you neither."

Miranda covered her face with her hands and was crying real tears. Fear had settled into her bones along with the endless prison sentence that stretched out before her.

***

Miranda was constantly harassed by the other inmates. She took many beatings from her peers, so much so that her bruises had bruises.

Stella never let Miranda rest. Just to annoy her, she'd shove Miranda's pillow in the toilet and would laugh as she pulled out the soaking blob. She smeared handfuls of Vaseline between Miranda's sheets. Stella often gave her an open-hand slap when she entered the cell or stuck out her foot to watch her splat on the floor. But the worst was when she wouldn't give her permission to pee and she would hold it in as long as she could before finally peeing on her bed.

Miranda didn't dare fight back. She was living a life of abuse from her fellow prisoners and neglect from the guards, who often looked the other way. She was slowly but surely learning what it was like to be one of her children.

After a month in prison, Miranda was going through the cafeteria line. She put one of everything on her tray, still trying to substitute drugs with food. Her head bobbed and her eyes darted around looking for the demons that would inevitably come to haunt her, the other inmates. After making it through the line with her tray of food, she let out a sigh of relief. She moved quickly to a table where no one was sitting. She placed her tray down and lifted her fork to her mouth and shoveled in a piece of meatloaf. Before she could take another bite, an inmate swaggered over and squirted a syringe full of bleach onto her food.

"Don't forget your dope, Needle-dick," the woman snarled.

Miranda jumped back from the strong chemical smell and slunk into the seat, defeated. This happened to her at least once a day. The other criminals would not let her get off easily for what she'd done.

Almost six months after Miranda arrived at Berwick State Correctional Institution, she was found in the shower, killed by an injection of bleach. When the guards discovered her body, her arm was tied off with a canvas belt and the empty needle hung from her arm. They were never able to

determine if Miranda had committed suicide or if she'd been murdered by another inmate.

When Rainey was informed of her mother's death, she didn't feel sorry for her. She believed Miranda had gotten what she put out. She hoped that her mother's time in prison made her realize how much she had abused her family and that she would serve eternity in hell grappling with painful remorse.

Chapter One Hundred Seven

Waynesburg, Pennsylvania, State Correctional Institution for Men

As a guard escorted Peter through the common area, a burly man with a shaved head, long mustache, scraggly beard, and a flat nose stared at him with contempt from a table in the corner.

Peter stood before the cell door where he would spend the rest of his life. His cellmate, a thin, nervous man, looked at him and rubbed his face, then rubbed his arms. "Why's he gotta cell with me? I mind my own business. I don't need none of his shit coming at me."

The guard sneered at the man. "Shut up, Slim. This ain't band camp. You get what you get here. If you wanted to pick who you slept with you shouldn't have broken the law."

The guard turned and left the two men standing in the cell facing each other.

Slim said, "I ain't hanging with you. It ain't nothing personal, man, I dig my dope too, but you did some stuff that guys in here don't take kindly to. Hell, I tried to rob a grocery store, but I wouldn't have killed nobody or sold my kid to some scab. I mean, if I had a kid, which I don't," he rambled.

"Listen, dude. Shut up. I don't need friends like you," Peter said with blunt force.

"If you say so. Not sure how you can be so calm. Oh, unless . . . you don't know, do you?" he asked with a crooked smile. Then he shrieked with forced laughter, slapping his thighs and moving about the cell spastically.

"Know what? You asshole," Peter bit back.

"That," Slim said, pointing to Dragon, coming up behind him.

Dragon had to duck his head to fit through the cell door. He glared at Slim and threw his thumb over his shoulder. "Get the fuck out."

Slim scurried away like a mouse, his head ducked low and his boney shoulders bent forward.

Peter stood taller as he faced the man defiantly.

Dragon chuckled. "Are you puffing out your chest?" he said, springing forward and grabbing him with one hand around the throat.

Peter clawed at the man with both hands. As the seconds ticked on and he could get no air into his lungs, his face turned bright red and the veins in his neck and face were plump and throbbing. When Peter thought he would die, Dragon let go and Peter collapsed to the floor, pulling air into his lungs and sputtering.

He put his palms up. "Look, man. I'm mellow, I ain't gonna give you a hard time in here. I just wanna serve my time in peace."

Dragon crossed his arms over his chest as he stood over him like a giant. "Get up."

Peter struggled to his feet and held onto the bunk to steady himself. That's when he saw the Devils Angels tattoo on Dragon's arm.

"Oh, man. Cool, you're a Devils Angel. I lived in Kensington and seen you all riding before. Cool biker group," he sputtered nervously. "I always wanted to be a biker but my girlfriend held me down a lot."

"Oh, really?" Dragon asked. "You know anybody that's ever been in the Devils Angels?" His fist slipped inside his other hand and he held the position.

"Nah. I never got the chance to meet anybody so it's cool to get to meet you now. Maybe I can be a part of your group in here. I mean, I know it ain't the same as on the outside, but you know, it's something, right? I bet you have some harsh stories."

Dragon scoffed. He intentionally scratched his face with his index finger. "Let me think. There's a story I wanna tell you."

Peter's shoulders relaxed into their natural position. "Yeah, sure, man, I got plenty of time," he cackled.

"Well, I had a brother in the Devils Angels. One night, we were out on our bikes cruising in South Philly and we stopped at this steak joint to get a bite to eat. So, I'm in line waiting to order for me and Stoker while he sat on his bike, he was the vice president of our club, so we give our leaders respect. Anyway, I'm standing there and I'm trying to decide what I want on my cheesesteak. The next thing I know there are gunshots—Bam! Bam! Bam! I drop down into a squatting position, like this," he said. Dragon

remained in a low squat and now he looked up at Peter, who was smiling and enjoying the story. "You getting what I'm saying?"

Peter gave him an enthusiastic nod.

"Good. Anyway, I look over and see Stoker, right? And he's got his gun in his hand and he yells, 'Gotta go!' I turn and see three guys running toward me so I pull out my gun and fire off a few shots. I run to my bike and we're flying down the streets of South Philly. When we get back to the clubhouse, Stoker tells me that the guy he shot had a gun about six inches from the back of my head. Stoker saved my life that night, and even though he's dead now, I still owe him."

"How did he die?"

"Murdered, just like I would've been." He shook his head slowly. "I wish I could've been there to save him."

"Did the Devils Angels get revenge on the person who killed him?" Peter asked, like a child being told a bedtime story.

"Hold up, bitch, I ain't done my story."

Peter's head flinched back. "Oh, sorry. Go ahead," he said, extending his hand out as an invitation to continue.

"Well, Stoker had this ol' lady. Beautiful girl. She was tough as nails, didn't let any of the other bitches push her around. She'd brawl with someone quicker than looking at them. The men all loved that about her. She was no drama, man." Dragon put his thumb and index finger to his chin in an exaggerated thinking gesture. "I can't remember her name now . . . did you tell me your name yet, dude?"

"Peter. Peter Paxton," he said with a grin.

Dragon pointed at him. "Yeah, that's it. Her name was Rainey Paxton. That was the girl. She's your daughter, ain't she?"

Peter gulped in a breath of air and held it in his lungs. Beads of sweat formed over his lip. His body flooded with deathly dread. He backed a few steps away. "Yeah, she's my kid."

Dragon advanced on him. "Yeah, motherfucker, that's what I heard. Welcome to hell. You don't need to worry, I ain't gonna kill you."

Peter released an audible breath.

"Instead, me and my brothers, I have ten of them in here with me, we're going to make every day of your life a living hell. That's what Stoker would want us to do. Man, Stoker really loved Rainey—wanted to marry her someday."

Peter pressed his hands to his stomach. His face drained of color and he thought his knees would give out.

Dragon ran his hand through his long beard. "Is it true she served time for dope that wasn't hers and that you and your whore girlfriend threatened to hurt her little sister if she told anybody the truth?"

Peter took a few more steps backward until his back was against the wall. He blinked rapidly and willed the wall to open up and swallow him. "Things got messed up, man. I was strung out on heroin and didn't know what I was doing. I went along with her mother, she's the one who did all the bad shit to Rainey."

"Oh, yeah? That's not the way she told it to Stoker. When she got outta juvie after covering your ass and Jiggy's ass, she tried to go home and you cold-cocked her when she wasn't looking. Knocked her lights out and she woke up in the Badlands. The fucking Badlands, dude," he said, jerking his chin out as he spoke. "Who the hell drops their seventeen-year-old kid off there? I mean," he said, turning his back to Peter and looking out into the common room, "do you have any idea what could've happened to her?"

He looked at Peter over his shoulder. "Do you?"

Peter shook his head, hunching over, trying to stop his arms and legs from shaking.

Dragon took a few steps toward him. He stopped and leaned against the top bunk. "Well, for one, she could've been killed. Or raped." He tilted his head and looked away. "Or she could've been taken by one of the gangs. Beaten, raped, shot up with dope, and turned out to hook."

"I swear, man," Peter said, holding his stomach tighter, as if he were in pain. "I never meant to hurt Rainey. I love her. It was the drugs, man. They were controlling me. You know? I couldn't shake the dope. That wasn't me, it was the dope that did that to her."

The man sneered. "Really? See, in this hellhole, we don't care about your excuses. In prison there ain't no excuse for doing bad shit to kids."

Peter's complexion became sickly and fear etched deep lines into his face. He dragged his hands over his pant legs. "So, what do you want from me?"

"I ain't done yet," Dragon spat. "I learned a few days ago that you have another daughter. Ivy, is it?"

Peter flinched and nodded.

"Yeah, you sold her to Jiggy? So you could get high? Wow, dude, that right there is a reason to have your ass beat every fucking day of your pathetic life."

"I'm sorry," he muttered in a soft voice.

"Nah, you ain't sorry. But you're gonna be."

"Wha . . . wha . . . are you gonna do to me?"

"Oh, we're gonna do everything to you except kill you, because that would make it too easy on you. Welcome home, bitch," Dragon said, then turned and left the cell.

Peter slid down the wall, pulled his knees up, and wrapped his arms around them. Helplessness settled over him realizing, he would live the rest of his life on earth in hell.

***

It was right before Thanksgiving when Rainey went to visit Boulder and Kiki. She sat drinking coffee at their kitchen table.

"So, what's going on? Why did you want to talk to me?" she asked.

Boulder glanced at Kiki, and she smiled at him.

"I heard your mom died in prison," Boulder said.

Her features remained fixed, relaxed, unaffected; she had long ago stopped feeling anything for her parents. "Yep. She did. I guess that's what happens in prison."

Boulder nodded and lit a cigarette. "I have some news about your dad if you wanna hear it."

"Don't tell me he found a way to get out of prison," Rainey said, already annoyed at the thought that he found a loophole.

He shook his head. "Do you remember Dragon?"

She took a moment to process. She recalled the man who was the meanest member of the Devils Angels and also a devoted Stoker fan. She hadn't interacted with him much, but whenever she did, she'd found him to be respectful, and he always spoke highly of her dead boyfriend. "Of course. Stoker loved him. The two of them had the same sense of humor. What about him?"

"After you left here, Dragon was sent to prison."

Her mind swirled as she connected the dots. Both Boulder and Kiki had knowing smiles on their faces. She put her hand over her mouth. "Is he with my dad?"

Boulder nodded. "You know, Dragon dug you. He told me and Stoker that you were the kind of woman to marry. He always called you a warrior 'cause you never took any shit from anybody."

Rainey glanced at Kiki and cracked a smile. She wanted to ask Boulder if Dragon would kill her father, but knew he wouldn't appreciate such a question.

"I understand your dad was pretty shocked to find out that you were Stoker's ol' lady," he said.

She looked at him intently, as her anticipation for his punch line grew.

"He's gonna spend the rest of his life dealing with my members. Do you understand what I'm telling you?"

"I think so. If I had to guess and knowing the Devils Angels, my father will stay alive and wish they would kill him to stop the torture and pain," Rainey said, putting her hand over his.

Boulder nodded.

"Thank you, Boulder."

Chapter One Hundred Eight

Six Months Later

Rainey and Sam were on the sofa in their living room watching a movie when he laid across her lap, resting the back of his head on her thighs.

She looked down at him and smiled. “Can I help you?” she chuckled, looking back at the television.

“Now that you asked, there is something you can do for me.”

She ran her hand over her head to the ends of her hair. “Well? Spit it out. I wanna finish the movie. But I’m telling you now, if it involves me getting off this sofa and going into the kitchen for something, you can forget it,” she joked.

“I was thinking that I want to marry you. Let’s get married.”

Rainey tensed. Her words were stuck, taken back by Sam’s blunt proposal. “Umm, I wasn’t expecting you to say that right now. I’m not sure I’m ready to get married,” she admitted.

“Hmm. Well.” He sat up. “We’ve been living together for a while, and it’s been good, right?”

“Yeah.” She smiled. “It’s been great. It’s not you, it’s just that I want to do more with my life before I get married and have children.”

“Whoa, whoa!” He cocked his head and gave her a mischievous grin. “Who said anything about kids?”

She swatted his shoulder playfully.

A moment of silence stretched out before them, the air gaining thickness.

“Are you saying no?” he asked.

Rainey shook her head. "I'm saying not now." She leaned in to kiss him, and when they separated, she eyed him up and down. "Are you trying to marry me for my money?" she teased to lighten the mood.

"Of course. What? Do you think I'm stupid?"

Sam pressed her down on the sofa and pulled her clothes off.

When they were finished, Rainey lay in his arms thinking of all she'd lost and all she'd gained. She knew in her heart that if she ever were to marry, Sam would be the one for her. He treated her as an equal, but more importantly, Sam respected her. Feeling grounded that he'd never stray from his promises or diminish her dreams, she'd grown to depend on his love.

Rainey didn't know what the future held for them but was optimistic it would be filled with happiness.

***

The following day, Rainey went to see Rosemary and told her about the marriage proposal.

"I can't see why you don't just go on and marry the man. You know he loves you."

Rainey nodded. "I love him too, but I'm not ready."

"Well, it's important you wait until you're ready then. Marriage is a big step and I think you'll be great at it. I can't wait to get me some grandbabies, though," Rosemary chirped.

Rainey giggled and kissed Rosemary on the cheek. "You're the best friend and mom I've ever had."

Rosemary's eyes welled and she pulled Rainey into her. "You and me, we been through a lot together. But I know, as sure as we stand here today, we'll always be with each other 'til the end of time."

Rainey rested her head on Rosemary's shoulder, knowing that between Sam and Rosemary, she had finally found the place where she belonged.

Continue reading . . .

Believe Like A Child Sample

Read an excerpt of Paige's debut novel **Believe Like A Child.** The beginning of this book is based on her real life and the remainder of the book is fiction.

How It All Began

Alessa awoke in the middle of the night to find her nightgown bunched up around her chest and her uncle's fingers between her legs. Just seven years old, she was scared and confused by what her so-called protector was doing to her and pretended to still be asleep, hoping it would make him stop. Alessa didn't know if what he was doing was right or wrong; all she knew was that it filled her with dread. Ten minutes later, she felt as if she were going to explode right there in her uncle's bed from the terror welling up inside her. She pretended to be just waking up, and gathered the courage to look up at him with wide, terrified eyes.

"Just lie back and be quiet," he rasped. "I'll make you feel really good."

Then he placed his thick, wet mouth, still stinking of cigars, over hers and continued to explore her undeveloped body until he had finally entered her. Alessa was young, but knew instinctively that no one would believe her, if she reported what her uncle had just done to her.

Alessa was the youngest of four children and the only introvert in the group. While her family was loud and opinionated, she was quiet and timid. And because she was so different from the rest of them, she often found herself watching the chaos that ensued during family gatherings from the periphery, like an outsider who didn't belong. She wondered why God had placed her with them. She couldn't relate to her parents; nor did she share any of the qualities that characterized her siblings. In the

constant arguing and heated debates that they had with each other, the seven-year-old found herself lost and forgotten.

Alessa lacked all of the right characteristics for becoming anything important in life. Shy and unexceptional, with rarely a smile to light up her solemn expression, she led people to believe she was a miserable little child. Her lank hair and large, serious brown eyes made her look homely. Her small frame was always draped in threadbare hand-me-downs that were always too big for her and never seemed to sit on her the way they did on her two older sisters. The youngest in the family, she stood in stark contrast to her siblings—Anna, the firstborn, and Rosabella—and Anthony, the brother who came between the two. All three flaunted thick black hair, beautiful brown eyes and radiant olive complexions. From the time she was very young, Alessa had known she was not like the rest of them. The sheer force of their outgoing personalities appealed to all and overshadowed her meek demeanor. Simply put, Alessa was forgettable.

Their maternal grandmother, who they called Grammy, lived with the family and since their mother, Caterina, was the youngest of fourteen siblings, they always had people visiting. Being an insignificant part of such a large family was unbearable for the solitary seven-year-old. She would listen to them argue with each other over the most trivial matters, as they spent hours sitting around the kitchen table, drinking coffee and passing judgment on people they knew, bitterly criticizing the way they lived their lives or raised their children. As each of these evenings drew to a close, someone would invariably stomp out of the house either in a fit of silent rage or screaming at another family member. The constant friction was traumatic for the little girl, a fact that no one else in her family sensed or understood. Turmoil was what her family thrived on, whereas all she wanted was to be in the company of people who would make her feel she belonged.

Alessa found an ally in Grammy who, given the limited number of bedrooms in their house, shared one with her. The child loved sleeping with Grammy whose very presence instilled in her a sense of security amid the ominous darkness teeming with imaginary monsters that settled around her bed at night. Every evening, when it was time for bed, Alessa would snuggle up close, her small arm linked as tightly as a vice through her grandmother's. As Alessa lay beside her, Grammy would go through her rosary beads and murmur her evening prayers, assuring her granddaughter that monsters didn't exist.

Alessa's grandmother was a happy woman. Her cheerful face was framed by short, curly gray hair and her skin felt as soft and smooth as silk. The matriarch of the family, she was a gentle soul, loved and respected because of her kindness to others. She often invited neighbors and relatives to their home so she could provide them with a hot meal. Even though she wasn't a wealthy woman, she believed in sharing what God had provided her. She would knit for hours on end so she could gift afghans in the winter to people she knew. Alessa would squeeze in beside her grandmother, as she sat knitting on her rocking chair, and often find herself dozing off, lulled by the sound of her infinitely soothing voice. In her company, Alessa always felt tranquil and completely at peace.

The family was poor and enjoyed few luxuries. One of Alessa's most memorable ones was the weeklong vacation she had taken with her grandmother in Atlantic City, New Jersey, as a five-year-old. At the Chalfonte-Haddon Hall Hotel where they stayed, the child had felt as though she were in heaven. Wearing the new bathing suit her grandmother had bought her, she had played on the beach, building sand castles and jumping the waves. She had loved eating in the elegant dining room where she could choose whatever delicacies she wanted from the dessert table. The waiters were nice to her and attentive to their every need. Grammy had let her order Shirley Temples that were served in tall glasses with crushed ice and topped with a cherry. The vacation in Atlantic City was Alessa's only good childhood memory. She would relive that week a million times in her mind, as she grew older and found less and less to look forward to.

When Alessa was six years old her grandmother died. Unable to imagine life without her, the child was devastated by her loss and felt there was no longer a place in her home that she could call safe. She felt bereft and abandoned without her ally, but soon found solace in a new one. It was her Uncle Danny who held and comforted her through her bereavement. She felt special and deeply loved because of the kindness he showered upon her during those dark days following Grammy's death.

Everyone loved her Uncle Danny. He was extremely popular, a family icon, the man with all the money, and everyone sought his company. He often told stories about the mafia and most people secretly believed he worked for them. But eventually, Alessa realized, they were just stories concocted to make everyone live in awe of him. Uncle Danny's tales were so persuasive that most people who knew him ended up giving him far more

respect than he deserved. He wielded a lot of clout and everyone around him automatically bowed to his demands.

Six long months after her grandmother had passed away and shortly after her Uncle Danny's live-in girlfriend died tragically in a car accident, he moved in with Alessa's family.

"After all," Caterina told her husband, "we need the money. We can't keep this house going and raise the kids, if we don't get some help."

It was she, in fact, who had invited her brother to move in with them. Danny promptly accepted the offer and before they knew it, he had taken over one of the four bedrooms in their house and, along with it, Alessa's life.

When her uncle first moved in, the little girl was excited at the prospect of having him there. Uncle Danny loved her more than anyone else in the family did and was almost a substitute for her grandmother. He had an air of confidence about him that made Alessa feel utterly safe when she was by his side. He was generous and loving with her and made her feel special, like she was the only person on earth.

Grief-stricken and vulnerable and still fearful of the monsters that lurked in her imagination, she turned to Uncle Danny who found the perfect reason to console her. Shortly after he moved into her house, Alessa's uncle invited her to sleep in his bed. Just as she had done with her grandmother, the child would link her arm through his as she lay waiting to fall asleep. For the next several months, Alessa slept peacefully next to her protector, unafraid that the monsters of the night would attack her—until the night he raped her.

Alessa's parents knew that their youngest child had been sleeping in Danny's bed, but any concern they might have had over the situation was silenced when the income from their new tenant promptly alleviated their anxieties about how they would pay their bills. Caterina chose to believe her brother was in the mafia, a fact she took great pride in. She had a twisted view of reality and of the world in general. As far as she was concerned, the world revolved around this overgrown beast, her older brother. After all, he was paying her seven hundred fifty dollars a month just to live in their house, a sum Alessa's whole family lived off. Her parents didn't go to work. Her father couldn't, because he had been disabled in combat during the war; and her mother just wouldn't, claiming she "needed" to stay home with the kids.

Until Uncle Danny moved in, the family had survived solely on welfare. In middle-class circles, they were known as poor white trash. Alessa was the golden goose Caterina needed to indulge her unwillingness to work and keep her finances afloat. In a short period of time, the child became the ultimate sacrificial lamb, the bargaining chip her family could use to retain their home, buy the things they needed, and maintain the lifestyle they could ill afford otherwise.

The first time Alessa's uncle raped her, she felt isolated and helpless. The abuse became more frequent thereafter. It did occur to the child that she should tell her mother about her uncle's behavior, but Danny enjoyed a certain standing both in her family and in the neighborhood where they lived and she was not confident about being taken seriously. By abusing her, he had stripped her of all confidence and she felt entirely defenseless, unable to resist his assaults, and at times, she felt like it was her who had caused the abuse.

What confused Alessa even more was her uncle's assertion that whatever took place between them was a natural thing shared between two people who loved each other. After that first night, she had started sleeping in her own bed, but Uncle Danny would still wake her up in the middle of the night to quench his own sick desires. His six-foot-four-inch, two-hundred-and-seventy-five-pound body would crush her small frame so she could barely breathe in her tiny single bed.

thought, it would have been a great release for her. She could smell her own feces and had to hold back the vomit that was threatening to gush forth from her mouth. The excruciating pain, as he ripped through her, was like fire scorching her insides. She was afraid he would tear her in half.

Through his harsh breathing, she heard him repeat, "This is good and tight." He kept telling her he loved her, until he came. Finally, he collapsed next to her on the tiny bed that barely had enough room for one person. She cried that night, until the tears wouldn't come anymore. And even when she finally fell asleep, there was no shelter from her pain. She dreamed of faceless men touching her, pawing her all over with their filthy hands. She couldn't escape the horrendous nightmare she was living through, not even in her sleep.

That terrible night, it finally dawned on her that the monsters she had always feared lived under her bed had never existed. The only real monster had a name: Uncle Danny, the ogre who had stripped her of her innocence and left nothing, but an empty shell. Her childhood, her very life, had been stolen from her. She no longer knew who she was; nor did she dare to contemplate her future. She had learned that life was flawed and just making it through each day would take all her strength and challenge her powers of endurance. Her rough childhood, robbed of its innocence, would arm her with the resilience to hold onto her sanity later in life.

Despite her moments of dark despair, Alessa had faith that she would eventually rise above the sordidness of her life and come through. Her belief in herself had been instilled early in life by her beloved grandmother who had chosen her name for her, imagining that she had seen something unique and exciting in the newborn. Alessa meant "defender of mankind". That is how her grandmother had visualized her when she looked into the baby's eyes and probed her soul. Despite Caterina's attempts to undermine her youngest child at every opportunity, Alessa's grandmother had been firm in her belief that one day, her favorite grandchild would be strong and resilient and the inspiration for many; but, most importantly, she would be a force to reckon with.

BUY NOW: Believe Like A Child (Home Street Home Series: Book One)

The HOME STREET HOME SERIES is a collection of novels that can be read in any order.

More books by Paige

Home Street Home Series (can be read in any order):
Believe Like A Child
When Smiles Fade
One Among Us
Mean Little People
Never Be Alone
My Final Breath

Rainey Paxton Series (must be read in order):
A Little Pinprick
A Little High

A Note From Paige

Dear Dearth Reader,

I want to take a moment to thank you for reading and supporting my work. I appreciate you spreading the word about my books to family, friends and co-workers. If you enjoyed this book please go to Amazon and leave a short review so that other readers can determine if this is the right book for them . . . great reviews mean so much to me and keep me writing. Thank you!

~Paige